1964

Th book m

MUSIC, ACOUSTICS & ARCHITECTURE

by LEO L. BERANEK

JOHN WILEY & SONS, INC.,

New York   London

With the editorial assistance of GERALDINE STONE

Architectural drawings by WILFRED A. MALMLUND

Library of Congress Catalog Card Number: 62–19866
Printed in the United States of America

Foreword

The scene: backstage just prior to the inaugural concert in a brand-new auditorium. Cast of characters: the conductor, the architect, and the local manager. Each has his own particular interest in the hall: the manager hopes that every seat will always be filled; the architect hopes that his fine structure will find favor with the public; the conductor hopes that the orchestra will rise to the occasion and give that extra "something" which transforms a fine concert into a great one.

But behind all these hopes lurks one unanswered question: How will the new hall "sound"?

Upon the answer to this question depend the future audiences on which the manager counts. Upon the answer depends the success of the architect's every effort. Upon this answer depends the sound of the orchestra and the resulting communication of great art.

How will the hall "sound"? But on what does the answer to this question depend?

Every intelligent musician and music lover knows the answer: acoustics. For it is when the acoustic properties of a hall are good that the manager, the architect, and the conductor all know that their efforts will be enhanced rather than baffled.

Each one dreams, in his rare moments of leisure, of a perfect concert hall, in which every listener has an opportunity both to see and to hear unimpeded. Grace of line wedded to the fullest possible use of space is the dream of the architect. And the conductor dreams always of the ideal hall in which his musicians can play "normally," without undue effort, and without the annoying adjustments of balance that are all too essential in many of our concert halls today. Above all, the conductor looks for a hall in which the sound that he hears on the podium is identical with the sound heard in any seat, regardless of its location.

How often, while on tour with the Philadelphia Orchestra, I have had to depend on a second pair of ears, those of William Smith, my assistant conductor, who roams through the unfamiliar auditorium during the first work on the program. As soon as it is over he signals to me from the wings to let me know whether the strings are sufficiently brilliant, whether the brass or the percussion is too heavy, whether the woodwinds are "in balance" with the more penetrating brass or the large mass of string tone.

Think of the score of Debussy's *La Mer*, for instance. Here the composer has achieved one of the most delicately wrought of musical mechanisms. Its success requires not only expert execution but also the best possible hearing conditions. There is hardly a bar of this score that does not require the most sensitive attention from both the musician and the listener. Imagine the sorry result of this acute mutual effort if the music fails to "sound," if excessive reverberation blurs the "colors" or excessive dryness robs the sound of its lustre.

But the question remains: On what does the sound of the hall depend?

Until recently the answer has been: Lady Luck. This does not imply that acoustics has been ignored. But until recently, although there has been some sense, there has been little science in this field. With the appearance of this book—which is the fruit of years of laborious study and analysis by Leo Beranek—the sense is greatly enlarged and the science is significantly stated in unmistakable terms.

Dr. Beranek is skilled in the ways of both music and architecture, and he has gone to great pains to heighten the contribution of each of these arts to acoustical success. He has found a way to apply scientific method to the analysis of acoustical concepts without ever losing sight of the aesthetic demands of the music itself.

We can be especially grateful for the numerous explanatory drawings, as well as for the superb photographs and the plans of the great halls of the world. I have learned many new things about halls that I have long looked upon as "old friends." And, as scientific method demands, Dr. Beranek has thoroughly exploded a number of "sacred" myths, still regarded as gospel truth by many musicians.

The climax of the volume is the description of the care taken in the planning of Philharmonic Hall in Lincoln Center for the Performing Arts, in New York. The book ends with an exciting account of the "tuning period" during which acoustical tests, involving a full symphony orchestra and days of laborious trial and error culminated in the sure knowledge that good acoustics need not be hit-or-miss. Lady Luck has finally been supplanted by careful analysis and the painstaking application of new but firmly grounded acoustic principles.

With the appearance of this book, musical architecture stands at the threshold of new and exciting things. I express the gratitude and joy of all conscientious musicians in hailing the new era that this study must engender.

Philadelphia, July 1962

Eugene Ormandy

Preface

This book is offered to music lovers and musicians, to architects and acousticians, to everyone who is interested in the sounds of music. A half century ago most listeners had little opportunity to know any setting for music besides their homes and local halls. People seldom traveled to New York, London, Vienna, Bayreuth, or Milan to experience the excitement of performances in a new environment. Today many music lovers have traveled widely and have encountered, perhaps with surprise, the striking differences that characterize the acoustics of the world's many halls. Even the listener who stays at home experiences a kaleidoscope of sound through radio broadcasts and recordings.

Every interest and experience is heightened by some knowledge of the inside story. My own search for the inside story of halls for music has led me to a hundred interviews with conductors of operas and symphony orchestras, performers, and music critics; to listening to music in some sixty halls; and to the collecting of precise acoustical measurements and accurate architectural drawings and photographs. I have tried to tell this story as simply as possible, while still maintaining technical accuracy.

What I have written here pertains to any concert hall or opera house. But in a more limited sense this book is the story of the acoustical planning of Philharmonic Hall, and some preliminary planning for the proposed Metropolitan Opera House, at Lincoln Center for the Performing Arts in New York. Max Abramovitz, the architect for Philharmonic Hall, was unsparing in his efforts to incorporate into his design the features my acoustical colleagues and I felt were necessary if the hall was to meet the exacting standards of the music lovers of a great city. An exciting new principle—planned flexibility and acoustical tuning and adjustment—has been built into the design of Philharmonic Hall. The musicians, the music lovers, and the music critics—the regular patrons of the hall—will judge whether our efforts have provided New York with an acoustical setting appropriate for the music of today's symphonic repertoire.

This book is not the fruit of my efforts alone. Many people have contributed to its substance and its preparation, and their assistance is gratefully acknowledged. Some are named below, others in the pages of the text. But let no one but the author be held responsible for any detail of the contents presented here. Errors and differences are bound to turn up in spite of our efforts to eliminate them, and I can only hope that my readers will be kind enough to point them out to me.

Credits and Acknowledgments

The architects who designed all fifty-four halls of Chapter 6 are named. Where technical papers on the acoustics of the halls have been published, these are cited. Where no technical papers are available, it has been impossible to establish the identity of all the experts who advised on the acoustics.

It gives me pleasure to acknowledge the great assistance I have received from conductors, composers, musicians, orchestra and opera managers, hall managers, architects, acousticians, and musical friends, numbering several hundred. All were essential to a fruitful result.

I sought and received suggestions on Chapter 3, "Acoustics and Music," from Hope Bagenal, E. Power Biggs, Leonard S. Burkat, Martin F. Gardiner, Karl Geiringer, Klaus Liepmann, Daniel Pinkham, Caldwell Titcomb, and Edith Vogl. Chapters 7 through 13 were reviewed and commented on by William A. Allen, Peter H. Parkin, and T. Somerville of London; Willi Furrer of Bern; Lothar Cremer of Berlin; Erwin Meyer and H. Kuttruff of Goettingen; Helmut Mueller and Manfred Heckl of Munich. Among the many others who patiently read and commented on a seemingly endless succession of typescripts, particular thanks are due to William J. Cavanaugh, Howard D. Hershberger, David L. Klepper, Robert B. Newman, J. B. C. Purcell, and Theodore J. Schultz of Bolt Beranek and Newman.

My colleague, Russell Johnson, worked closely with me in the design of Philharmonic Hall and assisted in a number of the interviews and measurements.

Two persons made special contributions to the book: Wilfred A. Malmlund, whose untiring artistic efforts over a period of three years produced the magnificent architectural drawings of Chapters 6 and 15; and Geraldine Stone, who labored with me to convert difficult scientific concepts into easily understandable prose.

I wish to thank my secretary, Elizabeth M. Donnelly, and her staff, Elizabeth H. Jones, Shirley Jennings, and Helene Morgan, for handling voluminous correspondence and a train of manuscript drafts. And I am grateful to Devra Rowland, who reviewed the final typescript, and to Margaret Hasson, who prepared the name index.

Leo L. Beranek

Cambridge, Massachusetts
July 1962

Contents

MUSIC, ACOUSTICS & ARCHITECTURE

Musical Acoustics—Science or Myth?

"But I don't want to hear a pin drop," exclaimed Eugene Ormandy, throwing his arms upward for emphasis, "I want to hear the orchestra!" This explosive remark was made to the surprised manager of a world-famous concert hall who had just said that his hall had "perfect acoustics because everywhere in it one can hear the sound of a pin dropped on the stage." Mr. Ormandy shares the belief of most informed listeners that excellent acoustics for music are not simply a matter of the projection of faint sounds from the stage to the most distant seats.

What constitutes good acoustics for music? Is there agreement among musicians and listeners on which halls are good and which are not? Are there several kinds of good acoustics just as there are good white wines and good red wines? The technical literature offers no satisfactory counsel. Most written discussions of acoustics for music either express one man's opinion based on his own listening or conducting experience or conclude from a random collection of opinions that there is no rhyme or reason whatsoever to the subject.

I concur that there may be disagreement about acoustical quality. But I cannot agree with those people who would deny the existence of "good" and "bad," and who would call acoustics a mere matter of taste. If that were the case, acoustics would stand alone as the one thing in the world not possessed of different degrees of quality.

It was early in November 1955 that I settled back in my favorite lounge chair before a warm fire to enjoy a then-current issue of the *New Yorker*. [Joseph Wechsberg, "Our Far-Flung Correspondents—A Question of Reverberation," *The New Yorker*, November 5, 1955, p. 90.] My peace of mind evaporated as I came to a passage that read:

Most of the people who have set themselves up as consultants on matters of acoustics contend, not unnaturally, that by applying certain laws of physics and using certain testing devices they can determine in advance how hospitable to sound a new auditorium will be. The fact is, however, that several auditoriums built in Europe recently under the guidance of consultants who presumably applied the laws of physics and used the testing devices have turned out to have dreadful acoustics. When the . . . new concert hall, which was hailed in advance as Europe's finest auditorium, opened, it proved to be an acoustical atrocity. . . . Although years of acoustical study had gone into the design of the building, it was discovered after the first few concerts [that numerous changes had to be made]. This has been helpful, but the acoustics are still far from satisfactory. The sad truth is that while scientists in many fields can foretell with unvarying accuracy what will result from a combination of known factors, those who specialize in acoustics seem to be on no surer footing in making their forecasts than meteorologists are in making theirs. From the evidence, it appears that no one can say for sure what the acoustical qualities of an auditorium will be until it is finished, furnished, heated, and filled with musicians, music, and listeners. And if the qualities turn out to be disappointing, it will very likely be expensive to correct them—if it can be done at all.

This article was written about a concert hall built some years ago in another country, but the condemnation of modern acoustics—my field—cut deep. Reaching for a pencil, I jotted down the cities in which halls that I knew had been built since 1900: Paris, Copenhagen, Berlin, Munich, Liverpool, London, Caracas, Turku, Gothenburg, Chicago, San Francisco, Rochester, Cleveland. I was forced to admit that only two halls were relatively free from criticism, and in one of them draperies were being hung in an attempt to improve the balance and blend of the orchestra.

What is wrong with our present-day knowledge of acoustics? The twentieth century began auspiciously, with the opening of Symphony Hall in Boston, one of the world's finest concert halls. Everyone believed then that the essential laws of musical acoustics had been formulated. But something was wrong. Subsequent halls were not so successful as Boston's, and for what reasons nobody was sure.

The *New Yorker* seemed to have fired its challenge directly at me. I was probably in a unique position to respond to it. I had training and experience in both physical and psychological acoustics. I had played in orchestras at Cornell College in Iowa and Harvard University. For many years I had been privileged to attend concerts in America and in many foreign cities. International meetings on acoustics had brought me into contact with acousticians who could help me to obtain acoustical data on foreign halls. But most important, my acoustical consulting took me to

Europe and South America and gave me the opportunity to hear music in many halls in many cities.

As I began to think about the many facets of architecture, acoustics, and music that I would need to bring together, I resolved to visit the world's best-known halls and to listen to music in them, to collect architectural drawings and photographs, to take acoustical data, to interview conductors, musicians, music critics, and experienced listeners wherever I could meet them; in other words, to begin the systematic correlation of acoustical data and musical assessment that was requisite to a real understanding of the application of acoustics to the purposes of music in concert halls and opera houses.

In the next six years, I traveled in twenty nations on five continents. I heard music in over sixty halls—as far north as Helsinki and Turku, as far south as Buenos Aires, as far east as Moscow and Jerusalem, as far west as San Francisco. The acoustical behavior, the architectural drawings, the thoughtful comments of musicians and critics, together with my own experience listening in fifty-four concert halls and opera houses, are the meat of this book. From these sources, the attributes of acoustics that contribute most to musical quality have been isolated, and a new formulation has been devised for rating the acoustics of halls for music.

To illustrate the need for an advance in our understanding of musical acoustics, I should like to relate my own experience with the acoustical design of a concert hall that was undertaken by my firm in 1951. The architect and I combed the literature to get as much information as possible on the construction and acoustical performance of some of the world's best-known halls. We met with the local orchestra and learned their experiences in the various halls in which they had played on tour. Given the alternatives of a high-ceilinged rectangular-shaped hall, of the type of Symphony Hall, Boston, and a modern, low-ceilinged fan-shaped hall, modeled after one the orchestra had played in on tour, the architect and the building committee, swayed by considerations of aesthetics and comfort, chose the low-ceilinged modern hall. The committee and I understood that the acoustics of these differently shaped halls were different, but the acoustical literature offered no definitive basis for a choice between them. By opening day, however, my interviews with musicians and professional music critics, correlated with data newly taken on a number of halls, began to suggest that the new hall would not rank among the world's greatest auditoriums. It was too late to make changes; the interior was finished. The hall that had been chosen for comfort and beauty was now ready to be judged for its acoustical quality.

As I write this page, I have before me two sentences from a *Saturday Review* article written by Irving Kolodin after a visit to the hall, "The music tends to spread out and dissipate in the modified U-shaped room. . . . There would seem to be some relatively simple solution to this problem, and it is likely to be achieved once the acousticians and their graphs have been retired to a proper place of honor in history."

I hope that my acoustical colleagues and I are not about to be retired, with or without honor, as the writer seems to expect, but if we are, who should take our place? The mythology of the past? Committees, promoters, seat designers? The choice is not between scientists and oracles, but between well-validated technical knowledge, incomplete though it may be, and the old wives' tales that have plagued us.

What are some of the myths that purport to account for the physical properties of the travel of sound?

SOME ACOUSTICAL MYTHOLOGY

Acoustics is one of the youngest classical sciences. Lord Rayleigh, an English physicist, recorded the theoretical foundations of the science in 1877. The first major advances in the application of acoustics to architecture were made by Wallace Clement Sabine in the period between 1898 and 1905. It was not until the second quarter of the twentieth century, following the development of the vacuum-tube amplifier, loudspeakers, and noise-free microphones, that acousticians began to amass the accurate data that would make of acoustics an effective engineering science. For before electronic equipment was invented, the student of acoustics lacked both a means to produce sounds that would meet his specifications, and a means to measure the strength of the sounds that were produced. Before these tools were available, the designer of a hall in which music was to be played could learn about acoustics only by observing other halls and speculating about which features were responsible for the glorious sonorities in one place and the muddled cacophony in another.

It is small wonder that in a thousand years a thousand myths arose to account for the mysteries of this subject. Or that these myths spread from city to city and age to age, added to and embellished, so that they have come down to us adorned with the patina of history, the credibility of axiom.

The owner of a famous concert hall may believe that the gold paint on the walls and statues is responsible for his hall's acoustical excellence. Another may believe that wooden beams in the attic benefit the sound of his hall. In both halls, the acoustics are undoubtedly excellent, and the feature the owner values is unquestionably present, but something more than deduction would be needed to demonstrate that these details do or do not significantly affect the quality of music performed therein.

Herbert von Karajan reminded me of one of the more deeply entrenched myths of acoustics when he said, "I don't suppose that you subscribe to the theory that broken wine bottles beneath the stage are good for the acoustics of a hall?" Indeed I do not. Precise acoustical measurements reveal that broken wine bottles under stages, in attics, in walls, or even heaped in the corners of a hall have no effect on acoustical quality. Broken wine bottles are often found inside the construction of European halls simply because workers, during the years of construction, flung the remnants of innumerable déjeuners into the most convenient and most hidden places. I invite anyone sufficiently interested to remove all the broken bottles from one of these halls and to demonstrate to himself that the effect on the acoustics is nil.

Some of the myths that have arisen from efforts to explain acoustical effects have persisted for generations and are accepted as fact by a great number of people. I shall take up several of them here. Later in the book (Chapter 6), where I describe the 54 concert halls and opera houses, some of these myths will flash into our view briefly, but illumined by the harsh light of facts, they will show clearly for the baseless superstitions they really are.

The whispering gallery

Many people have been awed by the description of a hall in which sound travels "perfectly" from one particular point to another particular point, and the myth has grown up that this feature must be a proof of extraordinary acoustics in the hall as a whole. Not only is this assumption unfounded, but any decision based on it may lead to further unsound and perhaps unfortunate consequences.

Let us suppose that a pin dropped into a stiff hat at one location in a hall can be heard clearly by a group of listeners seated in a particular distant location. If listeners seated in other parts of the hall cannot hear this demonstration of "perfect acoustics" it is hard to imagine the worth of the phenomenon. And, of course, to assume further that, because a hall with the pin-drop effect has several thousand seats, large halls have thus been shown to be capable of "perfect acoustics" is to compound an initial absurdity with a subsequent instance of pseudo logic.

In fact, a hall in which sound travels unusually well from one certain point to another is known as a "whispering gallery," and ever since Sabine's early writings (ca. 1900) has been considered an acoustical faux pas. The trouble is that where there is such excellent transmission of sound along one particular line, much of the sound produced at the source is carried along that line directly to one particular point and only a small portion of it is left to be transmitted to other points in the hall. Thus the hall cannot possibly be transmitting the same quality or quantity of sound to all its seats—it has one bright spot and is more or less dead elsewhere.

The Greek theater

Before responding to the question, "What are perfect acoustics—and did the Greeks have them?" we must define perfect acoustics. For musical performances, this is the subject of Chapter 3, "Acoustics and Music." To avoid duplication here, let us simply answer the questions, "For what purposes were the Greek outdoor theaters built?" and "Do we favor such theaters over indoor theaters where they exist in our country today?"

The Greek theater that I have in mind was built on the side of a hill, was semi-circular in shape, and was equipped with a sound-reflecting wall at the rear of the stage. It was used for speeches, drama, accompanied and unaccompanied song, choruses, and probably recitals by a few instruments. There was no music like the concert music that has been composed in Europe for musical groups since the thirteenth century.

The hillside site was chosen to reduce surrounding noise and to prevent nearby heads from interfering with the direct transmission of the sound to more remote ears—as would be true with a horizontal seating plan. The semi-circular shape was chosen to enable the greatest number of people to be seated as close as possible to the stage. A wall was erected at the rear of the stage to eliminate external noise and disturbing sights and to reflect the voices of the performers back into the audience.

It is generally believed that the performers in Greek theaters sang in loud voices. In many performances they wore masks which exaggerated their features so that they could be seen at greater distances. Small megaphones were sometimes built into these masks to amplify the performers' voices. The success of the Greek theater depended on absolute quiet—there was no nearby airway or autobahn—and on the adequate loudness of the performers' voices. The theater itself, when filled with an audience, was passive; its sole contribution to the speech or music was a single reflection of sound from the stage wall.

In order for the music of the eighteenth or nineteenth century to be performed effectively—to communicate to the audience faithfully the intent of the composer—the walls and ceiling of the concert hall in which it is played must set up a complex pattern of reverberation. Because the Greek theater is not enclosed, it makes a disappointing setting for the repertoire of a modern symphony orchestra. Most of us who have heard orchestral music performed outdoors in one of the large modern amphitheaters that are patterned after the Greek theater will attest to this fact. Not only do noise and weather intrude but in the rear of the theater the music may be deficient in loudness, and the fortissimos lacking in force. In any location, music composed in the style of the nineteenth century will lack the fullness of tone that can only come through reverberation.

The Greek theater in its time and place and for its purposes was highly successful. The assumption that it is excellent also for the performance of today's musical repertoire—particularly the music composed in the last century—must be viewed as one of the myths of acoustics.

Special external constructions

In the basement of the Philadelphia Academy of Music, there is a dry well in the shape of a gigantic teacup, about 20 feet in diameter and 11 feet deep, almost underneath the large chandelier that hangs from the center of the ceiling. This dry well is made of brick and cement, and many people who know of it believe that it was installed for acoustical purposes. As nearly as I have been able to determine, this tank was built beneath the floor to house an auxiliary supply of water, at a time (1857) when adequate fire protection was not yet available.

It is clearly not possible that a tank of this sort *beneath* a heavy wooden floor, heavy enough to support an audience, could affect the acoustics of the hall itself. In the first place, the cubic volume of this tank is only a half of one per cent that of the hall. But more important, a sound wave passing to an outside space through a floor or a plaster wall or a ceiling loses so great a part of its energy, that only a fraction of it arrives outside. A round-trip, double passage of the sound through that same surface, would entail so great a loss in energy that the hall would be impervious to its return. If an external cavity like this tank could exert an appreciable effect on the acoustics, think of the effect that would be exerted by external corridors, closets, electrical and ventilation shafts, attics, and all the other empty spaces that may surround an auditorium. Acoustical tests have amply verified that areas outside a room have only a minute effect on the acoustics inside the room, so long as there are no large openings such as open doors, windows, or grilles to provide a direct connection between the interior and exterior spaces.

Does a wooden interior ensure good acoustics?

On the analogy of the violin, many musicians are convinced that a concert hall should have a wooden lining on its inner walls. Since a violin is made of wood and the wood resonates and enhances its sound, they hypothesize that the side walls of a hall should be constructed to do the same thing.

Of course, surprises might await us if we were to crawl inside a violin and listen to music there. The sound of a violin as we hear it is produced by the vibration of its strings, which transmit energy into the belly and back of the instrument. These surfaces radiate sound in much the same way as does the lightweight paper cone of a loudspeaker; thus they must be thin, of light weight, and highly responsive to vibration. Thick, heavy surfaces could not easily be set into motion by the delicate vibrating strings, and thus a loud, clear tone would not emanate from a thick-walled violin.

In a concert hall, we do not want to radiate sounds beyond the walls of the hall, but rather we want to conserve the energy by keeping it inside. This requires that the walls be hard and heavy, made of plaster or masonry or thick wood. Contrary to popular impression, the great concert halls and opera houses of the world contain very little, if any, thin wood on the walls and ceilings—the very best of them are lined almost entirely with heavy plaster or thick, heavy wood—materials that keep the sound inside for the enjoyment of the listener.

Can excellent acoustics be achieved in a large hall?

If you were to listen to a Mozart symphony in the Royal Albert Hall in London, whose cubic volume is a huge 3,000,000 cubic feet, and compare it with the same music played in the Concertgebouw in Amsterdam or the Stadt-Casino in Basel, whose volumes are 663,000 and 370,000 cubic feet, respectively, you would feel immediately that large size has a detrimental effect on many kinds of music. Of course, you might have the opposite experience if you were to listen to a 300-piece military band in one of these smaller halls.

In a large hall, the time required for the sound to travel around the room is so great that the reverberant sound becomes dissociated from the sound that emanates from the stage, and a sort of general muddle results. In addition, the loudness of the sound that travels directly from the performer to the listener may diminish so much that it almost merges into the audience noise. A singer or a solo instrumentalist who stands on the stage of an enormous auditorium, hardly able to distinguish faces in the faraway rows of straining listeners, is struck with the foreboding that no effort he can make will be great enough to fill adequately that vast volume of space.

Small wonder that his voice or his instrument may sound thin and uncertain. Large halls and excellent acoustics are not easy to marry.

Can perfect proportions be specified?

If the Boston Symphony Orchestra were to place itself along one side of its long, rectangular hall, and the audience were to stretch from the stage to the rear of the hall, turned 90 degrees so as to face the newly placed orchestra, would the music please the listeners as well as the present arrangement does? If the roof were to be rolled back, leaving the hall open to the sky, or if the balconies were to be eliminated and a new ceiling hung a few feet above the audience's heads, would the acoustics change? Clearly, great differences would result from any one of these radical changes, and one of the tasks of modern acoustics is to try to find formulas that can predict the effect of different proportions on the acoustics of the hall.

As a matter of fact, the length of a hall is generally limited to the maximum distance from which people can see the stage. The width might well be set by acoustical considerations, but often it is determined by economics, the size of audience, the generosity of the seating, and the number and size of the balconies. Many older halls were designed to have a relatively small number of seats and were thus made quite narrow. The heights of the best of the older halls are nearly the same as the heights of the best halls built today. The height of a hall is closely associated with the after-ring, and the present height follows from listeners' concurrence on a certain preferred reverberation time.

As financial considerations pushed the walls of the concert hall farther and farther apart, the quality of the musical sound inevitably deteriorated. But the course of the deterioration with size can be stopped. Through new developments in acoustical science, countermeasures can be taken to create the acoustical equivalent of a decreased width. Reflectors or baffles provided at strategic locations at the sides of the proscenium and over the audience can make the sound travel in the paths of a narrower enclosure. Thus another myth of acoustics has been exposed—it is not a magic ratio of dimensions that is requisite to good musical acoustics, but rather the factor of "acoustic narrowness," provided either by a narrow hall or by sound-reflecting baffles.

Are steel, glass, and concrete inimical to good acoustics?

Steel, glass, and concrete may, like thin wood, be misused in the construction of a hall intended primarily for music. If steel and glass account for a large part of the surface of a concert hall they are subject to the same acoustical requirements as are any other surface materials: they must be thick and heavy, so that sound cannot radiate through them. If they are used sparingly, for decoration, they can be quite satisfactory, provided they do not ring or vibrate. Concrete has nearly the same acoustical properties as plaster, which is the lining material of most successful halls. Some of the least successful halls have wooden interiors and only very small areas of glass. Two of the world's most highly praised halls—the Neues Gewandhaus of Leipzig, which was destroyed in World War II, and the Grosser Musikvereinssaal in Vienna—feature large glass clerestories. We must look further to find the factors that account for the good and bad acoustics of concert halls.

Do the acoustics improve as a hall ages?

Many of the halls that are best loved were built in the last century, and this fact has given rise to the notion that not the original construction but the process of aging has somehow generated the excellence. We can be quite certain, however, that unless the structure or the seating, or the draperies, carpeting, or other sound-absorbent materials are changed, the acoustics of a hall remain unchanged throughout its life.

Good and bad halls exist in every age, and good and bad halls have probably been built in every period. It is more than likely that the old halls that are still standing are among the best that were built. Very few halls that compared badly with their contemporaries are still with us. In fact, poor halls are often destroyed or replaced before they are 50 years old, as Boston's most recent Opera House (1909 to 1958) and New York's Italian Opera House (1833 to 1839) remind us. On the other hand, heroic measures are often taken to preserve good halls; witness the public's response to the news that Carnegie Hall in New York was to be destroyed. A law was rushed through the New York State Legislature making possible its acquisition by the City of New York. A citizens' committee was formed to pressure the city into buying it and leasing it to an operating group. Carnegie Hall was saved in 1960 because it was a hall with a tradition of great music and fine acoustics, and many people, both musicians and music lovers, rallied to its rescue. But because the old halls that have survived are generally good ones, and because time has not yet weeded out the poorer of the new halls, it is easy to conclude that halls, like cognac, grow better with the passing years.

Perhaps the question whether concert halls improve with age should be framed to ask, does the reputation of a concert hall grow better with the passage of time? And the answer might well be, yes. A good hall, adorned by distinguished artists, may develop the aura of a great hall. And the excellence of a hall that has been well loved may, when it no longer exists, seem beyond comparison with that of any hall whose idiosyncrasies can still be probed.

2
Sounds and Listeners

Acoustical phenomena have been an unavoidable part of man's environment since the earliest times. Most living organisms not only produce sound but respond to it. It is likely that man, taking shelter from the elements, first discovered acoustical effects in caves and in inlets along the sea. The inadvertent production of acoustical effects may have led to the development of musical instruments. Primitive man would hardly have failed to notice the sound produced when a hollow log is pounded by the wings of a large bird. He would soon have discovered that stretching an animal's skin over the open end of such a log would create a drum with loud and interesting resonances. From ancient instruments of warfare, such as the bow, he could learn of the vibratory sound made by a stretched string. From his own voice, which is a wind instrument, he could learn of the sound-producing characteristics of a pipe driven by a vibrating reed. In those familiar encounters—with the cave, the percussion instrument, the stretched string, and the human throat and mouth—lie the elements of all acoustics.

Sound is created by materials that vibrate. The vibrating surfaces of strings or membranes set into motion the molecules of the air surrounding them. Not content with vibrating alone, these moving air molecules jostle their neighbors and produce an outward-traveling wave which progresses at a speed of 1130 feet per second. Sound waves can easily be heard outdoors at a distance of several hundred or even, under favorable conditions of the atmosphere, several thousand feet.

Audible sound involves the ear. The vibration of the air particles in a sound wave, minute as it is, sets the eardrums in motion. The nervous system is so sensitive that it responds to a movement of the eardrum equal to only one-tenth the diameter of a hydrogen molecule! The manner in which the ear transforms physical vibrations into recognizable sounds that can arouse understanding and emotions has engaged the attention of psychologists, physiologists, physicists, and linguists, and many of the answers are still being sought.

Not all vibrations, however, are alike. A long string or a long pipe or a large drum vibrates slowly and produces a sound of low frequency, a

13

low-pitched sound.* If a string or pipe is made shorter—for example, when a violinist presses a string against the fingerboard of his instrument—the vibrations are more rapid and produce a sound of higher pitch. Size has a similar effect on the pitch of a drum. Vibrations differ from each other also in the intensity of their motion. A performer may cause a string, a pipe, or a drum of any size, and hence of any pitch, to vibrate with greater or smaller amplitude, and by so doing he produces a louder or fainter tone. And finally, a string or a membrane that is made to vibrate in several different ways will radiate several sounds simultaneously, which results in a sound of a particular timbre. We can say, therefore, that musical sounds have pitch, loudness, and the quality that makes it possible to distinguish one instrument from another, timbre.

Strings and organ pipes

The motion of the stretched string of a member of the viol family provides the most easily visualized types of vibration and gives us insight into the more complicated problems of room acoustics. Although it is not possible to produce a pure tone with a violinist's bow, in the laboratory a string can be made to sound only at its fundamental frequency, the lowest tone possible for its length and tension. A string can also be made to sound at each of a series of higher tones, whose frequencies are multiples of the frequency of the fundamental. Each of these vibrations corresponds to a different form of motion of the string.

Scientists call each way in which a string may vibrate a *normal mode of vibration,* and a single string can vibrate in many normal modes of vibration simultaneously. Each normal mode has its own *normal* or *resonance frequency.* The fundamental sound of a string is produced by a mode of vibration in which the center part oscillates at a larger amplitude than any other part, as can be seen in *(a)* of Figure 2.1. The large amplitude at the center gradually tapers off to zero at the two clamped ends.

* In acoustics, frequency is the physical measure of the number of vibrations per second in a pure tone, whereas pitch refers to the subjective impression of frequency. On the whole, the musician uses pitch to define his musical scale in the way the scientist uses frequency.

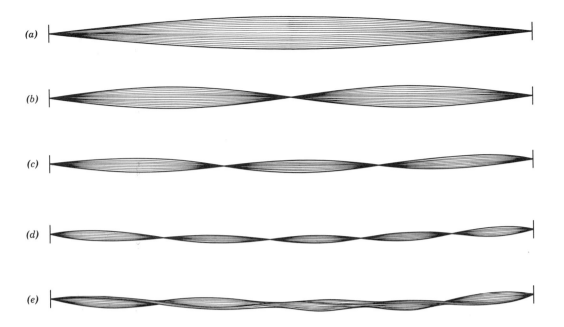

Figure 2.1. Vibration of a string: *(a)* at its fundamental or first harmonic; *(b)* at its second harmonic; *(c)* at its third harmonic; *(d)* at its fifth harmonic; and *(e)* in several harmonics simultaneously.

In music these modes of vibration are known as harmonics, because their frequencies are harmonically related to each other. Thus the lowest mode of vibration for a string is also called the fundamental or the first harmonic. To produce the second harmonic, illustrated in *(b)* of Figure 2.1, the string vibrates in two segments as though it were clamped not only at the two ends but also at the middle. The frequency of this mode of vibration is exactly twice that of the fundamental, and its pitch is thus one octave higher.

To produce the third harmonic, a point on each side of the middle as well as the two ends stands still [see *(c)* of Figure 2.1]. Between the two points of zero motion there are regions of large amplitude. Here the frequency is three times that of the fundamental, and the pitch is an octave and a fifth above the fundamental.

It is also possible to excite the string in such a way that four points of zero amplitude occur [see *(d)*]. This happens at the fifth harmonic. Again, halfway between points of zero amplitude there are large excursions of the string.

In *(e)*, a complex form of vibration is shown in which a number of the possible modes of vibration occur simultaneously. Indeed, when a violinist bows a string, by proper placement of the bow along the string and by correct fingering, he produces a sound that consists not of the fundamental or one of the higher harmonics alone, but rather of a combination of many harmonics. It is the particular combination of different forms of vibration, harmonically related to each other, that gives an instrument its peculiar *timbre*—a sound quality different from the timbre of all other instruments even when they are sounding the same fundamental tone.

Once the string is set in motion in one or more of its harmonic modes of vibration, it takes a little while for the vibration to die down. This persistence of sound, which diminishes in amplitude after the bow is removed, is called the *after-ring*.

The rate at which sound decays is different for different modes of vibration. When several harmonics are excited simultaneously by bowing and the bow is removed from the string, the higher harmonics generally die down first, leaving the fundamental tone to persist alone for a little longer. A violinist can suppress the tone simply by leaving the bow in stationary contact with the string.

Now let us consider a closed organ pipe. In an organ pipe it is not the solid matter that is in motion but rather the particles of air inside the pipe. These air particles are set in motion by a jet of air at the embouchure, and a sound wave results, which travels to the far end of the pipe. There it is reflected back to the opposite end, where again it is reflected, and so it goes back and forth, combining with its continuously generated self. At the two ends of the pipe, which are rigid, there is obviously no net motion of the air particles, just as there was no motion at the ends of the string. The organ pipe, like the string, has many possible modes of vibration, each with its own normal or resonance frequency.

In producing the mode of vibration with the lowest frequency—the fundamental—the air particles halfway between the ends of the pipe vibrate vigorously along the axis of the pipe. For the second harmonic, the air particles at the center stand still, and at two positions halfway between the ends and the middle there are intense vibrations. Just as for the string, the second harmonic is an octave higher in pitch than the fundamental. For the third harmonic, there are two positions along the pipe at which the particle motion is zero, while between these positions and the ends there are three positions of vigorous vibration.

When the air to the embouchure is stopped, the sound gradually dies

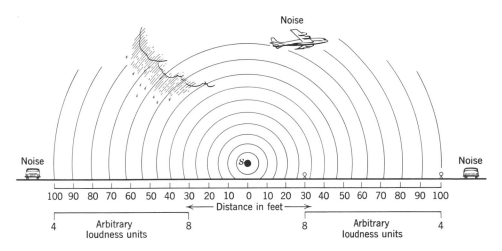

Figure 2.2. Sound in an open field with no wind. The sound at 100 feet is one-half as loud as that at 30 feet, although the amplitude of vibration of the air particles is roughly one-third. The weather and the noise produced by automobiles and aircraft make listening outdoors difficult.

down or decays. In an organ pipe, just as with a string, several modes of vibration can occur simultaneously, each with its own frequency, intensity, and rate of decay.

We are now ready to consider sound in larger spaces—out of doors and in rooms.

Sound in an open field

All of us have stood at one time or another in an open field and listened to sounds emanating from a distant source. If the source is steady, the sound becomes louder as we approach it. As we walk away from it, it becomes fainter. Because there are no reflected waves (as in the closed end of an organ pipe) the vibration of the air particles in the sound wave decreases in amplitude as the wave recedes from the sound source. In fact, the amplitude of the sound wave that reaches us drops to one-half as we double the distance between us and the source of sound.

In Figure 2.2 a source of sound is located at the point S just above the ground. The source radiates sound uniformly in all directions. If there is wind, the sound will be louder downwind and weaker upwind. Wind also produces turbulence which distorts the sound.

First let us set up an arbitrary scale of loudness units so that, if we stand 30 feet from a source of sound, its loudness will be called 8 units.* As we move away from the source of sound, the loudness drops. At a

* By "loudness" we mean a subjective evaluation rather than a physical measurement of how strong a sound is. The unit of loudness commonly used by acousticians is the sone, but since we have no continuing need for the sone in this book, we shall not introduce it here.

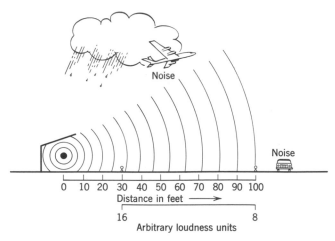

Figure 2.3. Sound from an orchestra enclosure in an open field with no wind. The enclosure has doubled the loudness of the sound over that in Figure 2.2. The weather and some noise still interfere with listening.

distance of 100 feet, the amplitude of vibration of the air particles is roughly one-third what it was at 30 feet. But although there is a three-to-one decrease in movement of the air particles and, hence, of the eardrum, we hear only a two-to-one drop in its loudness. At a distance of 100 feet from the source, the loudness of the sound is now 4 on our arbitrary scale.

One of the difficulties we encounter when we try to listen to a sound outdoors is our inability to hear one sound alone. We find ourselves subjected to the sounds of passing automobiles, children playing, the rustling of leaves, and, even far out in the country, aircraft passing overhead. Above all, in the open, we are subject to the vagaries of the weather. If there is a small musical source, and we are quite close to it—for example, a string quartet playing on an open lawn—we may hear it quite well. But at some distance from a source of music, when there are various kinds of noises, and perhaps wind as well, listening is difficult and may be unrewarding.

Sound outdoors with an acoustical enclosure and no audience

How can listening conditions outdoors be improved? If an acoustical enclosure is added around the sides and above the source of the sound (see Figure 2.3) two improvements result. First, a barrier is created that shields the listener from extraneous noises coming from one side. And second, the enclosure gathers up the sound that would normally have been radiated upward and toward the back of the orchestra and redirects it toward the audience. The loudness at 30 feet and at 100 feet has approximately doubled to 16 units and 8 units. Of course, the listener is still susceptible to interference from traffic and aircraft noise, and he is still at the mercy of the weather.

An acoustical enclosure also provides two valuable assets for the

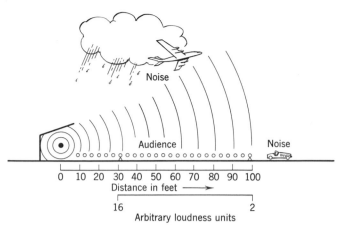

Figure 2.4. Sound from an orchestra enclosure with an audience. The loudness of sound decreases rapidly as it travels over an audience. We see that the loudness has decreased at the rear to one-fourth its value at the rear in Figure 2.3.

performers within it. It enables each musician to hear himself and the other musicians better since the sounds are amplified by the acoustical enclosure and reflected back to his ears. Also it contributes to blending the orchestral sound, so that when it emerges from the enclosure it sounds more cohesive than a collection of instruments playing separately though in good ensemble.

Sound outdoors with an enclosure and an audience

The desirable state of affairs just described is upset, however, when an audience is assembled, as is shown in Figure 2.4. The people absorb sound. When a sound wave is radiated outward from the orchestra enclosure across the heads of an audience seated on a horizontal floor, the loudness of the sound drops more rapidly with increasing distance from the stage than it would if there were no people present. At the rear, the music is about one-eighth as loud as it is at the front. In other words, the sound at the rear is about one-fourth as loud with an audience as without one.

For a demonstration of this effect, compare the loudness heard sitting and standing at the rear of an outdoor gathering on level ground. It is startling how much louder the sound becomes when you stand up. Incidentally, this experiment demonstrates the absurdity of seating an audience in the manner illustrated in Figure 2.5. Since sound does not easily bend around corners, in the arrangement shown the loudness at the rear would drop by about another factor of 4. The ancient Egyptians, Greeks, and Romans recognized this elementary principle, and they built their outdoor stadiums with the seats sloping upward or raked.

Steeply raked seating offers many advantages (Figure 2.6). First, the noise from sources at the back of the audience has been eliminated. The noise from behind the orchestra can be eliminated by the erection of a wall

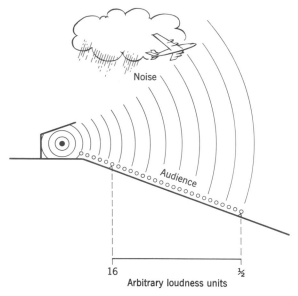

Figure 2.5. A poor way to listen outdoors. The sound at the rear is one-fourth as loud as it is at the rear in Figure 2.4.

behind the orchestra enclosure. There is also a gain in loudness since each person's ears are no longer blocked by the heads in front of him. The loudness at the back of the audience is about the same as it would be if there were no people seated between the orchestra and the back row. We have not eliminated the noise of aircraft, nor are we protected from the weather. In a very dry climate, such as Greece or Palestine, this type of stadium has been quite successful for music or drama, particularly at night, when the winds have died down and after the heat of the day. Today, however, airplanes fly everywhere and at all hours. The stadium sketched in Figure 2.6 is reminiscent of Lewissohn Stadium in New York, but at Lewissohn Stadium there is a wide plateau between the orchestra enclosure and the first rows, with openings to the street on the sides. Anyone who has attended concerts at the Lewissohn Stadium on a summer evening does not need to be told that noise is distracting—noise from aircraft, city traffic, children playing, and other activities in the surrounding areas.

Sound in an absorbent room with an audience

To protect our stadium from weather and noise, it is necessary only to erect side walls and a roof over the whole seating area, and to line them with highly efficient sound-absorbing materials (see Figure 2.7). The acoustical conditions have not changed, since the sound that radiates upward and to the sides is completely absorbed, as it was in the open space. But noise from aircraft and the ill effects of the weather are now eliminated. Music played here is "pure," heard just as it is emitted by the orchestra

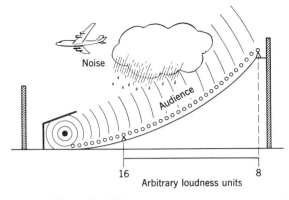

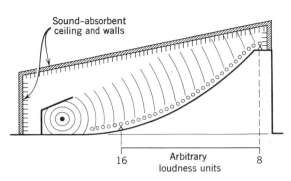

Figure 2.6. The loudness of sound at the rear of an audience is enhanced by sloping the seating upwards. Here the loudness is about the same as in Figure 2.3. In addition the noise from sources on the ground is reduced.

Figure 2.7. A means for eliminating noise and weather while preserving outdoor conditions. No enhancement of sound is provided because there is no reverberation in a room whose walls are highly sound absorbent.

without embellishment by room acoustics. A room of this kind, lined with sound-absorbing material is called acoustically "dead," because it does not alter the music in any way.

We are now ready to investigate what happens when we bring a source of sound into a hard-walled auditorium, a "live" hall, like the one illustrated in Figure 2.8.

Sound in a reverberant hall with an audience

A reverberant room can be envisaged as a kind of oversized organ pipe. Sound waves are reflected back and forth between every pair of parallel walls; they also travel obliquely in ways that may involve four or six walls. If the room is irregularly shaped the sound waves travel every conceivable way, crossing through each other, repeating on themselves, and in their travel building up normal modes of vibration that are highly complex. In a concert hall thousands of such modes are established. Those with the lowest normal frequencies lie well below the audible range. Since there are so many disparate distances in a room, the frequencies of most modes of vibration are not harmonically related, as they are on a violin string or in an organ pipe where only one length is involved.

The modes of vibration of a hall are so numerous that a single tone sounded by a violin may excite several hundred of them. For example, if a musical instrument sounds a tone with five harmonics, all the possible modes of vibration in the room that have normal frequencies somewhere near these five harmonics are set into vibration. Thus five groups of modes of vibration are excited, each group containing perhaps fifty or more individual modes of vibration, and each group of modes dying away at its own rate. These excited groups of "organ pipes of the hall" cause the tone of the violin to

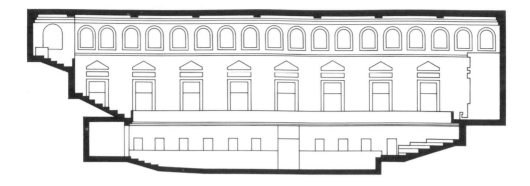

Figure 2.8. A concert hall with plaster ceiling and walls. This style of hall was built in the nineteenth century. It is quite reverberant and is particularly well suited to the music written in the nineteenth century.

persist for a short time after the original tone is stopped. This persistence of sound, with its gradual decay, is called *reverberation.*

The sound in a "live" room is composed of two parts, the direct sound and the reverberant sound. The "true" tone of an instrument is carried in the part that travels directly to a listener's ears, the direct sound. A fraction of a second later, he hears the first reflection from the walls and ceiling. And then, as these waves travel back and forth in the hall, they produce many normal modes of vibration, each of which decays at its own speed, producing the reverberant part of the sound. In a very large room or in a cathedral, the reverberant sound may persist for several seconds, generally for a longer time at the bass than at the treble.

A *live* room is acoustically superior to a *dead* room. Some of the advantages it affords will be discussed in the following paragraphs.

More uniform loudness: In a hall, as well as outdoors, the direct sound from a musical instrument diminishes in loudness at it travels away from its source. At the back of the hall the loudness of the direct sound may have dropped to as low as one-eighth its original level. This difference in loudness between the back and the front of the hall depends on the rake of the seats and the nature of the reflecting surfaces around the stage and at the front of the audience. It is relatively common for the direct sound that reaches the rear of an auditorium to be between three-quarters and one-quarter of the loudness at the front. But in a "live" room, the direct sound is heard in combination with reverberant sound, and the listener has the impression that the loudness is more uniform here than in a sound-absorbent space (Figure 2.7) or outdoors, where the sound does not reverberate. This does not mean that the sound is the same at every seat. At the front of a live hall, the direct sound is loud, and the reverberation is not pronounced. At the rear the direct sound is weaker and the reverberation is more apparent.

SOUNDS AND LISTENERS

Hence, the acoustical "texture" of the music at the front of the hall differs from that at the rear. There are other places in the hall where the acoustical texture changes, for instance, under a balcony, where one is shielded from hearing part of the reverberant sound, or in a particular location where faults in the design have caused the sound to focus.

Enhancement of bass and treble: Two advantages of a live hall are the enhancement of the bass and of the treble. The effect of reverberation in a hall is to increase the loudness of the sound, particularly at locations far removed from the source. Through the choice of certain materials for the surfaces of the hall, the reverberation time at low frequencies can be made long or short compared to that at high frequencies, and the loudness of the bass can thus be enhanced relative to the treble, or vice versa. The brilliance of the treble can also be enhanced through the strategic placement of sound-reflecting surfaces.

Fullness of tone: Reverberation sustains the tones that are sounded in the hall, fills the spaces between them, and causes each tone to blend somewhat with its predecessor, with results that are more than a mere enhancement of loudness. This blending of one tone with another gives music a special, usually desirable character that is called fullness of tone. Certain compositions depend very strongly upon fullness of tone and would sound thin without it. But a very long reverberation time does not benefit all styles of music; indeed the next chapter discusses the various periods of musical composition and the degree of fullness of tone that is most compatible with music of different styles.

Range of crescendo: A live hall augments the range of crescendos and diminuendos. The reverberation in a room is not obvious when the orchestra is playing pianissimo. However, as the intensity of the music swells, the participation of the hall becomes more and more apparent. The reverberation intensifies the growth of the sound. To hear a full orchestra at double forte in a responsive concert hall can be a stirring experience.

Sound diffusion: Sound diffusion is another consequence of reverberation. In a live hall the music arrives at a listener's ears from all directions. The listener has the sensuous experience of feeling bathed in a sea of sound that comes from all directions. Listening in a dead hall is like listening outdoors—the sound all comes from one direction.

Intimacy and texture: Two other advantages, acoustical intimacy and texture, will be discussed in later chapters after some additional concepts have been introduced.

Decibels

The word decibel impresses the non-specialist as a kind of yardstick by which the strength of sounds is measured. The decibel is a logarithm of the ratio of two amounts of power, and it can properly be applied to the measurement of any kind of power transmission, even the transmission of visible light. When the decibel is used as an acoustic measure the number of decibels is defined at ten times the logarithm of the ratio between two sound powers. Often one of these powers is defined as the faintest sound power that can be detected by the average young listener. This very low level is called a *reference sound intensity,* and by international agreement it is defined as 10^{-16} watt per square centimeter. Consequently the lowest sound level that a listener hears is the ratio of this lowest audible sound power divided by itself, which equals 1, and the logarithm of 1 is 0. Thus, 0 decibels is the threshold of hearing. The scale that concerns us in musical acoustics extends up to about 120 decibels, at which level the ear begins to tickle; in this vicinity is the threshold of discomfort.

Doubling the acoustic power results in a constant increase in the number of decibels, regardless of where one starts. That is to say, when the acoustic power is multiplied by 2, the number of decibels is increased by 3, since 0.3 is the logarithm of 2 (and 0.3 is multiplied by 10, as was explained above). Thus quadrupling the sound power at the source increases the sound by 6 decibels; doubling it once again increases the sound by an additional 3 to 9 decibels. Ten times the power means an increase of 10 decibels, 100 times the power equals 20 decibels, 1000 times the power equals 30 decibels, and so forth. The range of audible sounds is illustrated in column *(a)* of Figure 2.9, and the accompanying sound-power ratios are given in column *(b)*.

Audience noise in a concert hall has a sound level of 20 to 40 decibels, depending upon how quietly the audience sits. The air conditioning may

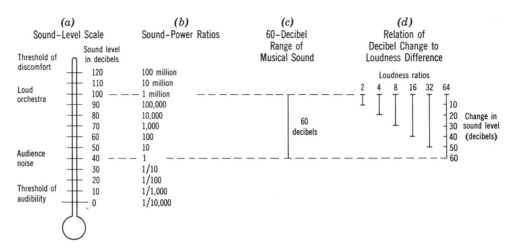

Figure 2.9. The decibel scale: *(a)* range in levels from threshold of audibility (0 to 10 decibels) to discomfort threshold (about 120 decibels); *(b)* scale of power ratios assuming 40 decibels as a reference power of 1; *(c)* 60-decibel range of musical sound; *(d)* each change of 10 decibels in sound level causes the loudness to double or half—thus, a change of 40 decibels would change the loudness by a factor of 16. The various scales show that a 1,000,000/1 power ratio equals a sound level increase of 60 decibels equals a loudness increase of 64 times.

also add about the same amount of noise. In a pianissimo passage, the sound of the string section in an orchestra may be barely audible above the audience and air-conditioning noise. During a double forte passage, accompanied by full percussion, the sound may go as high as 110 or 115 decibels. In some small halls, with a very large orchestra and heavy percussion, some listeners report that their ears "tickle." Since some people are more sensitive to loud sounds than others, there may be some who experience tickle in the ear before a level of 120 decibels has been reached. On the average, musical compositions have a range of about 60 decibels between their faintest and loudest sounds. Note that in Figure 2.9 this range is shown as extending from 40 to 100 decibels, but it varies from performance to performance and may on occasion reach considerably higher levels.

A change in sound level should not be confused with a change in loudness. Loudness refers to the subjective evaluation of how loud a sound seems, whereas decibels measure the amount of energy in a sound wave. When we increase the energy in a sound wave, the loudness increases also, but the relation between them is not linear. Two identical bells rung at the same time do not sound twice as loud as one of them alone, in much the same way that two 40-watt bulbs do not make a room twice as bright as one. It takes about 10 decibels added to the energy in a sound wave to double the loudness; when we add 20 decibels, the loudness becomes four times as great. And conversely, when 10 decibels are subtracted, the sound becomes half as loud, and when 20 decibels are subtracted, a fourth as loud. A chart

25

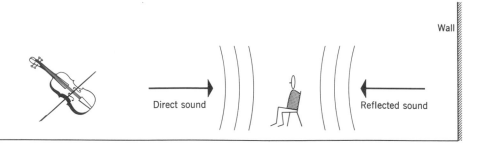

Figure 2.10. Direct sound travels straight from the violin to the listener and arrives first. The reflected sound has bounced off the wall and arrives a fraction of a second later.

illustrating this relation is shown in Figure 2.9, column *(d)*. Like the relation of power to the decibel scale, the relation of loudness to sound energy is constant, no matter where we start on the scale. All up and down the scale, an increase of 10 decibels corresponds to a doubling of the loudness.

Initial-time-delay gap

Figure 2.10 shows a violin producing a tone that travels outward in the direction of a listener. Some distance behind the listener is a wall. The sound that the listener hears first is the direct sound, the sound that travels directly to his ears from the violin. The sound he hears next has traveled from the violin to the wall behind him, bounced off the wall, and returned to him. In the time graph of Figure 2.11, the direct sound is shown arriving at the listener's ear first, followed, as the time scale at the bottom shows, by the reflected sound from the wall behind him.

Persons trained in listening—for example, blind people, who receive all their cues about the environment around them through senses other than the eye—can "measure" the size of a room or judge the distance to a wall behind them by the length of the time interval between the direct sound and the first reflected sound. The ability of a blind listener to judge the size of a room was remarked on by Erasmus Darwin in his famous *Zoonomia,* written in 1795 (Volume II, page 487). He wrote, "The late blind Justice Fielding walked for the first time into my room, when he once visited me, and after speaking a few words said, 'This room is about 22 feet long, 18 wide and 12 high;' all of which he guessed by the ear with great accuracy." This ability to observe the size of a hall by listening is not limited to the blind. Experienced music listeners may be able to sense the approximate size of a hall by the sound of music played in it, that is to say, by the length of the "initial-time-delay gap."

The initial-time-delay gap is the difference in times of arrival at a listener's position between the direct sound and the first reflected sound.

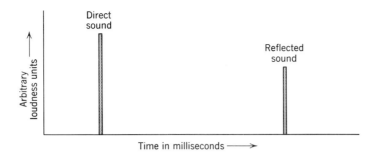

Figure 2.11. A time graph showing, reading from left to right, that the reflected sound arrives at a listener's ears a fraction of a second after the direct sound.

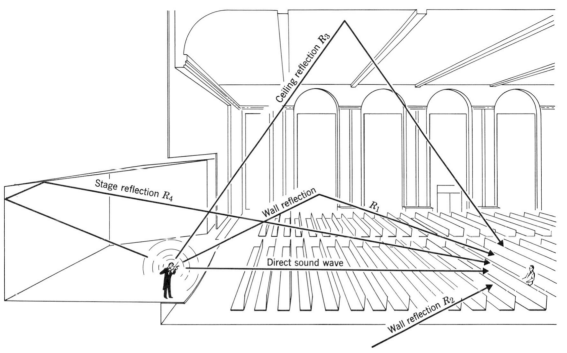

Figure 2.12. Showing the paths of direct sound and several reflected sound waves in a concert hall. Reflections also occur from balcony faces, rear wall, niches, and any other reflecting surfaces.

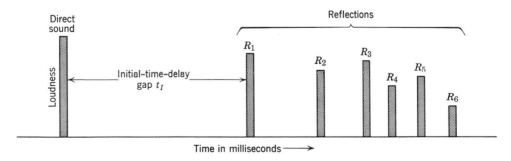

Figure 2.13. Time diagram showing that at a listener's ears, the sound that travels directly from the performer arrives first, and after a gap, reflections from the walls, ceiling, stage enclosure, and other reflecting surfaces arrive in rapid succession. The height of a bar suggests the loudness of the sound. This kind of diagram is called a reflection pattern, and the initial-time-delay gap can be measured from it.

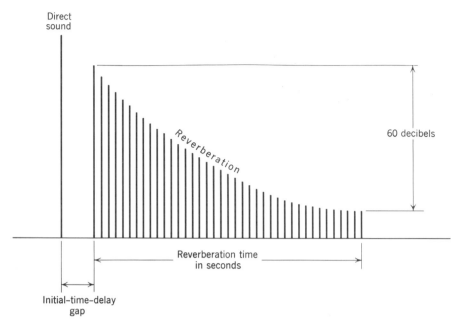

Figure 2.14. A sound-decay diagram measured at a listener's ears. Here the direct sound enters at the left of the diagram. The initial-time-delay gap is followed by a succession of sound reflections. The reverberation time of the room is defined as the length of time required for the reverberant sound to decay 60 decibels.

Although it has seldom been used as a factor in the design of halls for music prior to the studies discussed in this book, the initial-time-delay gap turns out to be one of the most powerful measures of the acoustical quality of halls for music. Its significance will be discussed at length in Chapter 9; the method by which it is measured is given in Appendix 3.

Figure 2.12 shows a room in which a soloist is sounding a tone. The direct sound travels from the instrument to the listener. Sound also travels to the listener via reflections from each of the walls, the ceiling, the stage enclosure, and, if there is a balcony, the balcony faces. The time diagram of Figure 2.13 shows the direct sound arriving ahead of all the reflections since it travels by the shortest possible path. After an initial time delay, the first reflection R_1 arrives from the surface closest to the listener. Almost immediately, a second reflection R_2 arrives from the next closest surface, then a third reflection R_3 arrives from a third surface, and so on. The plot of Figure 2.13 is called a *reflection pattern.*

Reverberation and reverberation time

Sound travels at a speed of about 1130 feet per second. If the walls and ceiling of a room are not absorbent, that is to say, if they are not covered with sound-absorbing draperies or porous materials, the sound will not just reflect once from each wall, but will bounce from wall to wall, passing by the listener's ear many times in a second and creating many modes of vibration in the room. Obviously, the sound loses some energy both at the walls and in its excursion through the air, and thus the level of the sound decreases each time it traverses the room and is reflected. In other words, the levels of the normal modes of vibration decay with time.

In acoustics, *reverberation* is defined as the sound that persists in a room after the tone that created it is stopped (see Figure 2.14). The length of time it takes for the level of the sound to decay by 60 decibels is defined as the *reverberation time*. It is generally measured in seconds.

Echo

An echo is a sound reflection that is excessively delayed after the direct sound and is loud enough to be obtrusive. A reflection is generally heard as an echo if it is delayed after the direct sound more than about 70 milliseconds, and is sufficiently loud to be heard clearly above the general reverberation.

3
Acoustics and Music

Daniel Pinkham, composer-conductor, organist and choir director at King's Chapel in Boston, says, "I am acutely aware of the different acoustics in which I perform or for which I write. My experience of performing in and writing for King's Chapel has changed my whole point of view about musical acoustics. I had long felt, as many of my colleagues do, that the only tolerable acoustics for church music is a room with a long reverberation time. But I am now convinced that this is too broad a generalization; some church music, if it is carefully selected and performed, can actually sound to best advantage in a moderately dry room."

Daniel Pinkham sounds the theme for this chapter when he observes that acoustics plays a part in all stages of the musical process—in composition, in performance, and in listening. This observation is neither novel nor unique. Bach knew the difference between the live acoustics of the St. Jacobi Kirche in Luebeck and the relatively dry acoustics of the Thomaskirche in Leipzig. His compositions for organ, written for churches like the St. Jacobi, differ markedly in style from his *St. Matthew Passion*, written for the Thomaskirche.

ACOUSTICS AND COMPOSITION

Music is sound or a combination of sounds that varies continuously or discontinuously with time, usually rhythmically, changing in pitch, timbre, and loudness in such a way as to communicate something to listeners in its own terms. The composition and performance of music are arts.

Acoustics, taken in the broadest sense, is the science of sound. Frequency, amplitude, wave form, resonance, manner of propagation, and responses to tones—these are some of the things about which acousticians ask questions and formulate answers. In a more restricted and popular sense, acoustics is defined as those qualities of a space that affect the production, transmission, and perception of music or speech.

The art of music and the science of sound must fuse if criteria are to be established for the design of halls in which music is to be played, since the experience of music can never be divorced from the acoustics of the space in which it is performed. Depending on how a hall affects what they hear, the musicians play differently; both consciously and unconsciously they adjust their performances to the acoustics. The hall must transfer their music to the listeners, preserving the musical qualities of intimacy, definition, timbre, balance, and dynamic range; it must contribute fullness of tone, loudness, and a wide range of crescendo and decrescendo. In short, a fine hall enhances the music in some ways, without detracting from it in others.

When I first contemplated this study, I wondered whether individual musical preferences would be so diverse or so arbitrary as to preclude the establishment of criteria for the design of halls for the presentation of music. I have found considerable agreement among musicians and skilled listeners, not only on what constitutes good acoustics, but even on their acoustical preferences for music written in various styles. That is to say, among musicians and music critics there is indeed a preference for performing and hearing the concertos of Bach in small halls with relatively low reverberation times and the richly orchestrated symphonic compositions of the late nineteenth century in larger, relatively reverberant halls.

This agreement bolsters the view that associated with each style of musical composition there is an optimum acoustical environment for its performance. This is not to say that every piece of music has a certain acoustical space for which it was designed, in the way that a building is designed for a specific plot of land. But many musical compositions seem to have been written for performance in particular acoustical settings. Thurston Dart, the musicologist, says [*The Interpretation of Music*, Hutchinson's University Library, Hutchinson House, London, pp. 56–57 (1954)]:

But even a superficial study shows that early composers were very aware of the effect on their music of the surroundings in which it was to be performed, and that they deliberately shaped their music accordingly. Musical acoustics may be roughly divided into "resonant," "room," and "outdoor." Plainsong is resonant music; so is the harmonic style of Léonin and Pérotin. . . . Pérotin's music, in fact, is perfectly adapted to the acoustics of the highly resonant cathedral (Notre Dame, Paris) for which it was written. . . . Gabrieli's music for brass consort is resonant, written for the Cathedral of St. Mark's; music for brass consort by Hassler or Matthew Locke is open-air music, using quite a different style from the same composers' music for stringed instruments, designed to be played indoors. Purcell distinguished in style between the music he wrote for Westminster Abbey and the music he wrote for the Chapel Royal; both styles differ from that of his theatre music, written for performance in completely "dead" surroundings. The forms used by Mozart and Haydn in their chamber and orchestral music are identical; but the details of style (counterpoint, ornamentation, rhythm, the layout of chords and the rate at which harmonies change) will vary according to whether they are writing room-music, concert-music or street-music.

Such a list could be extended indefinitely, though it is doubtful whether the list would include all the composers of the present day. Our own age has grown very insensitive to nuances of this kind.

A present-day example of considerable interest is provided by Daniel Pinkham:

Music that I have composed for King's Chapel in Boston is in a style which might sound muddy when performed in a reverberant concert hall but which sounds at its best in this rather dry environment, which transmits the details of each line with crystalline clarity while still providing a useful blend for the various lines.

In writing scores for moving pictures and TV, which are to be performed in acoustically dead recording studios, this approach must be carried even further, since any persistence of sound must be deliberately written into the music. When I was preparing my *Easter Cantata for Chorus, Brass and Percussion*, the rehearsals were held in Jordan Hall, Boston, which is fairly live. For the actual performance in a TV studio, I found that the only way to cope with the dead acoustics was to permit the percussion instruments to ring as long as they would, and this gave to the *whole sound* the impression of adequate reverberation. As a result of this experience, I have written my latest *Concertante No. 3 for Organ and Percussion Orchestra* so that the after-ring of the percussion following each phrase is deliberately carried over into the beginning of the next phrase; in a dead hall this will compensate for the lack of reverberation, while in a live hall it may either enhance the reverberant sound of the room or the percussion ring may be curtailed at the will of the performers to minimize confusion. On the other hand, I have found great difficulty, even with highly experienced musicians, in performing in a live hall some music which had originally been written for the dead acoustics of the TV studio.

Another example of a modern composer's awareness of the interaction between musical style and acoustics is revealing. Walter Piston was commissioned some years ago to write some music for radio. In an interview at the time of the performance he was asked, "Now, Mr. Piston, just what means did you use to adapt this music to radio?" Smiling, he replied, "Why I simply eliminated from it all the things that sound bad on radio."

Some composers appear not to be fully aware of the interrelation between acoustics and their music. For example, a writer who composes at the piano in his studio may fail to imagine adequately the acoustics of the hall and thus may indicate metronomic markings that, while appropriate in his dead studio, are so fast as to be impossible to perform in a reverberant hall. Boris Goldovsky, pianist and conductor, stated [*High Fidelity*, Vol. 11, p. 28 (April 1961)]:

> Verdi, for instance, could hardly have brought a metronome to an actual performance of *La Traviata* and estimated the tempo while the opera was in progress. He undoubtedly arrived at his metronomic markings by playing the score at home on the piano, probably singing the vocal lines to himself, with the result that . . . the home performance—ignoring the acoustics of the hall, the natural gravitational pull of the orchestra, and the effort of a professional singer to project the voice with full intensity—was siderably faster than the real thing. . . . Verdi's indication of 108 to the dotted quarter for *"Non sapete quale affeto"* is impossible.
>
> Now, the opening of [Beethoven's] *Hammerklavier* Sonata is noted 138 to the half-note, which is so unmanageable you think it must have been marked by a superman or a madman. But, *when you hum it*, it seems exactly right.

Clearly there is a strong relation between the composition and performance of music on one hand and the acoustics of the halls in which it is played on the other. Let us review some of the musical qualities that are most affected by the acoustics of a room in which music is performed.

MUSICAL QUALITIES AFFECTED BY ACOUSTICS

Fullness of tone

Suppose you are seated close to the stage of an outdoor stadium or in a room where there is no echo or reverberation. If a performer near you plays a tone, you hear the tone precisely as the instrument produced it. The build-up of the tone, its loudness, and its termination as you hear it are exactly characteristic of the instrument. The tones of wind instruments, other than large organ pipes, cease almost immediately after the excitation is stopped, though the tones of stringed instruments persist a little longer because of the vibrations of the strings and the wood.

In a reverberant concert hall, however, when a tone is sounded by any means, the reverberation of the hall causes the audible tone to last for about 2 seconds after the instrument has actually ceased to sound. The effect that this reverberation has on the music is to increase the "fullness of tone" of an instrument or an ensemble of instruments. Let us elaborate on this point.

A tone has a certain loudness at the ear of a listener even when it is sounded in a space that is acoustically "dead." But played in a reverberant room this same tone sounds louder. If the reverberation persists long enough, succeeding tones will blend with the reverberating tones. Reverberation in a room both increases the loudness of individual tones and changes the character of musical phrases through blending of the individual tones, and thus gives continuity to the musical line.

Reverberation is not in itself desirable or undesirable; it is one of the components available to the composer for producing a musical effect and as such is actually a part of the music. Some styles of music depend on the tying together of successive tones to produce their over-all effect. Many early choral compositions, particularly plainchant, were written to be performed in reverberant cathedrals and require considerable fullness of tone. When these compositions are performed in an acoustically dead environment, they suffer from a want of body and lose much of their power. Early composers often wrote pauses into the music to emphasize the after-ring of the church.

Three aspects of reverberation combine to increase the fullness of tone of an instrument or an ensemble: (1) the length of the reverberation time, (2) the loudness of the sound relative to that of the background noise, and (3) the ratio of the loudness of the reverberant sound to that of the direct sound. Reverberation time can be thought of as the length of time necessary for a loud sound in a room to die down to inaudibility (a more technical definition has been given in Chapter 2). The greater the cubic volume of a hall in relation to the audience seating area, the longer the reverberation time. The energy in a sound determines its loudness. Hence the loudness of the direct sound is determined by the energy of the sound that comes directly to a listener's ears from the instrument being played, and the loudness of the reverberant sound is determined by the energy in the sound that reaches the listener only after traveling around the room. The larger the ratio of the loudness of the reverberant to the direct sound, the greater the fullness of tone.

If the sending end of a hall is designed to guide the sound from the performers directly to the audience, most of the energy in the music reaches their ears directly. If the hall is designed so that the music rises freely into the upper reaches, the energy in the direct sound is dissipated. Halls can be built which combine these two features in various proportions. Thus the design of the room determines not only the reverberation time but also the ratio of the reverberant to the direct sound energy that reaches the audience, and hence both of the parameters that determine fullness of tone.

Definition or clarity

When a musician speaks of definition or clarity he means the degree to which the individual sounds in a musical performance stand apart, one from another. Definition depends critically on musical factors and the skill and intention of the performer, but it is also closely tied to the acoustics of the room. There are two kinds of definition, horizontal definition, which relates to tones played in succession, and vertical definition, which relates to tones played simultaneously.

Horizontal definition refers to the degree to which sounds that follow one another stand apart. The composer can specify certain musical factors that affect it: tempo, repetition of tones in a phrase, and the relative loudness of successive tones. The performer can vary the horizontal definition by the manner in which he phrases a passage.

The acoustical factors that affect horizontal definition are the length of the reverberation time and the ratio of the loudness of the direct sound to that of the reverberant sound—the same two factors that determine fullness of tone, but in inverse relation. That is to say, an increase in horizontal definition goes hand in hand with a decrease in fullness of tone.

Vertical definition refers to the degree to which sounds that occur simultaneously are heard separately. Vertical definition depends on the music, the performer, the acoustics of the room, and the acuteness of the listener. The composer specifies the vertical definition through his choice of simultaneous tones and their relation to the tones surrounding them (whether the composition is hymn-like, chordal, contrapuntal, or simply an accompanied melody), and his choice of instruments on which they are played. The performers can alter vertical definition by varying the dynamics of the various simultaneous sounds and through the precision of their ensemble.

Acoustical factors that may affect the vertical definition include the balance among the different instruments transmitted to the audience, the degree of blending of the tones of the different instruments in the stage enclosure, the relative response of the hall at low, middle, and high frequencies, and, once again, the ratio of the direct to the reverberant sound.

Definition, both horizontal and vertical, is the result of a complex of factors both musical and acoustical—a certain piece of music, played in a certain way, in a certain environment. The degree of definition that the composer intended is necessary in order for the music to be communicated faithfully to the audience. Gregorian chant, with its slow melodic lines that gradually build and recede, is performed with little horizontal definition; it is usually sung in a room with a very long reverberation time and a small ratio of direct to reverberant sound energy. Bach's *Toccata in D Minor* for organ needs a reverberation time of at least 3 seconds in order for the full sonorities to be realized. At the other end of the spectrum, a piano concerto by Mozart, with its rapid solo passages and the delicate interplay of piano and different orchestral voices, needs considerable horizontal and vertical definition. It should be performed in a room with a relatively short reverberation time and a large ratio of direct to reverberant sound energy. Mozart,

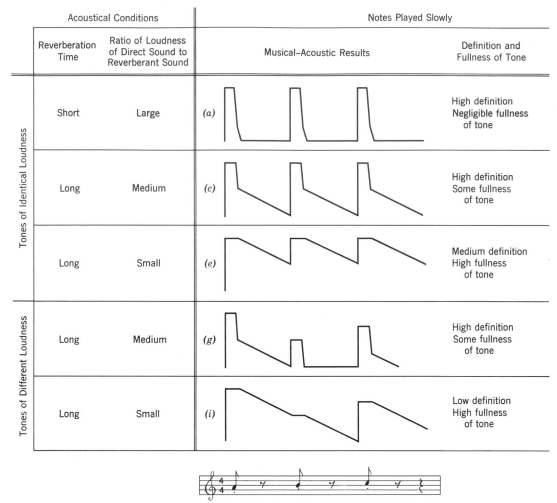

Acoustical Conditions			Notes Played Slowly	
Reverberation Time	Ratio of Loudness of Direct Sound to Reverberant Sound		Musical–Acoustic Results	Definition and Fullness of Tone
Tones of Identical Loudness				
Short	Large	(a)		High definition Negligible fullness of tone
Long	Medium	(c)		High definition Some fullness of tone
Long	Small	(e)		Medium definition High fullness of tone
Tones of Different Loudness				
Long	Medium	(g)		High definition Some fullness of tone
Long	Small	(i)		Low definition High fullness of tone

after listening to a performance of *Die Zauberflöte* from various locations in the hall and backstage, wrote in October 1791:

> By the way, you have no idea how charming the music sounds when you hear it from a box close to the orchestra—it sounds much better than from the gallery.

Mozart knew what later generations have confirmed, that his style of music sounds best where the ratio of direct to reverberant sound energy is large.

Speed of music relative to fullness of tone and definition

Fullness of tone and definition are both related to the speed with which music is played. The chart of Figure 3.1 shows the effect on music played slowly and music played rapidly of two different reverberation times and various ratios of the loudness of direct to reverberant sound.

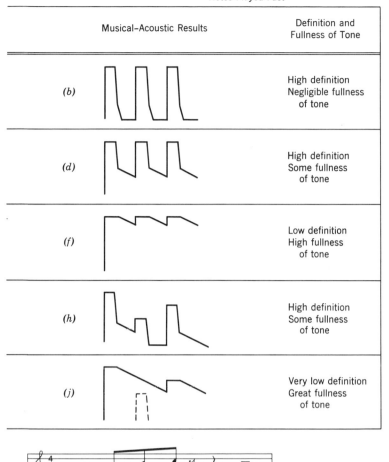

Notes Played Fast

Musical–Acoustic Results	Definition and Fullness of Tone
(b)	High definition Negligible fullness of tone
(d)	High definition Some fullness of tone
(f)	Low definition High fullness of tone
(h)	High definition Some fullness of tone
(j)	Very low definition Great fullness of tone

Figure 3.1. Chart illustrating the interrelations among speed of music, reverberation time, ratio of loudnesses of direct to reverberant sound, and the music itself (tempos are identical).

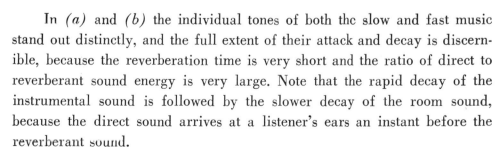

In *(a)* and *(b)* the individual tones of both the slow and fast music stand out distinctly, and the full extent of their attack and decay is discernible, because the reverberation time is very short and the ratio of direct to reverberant sound energy is very large. Note that the rapid decay of the instrumental sound is followed by the slower decay of the room sound, because the direct sound arrives at a listener's ears an instant before the reverberant sound.

In *(c)* we see the effect on slow music of a long reverberation time and a medium ratio of direct to reverberant sound energy. The full extent of the attack and part of the natural decay of the sound are heard before the reverberation in the room takes over. A certain amount of the natural decay of the instrumental tone is buried in the reverberation.

In *(d)*, because of the closer spacing of the tones in the fast music, part of the attack, as well as part of the natural decay of the tone, is buried in the

39

reverberation. The reverberation adds fullness to the tone, although the definition is still high.

In *(e)* the length of the reverberation time is the same as in *(c)*, but the ratio of the loudness of direct to reverberant sound is small. Here part of the attack and all of the natural instrumental decay of sound are obscured in the reverberation of the room. The tones are bonded one to another so that no one sound stands out clearly. When the speed of the music is increased, in *(f)*, each tone is still observable, but most of the natural attack and the decay of the instrument are buried in the reverberation. The music is almost continuous. Definition is sacrificed to fullness of tone; there is no possibility of a staccato sound.

Let us see how successive tones of different loudnesses fare in these rooms. When the music is played slowly and the ratio of the loudness of the direct to reverberant sound is fairly large, as in *(g)*, each tone is heard clearly. With the faster speed *(h)* some definition is sacrificed, but the tones are still distinct. In *(i)*, where the ratio of direct to reverberant sound loudness is decreased, the weakest tone is barely audible in the reverberation "tail" of the preceding tone. Finally, in *(j)*, when the music is fast, the weakest tone is lost completely inside the reverberation tail of the preceding tone; the definition is very low, and the fullness of the tone great.

The interplay of speed of music, definition, and fullness of tone illustrated in Figure 3.1 is characteristic of music performed in concert halls. If the composer pictures the acoustical environment in which his piece is likely to be played, he may be able to compose with a particular degree of definition and fullness of tone in mind. The performer is faced with the problem of selecting a tempo and phrasing that seem to him to fulfill the composer's intent. And if the performance is presented in an acoustically appropriate hall the audience is rewarded with music that accurately follows the composer's conception.

Intimacy

Acoustical intimacy is related to the audible aspect of a sound that indicates to a listener the size of the room in which it is produced. Each style of music sounds best in a hall with the appropriate degree of acoustical intimacy. It is not necessary that the room have a particular size, but only that it *sound* as though it were of the appropriate size. Acoustical intimacy is determined by the initial-time-delay gap—the difference in time of arrival of the direct sound and the first reflected sound (see Chapter 2 and Appendix 3).

In every period there has been chamber music composed for small groups of instruments to perform in small rooms. Between 1700 and 1900 most orchestral music was written to be played by larger groups in the relatively narrow concert halls of Europe, such as the Grosser Musikvereinssaal of Vienna. Choral and liturgical music was written for performance in large cathedrals, although some compositions were written for smaller, less reverberant churches or chapels. Opera has been intended primarily to be performed in relatively small horseshoe-shaped opera houses like La Scala in Milan or the Staatsoper of Vienna. In other words, the composer had a certain degree of intimacy in mind when he conceived his musical works. If the work is performed in a hall whose intimacy is not scaled to it, the listener immediately senses that something about the acoustics of the environment is inappropriate. More than any other factor in the acoustics of a hall —even more than fullness of tone and clarity—intimacy is closely allied with the degree of acceptability of a hall for music. It is an element of the composer's intent that must be borne in mind by those who perform his works. The organist E. Power Biggs says, "The listener immediately senses something wrong when he hears one of the organ works, such as those by Bach, played in a small college auditorium."

Because chamber music has for almost three centuries been written for performance in rooms of similar acoustical characteristics—intimacy and high definition, imparting relatively low fullness of tone—little need be said about the acoustical design of such rooms. The following discussion is therefore confined primarily to the acoustics of concert halls and opera houses, with occasional references to the acoustics of churches and cathedrals.

Timbre and tone color

Timbre is the quality of a sound that distinguishes one instrument from another, one voice from another. It derives from the particular combination and relative strengths of the harmonic overtones. Tone color is the effect produced by a combination of timbres—of voices and instruments in the performance of a musical composition. The composer can single out or combine the many varied timbres for particular effects. The conductor of an orchestra can modify these effects by his direction of the orchestra.

The timbre of a singer or an instrument, and the tone color of an orchestra, are also affected by the acoustical environment in which the music is produced. If a hall amplifies or absorbs the treble sound, either brittleness or a muffled quality may characterize the music. If the surfaces of the walls or ceiling absorb the low or middle frequencies, the full orchestra may sound deficient in basses or cellos. The stage enclosure or the main ceiling may project the sound of certain instruments toward some parts of the hall only and not toward others, thus differentially affecting the tone color.

At a concert I attended in a large hall in London, although I could see the hands of the harpist move across the strings, I could hear no sound from the harp, but only the stronger instruments. At intermission, I compared notes with a friend who sat in another part of the hall. He reported that he had never heard the harp played more beautifully. The tone color of an orchestra at a particular seat in an auditorium depends on how the sounds of the different instruments are directed to that part of the hall.

Loudness, noise, and dynamic range

A wide dynamic range, the spread between the faintest and the loudest musical sounds heard during a performance, is one mark of good acoustics in a hall. The dynamic range is limited at one end by the background noise in the hall and at the other end by the acoustical characteristics of the hall.

Even an attentive audience produces a certain amount of noise by breathing, coughing, shuffling, and so forth. A hall must be small enough for the pianissimo passages in a musical performance not to become lost in this noise; and at the other end of the dynamic range, a fortissimo passage must sound forth so as not to lose its impact. If a hall is quite small and very live, however, the music of a full symphony orchestra playing a heavily orchestrated composition may become so loud as to be almost painful to the ear. Clearly the upper end of the dynamic range must be controlled.

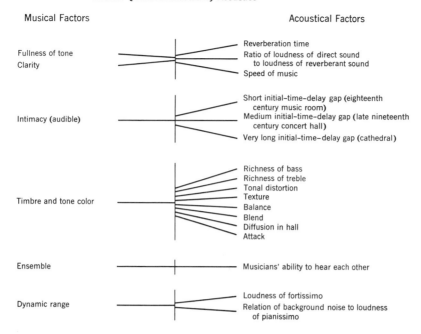

Figure 3.2. Chart showing the interrelations between the audible factors of music and the acoustical factors of the halls in which the music is performed.

The loudness of the reverberant sound in a hall decreases proportionally as the seating area of the audience and the amount of other sound-absorbing material in the room are increased. The loudness of the direct sound is a function of the distance of a listener from the stage, the design of the stage, and the reflecting surfaces at the stage-end of the hall and the ceiling. Although the minimum noise level attainable is set by the audience itself, needless to say, distracting noise from ventilation equipment and external sources should be lower than the audience noise.

The chart of Figure 3.2 summarizes the interrelations between the musical qualities heard in a hall and the acoustical factors that affect those qualities.

THE ACOUSTICAL SETTINGS FOR MUSIC OF VARIOUS STYLES

From interviews I have conducted with musicians and from the experience of the recording industry, it seems clear that today's listeners prefer particular kinds of acoustical spaces for the performance of music of particular styles. We may well ask whether the halls available when each style of music was composed had characteristics compatible with the acoustical preferences of today's audiences for listening to the same music. But this only raises the question: are the preferences of today's listeners a consequence of their listening experience, or does each style of music in fact require its own kind of acoustics?

At the outset, it is apparent that many early composers were constrained in their choice of musical material by the acoustics available to them for performance. It is certainly not a coincidence that Gregorian chant sounds best in acoustics similar to those of the medieval cathedrals in which it was originally performed—where the reverberation time may be as long as 5 to 10 seconds. For example, as Thurston Dart pointed out, the composer Giovanni Gabrieli, who was organist of St. Mark's Basilica at the turn of the seventeenth century, wrote chordal music in slow tempo for antiphonal choirs and assemblies of brass or wind instruments, music particularly well suited to the acoustics of a large reverberant church. It can be argued that between 1600 and 1900 there was a relation between architecture and music in Europe, and that the music of each of the stylistic periods—Renaissance, Baroque, Classical, and Romantic—coincided with a contemporary acoustical environment sympathetic to its performance. Indeed, only since 1900 and the advent of radio, recordings, television, and a variety of available concert halls and opera houses, has the composer had no clearly defined acoustics peculiar to his own time for which to write!

Organ music is somewhat different. It can hardly be assigned to "different periods" of composition, since a similar form is common to the work of all great organ composers. Nearly all such music benefits from the flattery of a long reverberation period.

Baroque period

The term Baroque is a convenient designation for the style of contrapuntal music written between 1600 and approximately 1750, and best exemplified by Bach and Handel in the north of Europe and Corelli and Vivaldi in Italy. These hundred and fifty years witnessed the evolution of music from an unaccompanied choral song to a more highly rhythmic, harmonic-thematic balance, where voice and instrument frequently combined in concert, and the parts were not all of equal melodic interest. Another aspect of Baroque music is the spacing of instrumental colors; each movement was played by a fixed group, the variety occurred only from one movement to another. In spite of differences in the music written by hundreds of composers scattered over much of Europe it is possible to speak of a

Baroque style for the purposes of acoustical analysis.

A conspicuous characteristic of the late Baroque period is several independent melodic lines, played or sung simultaneously, the combination emphasizing equal importance of several voices rather than a single accompanied solo melody. The independence of the melodic lines may be heightened by their being given to instruments of contrasting timbre. The sound is light, clear, and transparent. In Baroque music the detail is important and no portion of the sound should mask another.

Leonard Bernstein said in his *The Joy of Music* [Simon and Schuster, New York, pp. 232–233 (1959)]:

> Counterpoint *is* melody, only accompanied by one or more additional melodies, running along at the same time. . . . The art of counterpoint fixes rules for making two or more melodic lines go well together. . . . This music is difficult for us to listen to. But it's only a question of our having been spoiled by the music we hear most of the time, music which emphasizes harmony instead of counterpoint. In other words, we are used to hearing melody on top, with chords supporting it underneath like pillars—melody and harmony, a tune and its accompaniment. . . . But [in Bach's time and earlier] people used to listen to music differently. The ear was conditioned to hear *lines*, simultaneous melodic lines rather than chords. That was the natural way of music, strange though it seems to us. Counterpoint came before harmony which is a comparatively recent phenomenon.

What can we say about the acoustical environment for the performance of secular music in Bach's time? Baroque orchestral music was usually performed in relatively small rooms with hard reflecting walls, the rectangular ballroom of a palace, for instance, which had a high intimacy factor and, when occupied, a reverberation time longer than that of a conventional living room, but yet low—under 1.5 seconds.

Concerts were given either in music rooms or in small theaters like the Altesresidenz Theater in Munich, which was opened in 1753. In such a room the music sounded intimate, because of the many nearby sound-reflecting surfaces, and when an audience was present the reverberation time was short. Thus music played there had high definition and low fullness of tone.

The Baroque composer was familiar with these acoustical environments, and the music he wrote was scaled to them. Even today, we prefer listening to this highly articulated music in a small room, acoustically intimate, with a relatively low reverberation time.

Baroque sacred music is more difficult to relate to its environment than secular music. Most of the important churches of the eighteenth century were very large and highly reverberant, and the musical forms of earlier times, such as the plainchant, continued to be heard in them. On the other hand, a large body of the sacred music of this period was written for performance in private royal or ducal chapels with low reverberation times that make possible the brisk tempos of Bach's early fugues. Also the many converted and newly built Lutheran churches, in which the congregation occupied galleries as well as the main floor, and for which Bach composed many of his choral works, had a moderate reverberation—considerably less than that of the medieval cathedral. Hope Bagenal, architectural acoustician of England, writes,

> The reducing of reverberation in Lutheran churches by the inserted galleries, thus enabling string parts to be heard and distinguished and allowing a brisk tempo, was the most important single fact in the history of music because it leads directly to the *St. Matthew Passion* and the *B-Minor Mass*.

It was for this type of church, rather than the large cathedral, that Bach wrote some of his church music. While cantor of the Thomaskirche in Leipzig (a church about which a great deal is known) he wrote many of his large works, including the *Mass* and the *St. Matthew Passion*. From available lithographs, and from descriptions of the tapestries, altars, and so forth, we can estimate the acoustical qualities of the Thomaskirche. With a full congregation, the reverberation time must have been about 1.6 seconds at mid-frequencies and, when it was partly filled, a little over 2 seconds. The Thomaskirche was rebuilt during the nineteenth century with a higher ceiling. Today it has a reverberation time at mid-frequencies with full audience of about 1.9 seconds [L. Keibs and W. Kuhl, "Zur Akustik der Thomaskirche in Leipzig," *Acustica*, Vol. 9, pp. 365–370 (No. 5, 1959)]. The original reverberation time of 1.6 seconds is short for a church—a dry environment for ecclesiastical organ and choral music, as we think of it today.

Classical period

From 1750 until perhaps 1820 European audiences enjoyed music written in the style called "Classical." This was the period of the great symphonies of Haydn, Mozart, and Beethoven. In the eighteenth century, music was still commissioned by the court and the church, but a wider secular appeal now gave a new impetus to the composer. Publishers of music, entrepreneurs, and purveyors of public entertainment all increased the composer's area of influence and imposed changing demands upon him.

The most important development in the Classical period, from an acoustical point of view, was the appearance of the Classical symphony and sonata. These musical forms tied into a single unit independent musical ideas, some of them related, some contrasting. The way in which the ideas were put together—the structure of the music—sometimes became even more important than the musical material itself. Characteristic of the Classical period is a diminished contrapuntal emphasis, following the operatic idea of accompanied melody rather than the interweaving of equal parts which characterizes a Brandenburg Concerto. The strings carried the biggest part of the melodic material, but the woodwind passages became so prominent as to be entities in themselves. Larger movements were emphasized by the use of the full orchestra.

The first real concert halls were built in the last half of the eighteenth century, and they showed the influence of the court halls. For example, the Holywell Music Room in Oxford, England, which was completed in 1748 and recently has been restored, seats about 300 persons. When it is fully occupied its reverberation time is about 1.5 seconds at mid-frequencies. The Altes Gewandhaus, which stood in Leipzig from 1780 until it was razed in 1894, seated about 400 persons and, when fully occupied, had a reverberation time of not more than 1.3 seconds at mid-frequencies. The rectangular-shaped Redoutensaal of Vienna, which stood in Beethoven's time, seated an audience of about 400 people and had a reverberation time, with full audience, of about 1.4 seconds at mid-frequencies.

By the end of the eighteenth century, public concerts became more popular, owing mainly to historical and sociological developments but perhaps also to the new musical style of the Classical period. Throughout the eighteenth century, concerts had been performed in London and Paris, but it was not until the turn of the century that concert music began to appear as public entertainment in Leipzig, Berlin, Vienna, Stockholm, and elsewhere. Significantly, twelve of Haydn's symphonies were composed between 1791 and 1795 especially for Salomon's series of concerts at the Hanover Square Room in London.

The gradual rise in popularity of orchestral concerts led, toward the middle of the nineteenth century, to the construction of the first large halls specifically designed for concerts. These halls also had longer reverberation times. For example, the old Boston Music Hall, which opened in 1863, seated 2400 persons and had a reverberation time of over 1.8 seconds, with full audience. The longer reverberation times of the best of these large concert halls added to their fullness of tone and, hence, to the dramatic value of the music, while at the same time the clarity necessary for music written in the Classical style was preserved by their narrow, rectangular shapes.

Today the preferred reverberation times for music of the Classical period appear to be in the range of 1.5 to 1.7 seconds, which is reasonably consistent with the acoustics of the Leipzig, Oxford, and Vienna halls of that time. Beethoven's symphonies, particularly his later ones, showed the immense scope of his imagination—he wrote almost as though he anticipated the large reverberant halls which were built in the next half-century.

Romantic period

By the last years of Beethoven's life the emphasis in music had changed from elegant formal structure to the personal and emotional expression that is characteristic of the Romantic period. For the next hundred years, a succession of composers—from Schubert and Mendelssohn, through Brahms, Wagner, Tchaikovsky, Richard Strauss, Ravel, and Debussy—created a body of music that, together with the Classical symphonies, comprises the preponderant part of today's orchestral repertoire. From Haydn onward, each generation of composers increased the size and tone color of the orchestra and experimented with the expressive possibilities of controlled definition. The music no longer required the listener to separate out each sound that he heard to the same extent as in Baroque and Classical music: in some compositions a single melody is supported by complex orchestral harmonies; sometimes a number of melodies are interwoven, their details only partly discernible in the general impression of the sound; and in some musical passages no melody seems to emerge, only an outpouring of sound, perhaps rhythmic or dramatic, often expressive or emotional.

The music of the Romantic period thrives in an acoustical environment that provides high fullness of tone and low definition. Conductors and musicians confirm the experience of recording engineers that these qualities are achieved with a relatively long reverberation time, perhaps 1.9 to 2.2 seconds, and a small ratio of direct to reverberant sound.

Composers of this period sometimes wrote with a specific hall in mind. Wagner composed *Parsifal* expressly for his Festspielhaus in Bayreuth, Germany; Berlioz composed his *Requiem* for Les Invalides in Paris; and so on. In the last half of the nineteenth century halls built specifically for the performance of concert music reflected the desires of the composers for acoustics with high fullness of tone. The Grosser Musikvereinssaal in Vienna, for example, which was completed in 1870, has a reverberation at mid-frequencies of about 2 seconds when the hall is fully occupied. The hall is small enough for loud orchestral effects to sound very loud; its narrowness, emphasizing the direct sound, lends significant definition to the music. The Concertgebouw of Amsterdam, which was completed in 1887, also has a reverberation time of 2 seconds at mid-frequencies, but as it is wider it emphasizes the direct sound less; therefore, the music played in it emerges with less clarity and more fullness. The Concertgebouw has excellent acoustics for music of the late Romantic period.

Twentieth century

Since the 1880's, concert-going has grown into an established European and American custom. Attending concerts was very popular in the United States in the 1920's; the radio and the economic depression displaced concert-going during the next two decades, but again since the end of World War II, concerts have become increasingly popular.

The concert music of the twentieth century is extremely varied. Many contemporary composers have written for large orchestras along lines similar to those developed in the second half of the nineteenth century, though with the addition of new harmonies, new instruments, and new effects. In some of the other works there is evidence of a return to the smaller, clearer sound of earlier periods, which requires smaller instrumental combinations. And some innovators, experimenting with sounds from sources other than the conventional instruments, have resorted to the electronics laboratory, the tape recorder, even the computing machine, to furnish the components of a new music or at least a novel sound.

To be suitable to the needs of modern concert music, a hall must accommodate a great variety of styles. Music of the transparent, "intellectual" type wants a hall with relatively high definition, of the kind required for Bach. Modern halls have been built that fulfill this requirement—with reverberation times, when occupied, of the order of 1.4 seconds at mid-frequencies and with high definition. They have come to be referred to as "hi-fi" halls. Modern music of a more passionate or sentimental quality sounds best in a hall with high fullness of tone and low definition. But one hall cannot be ideal for all modern music unless its acoustics can be rendered variable.

The next half-century of music may confront the architect with acoustic requirements little explored to date. He may want to be able to adjust the height of a hall's ceiling quickly, in order to achieve a reverberation time and a ratio of direct to reverberant sound appropriate to the composition being performed. Perhaps reverberation will be added electronically to the hall or to individual instruments so that, in the course of a single composition, sharply defined chords can be presented at one moment and long sustained melodic lines at another. Perhaps in time, music will seldom be performed in a concert hall at all as stereophonic recordings and wide-screen television with stereophonic sound supplant the live concert. If that time comes reverberation could be added electronically and varied from one part of the composition to another. If purely electronic music should become the vogue, even the musician would be eliminated; the concert hall would pass from the scene, along with the symphony orchestra, the concert-goer, the usher, and the ticket-taker. The musical innovator and the electronic technician would then rule supreme—unless the electronic computer manages to displace them.

European
(non-Wagnerian) opera

The European opera house has been the most stable space for music ever designed. From at least 1700 on, the horseshoe-shaped theater has been built, with rings of boxes one atop the other, and capped by a gallery of low-priced seats. The form has reached its perfection in the Teatro alla Scala, the well-loved La Scala of Milan, which was completed in 1778. The horseshoe design has been copied in nearly every important city in Europe. Ubiquitous is the circular, tiered opera house; thus composers of opera have been able to write with only one kind of acoustics in mind.

Opera imposes different acoustical requirements from those for orchestral concerts. The vocal part must be considered as some form of communication not unlike speech. To preserve the libretto's intelligibility, especially at the tongue-twisting musical speeds of Mozart and Rossini, the reverberation time must be relatively short, so that successive syllables will not be masked by the reverberation of the immediately preceding sounds. This is the opposite of what is illustrated in Figure 3.1, *(i)* and *(j)*.

Except for the works of Wagner, European opera fits well into halls with acoustics suitable to the concert and chamber music of the Baroque period, that is to say, halls with high definition and relatively low fullness of tone. Many opera houses fulfill these requirements—La Scala, Le Fenice in Venice, San Carlo in Naples, the Paris Opera, Covent Garden in London, the Staatsoper in Vienna, and the Academy of Music in Philadelphia. In these houses the voices of the singers are projected to the audience with clarity and sufficient loudness, and the orchestra sounds clean and undistorted. Balance between the orchestra and the singers is assisted by the acoustical design as well as by the conductor's control of the orchestra.

In Europe, opera is nearly always performed in a language intelligible to the audience, and most European opera-goers stress the importance of understanding the words. In America, this has not been true. Opera is seldom sung in English and opera-goers do not expect to understand the language of every libretto. Erich Leinsdorf says of American opera-goers, "People come to an opera house to hear the music. Most of them either do not understand the language in which the opera is sung, or they have come so often to the opera that they follow the drama even if it is poorly articulated or masked by reverberation. In my opinion the music alone should govern the reverberation time for an opera house." It appears, therefore, that opera in America can be performed in houses with longer reverberation times than those of Europe. An example of such a house is the War Memorial Opera House in San Francisco where the reverberation time at mid-frequencies, with full audience, is about 1.6 seconds.

Wagnerian opera

Wagner broke with the tradition of Baroque-like opera and evolved a style that was wholly personal, yet within the traditions of the Romantic period. From his pen flowed some of the most unusual and stirring of operas, "musical dramas" as he called them. Wagner's rich Romantic music is best supported by high fullness of tone and low definition.

In an effort to achieve the perfect acoustical environment for his musical style, Wagner designed his own opera house—the Festspielhaus at Bayreuth, Germany—a house which combines a relatively long reverberation time, 1.6 seconds at mid-frequencies, fully occupied, with a thoroughly blended orchestral tone. Although a very large orchestra (100 to 130 pieces) is used, proper balance is maintained between singers and orchestra by means of a sunken and covered pit, which also imparts a mysterious quality to the music (see the discussion of the Bayreuth Festspielhaus in Chapter 6).

Wagner's orchestral passages, with their relatively slow speed, sound best in a hall with a long reverberation time, approximately 2 seconds at mid-frequencies; but in order for the libretto to be intelligible the reverberation time needs to be somewhat shorter, in the vicinity of the 1.6 seconds found in Bayreuth, or perhaps as high as 1.8 seconds if the ratio of direct to reverberant sound is high.

ACOUSTICS AND THE PERFORMERS

In addition to its direct effects on the music, the acoustics of the space in which music is presented can also affect music indirectly by influencing the way in which it is performed. Most musicians are sensitive to the sound of their music in a hall and automatically adjust their performance accordingly. Isaac Stern has said:

> Reverberation is of great help to a violinist. As he goes from one note to another the previous note perseveres and he has the feeling that each note is surrounded by strength. When this happens the violinist does not feel that his playing is bare or "naked"—there is a friendly aura surrounding each note. You want to hear clearly in a hall, but there should also be this desirable blending of the sound. If each successive note blends into the previous sound, it gives the violinist sound to work with. The resulting effect is very flattering. It is like walking with jet-assisted take-off.

Music for the organ is a special problem. Since the organ has no sustaining pedal, the tone stops very soon after a key is released. The performer can, with considerable effort, make partial compensation by his technique to achieve some fullness of tone, but technique alone cannot really substitute for reverberation. E. Power Biggs writes:

> An organist will take all the reverberation time he is given, and then ask for a bit more, for ample reverberation is part of organ music itself. Many of Bach's organ works are designed actually to exploit reverberation. Consider the pause that follows the ornamented proclamation that opens the famous *Toccata in D minor*. Obviously this is for the enjoyment of the notes as they remain suspended in air. In harmonic structure, Mendelssohn's organ music is tailored to ample acoustics, for the composer played frequently in the great spaces of St. Paul's Cathedral in London. Franck's organ music, as that of Bach, frequently contains alternation of sound and silence, and depends for its effect on a continuing trajectory of tone.
>
> Some organ music, the Hindemith Sonatas, many chorale preludes and shorter pieces, are enjoyable in any acoustic surroundings. Yet it must be added that certain modern French music depends so completely on a long

period of reverberation that, no matter how well played, in acoustically dead surroundings it falls apart into disconnected fragments. In general, a reverberation period of at least two seconds, and preferably more, is best for the organ and organ music.

Pianists appear to be satisfied with less reverberant spaces than other instrumentalists. One rarely hears a pianist complain of a short reverberation time with the same dissatisfaction as a violinist, probably because where slow chordal change is involved, the pianist can use his sustaining pedal to prolong notes. With his sustaining pedal he can also blend successive tones played at fast tempos. Too "dead" a hall prevents the pianist from hearing his music; a hall that is too live renders his music muddy. Because he has a technique for merging a tone with its successor, and because his instrument is itself loud and reverberant, he depends more on himself than on the hall to create the desired effects.

Many conductors are well aware of the effects that a hall may impart to the character of a performance. Conducting in an unfamiliar hall has an element of uncertainty about it. Rehearsal in an empty hall does not give the orchestra a sense of how the full hall will sound. For these reasons a visiting orchestra often shows up to disadvantage in a single engagement when it is compared with a resident orchestra that has learned to adjust its performance to the peculiarities of a hall. Moreover, history has amply demonstrated that the full potentialities of a new concert hall are seldom realized in its dedicatory concert.

Leopold Stokowski wrote me:

My experience has been that every concert hall in the world has different acoustical qualities and, as a concert hall is really an instrument for sound of music, the differences of each hall must be taken care of during rehearsals and concerts. Also, the differences of an empty hall and a full hall must be considered. All this becomes very difficult when one is on tour visiting new cities, performing in a new hall where sometimes one does not have an opportunity for rehearsal. Many considerations must be kept in mind, but one of the most important is reverberation in the low, medium, and high frequencies—in other words, over the whole tonal range. By keeping these considerations in mind, the clarity of the music in performance will enable the public to understand and receive the message that all great music contains.

Each conductor has his own musical style, a set of musical traits, that characterize him as surely as the styles of painters—Rembrandt, Van Gogh, Picasso, Sheeler—characterize them. A conductor's style is evident in his handling of any orchestra, playing any composer's works in any hall. But to achieve his style, the conductor must vary his technique to conform to the different acoustics of different halls. One conductor said to me, "I not only seat the orchestra differently according to the hall in which I play, but I handle the musicians differently."

In the 1930's, when Leopold Stokowski was conducting the Philadelphia Orchestra and Serge Koussevitsky the Boston Symphony Orchestra, some students of acoustics at Harvard University attempted to single out differences in their conducting techniques that apparently had been adopted to achieve their individual musical styles in the acoustics of their respective halls.

Leopold Stokowski is known for his emphasis on orchestral color—bar to bar and phrase to phrase—as well as on a long, rich, flowing melodic line. The Academy of Music in Philadelphia, in which he was the resident conductor from 1912 until 1936, has dry, clear, warm acoustics that lend high definition and rather low fullness of tone to compositions performed in it. It is a copy of the European horseshoe opera house, and was specifically planned for grand opera. In achieving his musical style in this hall, the Harvard study suggested, Stokowski had developed an orchestral technique that rounded and prolonged the attack and release of each tone, tended to blend successive notes, and gave the performance a flowing, silky tone. He required his violinists to practice free bowing to assure smooth orchestral texture. The violas, cellos, and basses were encouraged to produce a smooth, rich foundation to the full ensemble. Stokowski experimented with novel arrangements of the orchestra on the stage and with the dimensions and materials of the orchestra enclosure. Recording and radio engineers came to know him as the conductor most concerned with his acoustical surroundings. Stokowski's special style is clearly apparent when he conducts in other halls, but perhaps not to the same degree as in the Academy of Music, since he does not have as much time to adapt the technique of his musicians to the novel acoustical environment.

Serge Koussevitsky's primary interest was also orchestral color. But his style was more easily achieved in the lively acoustics of Symphony Hall—a hall with a relatively long reverberation time that imparts fullness of tone to any composition played in it. The Harvard group observed that Koussevitsky made his attacks and releases more abrupt than Stokowski's, and he depended on the hall to enhance the fullness of tone. The bowing techniques of the cellos and basses were not so critical, since the reverberation of Symphony Hall elongates and rounds the tones. Koussevitsky's violin tone—ringing, brilliant, and loud—was easy to achieve in the acoustics of Symphony Hall, so much so that even slight imprecisions could go unnoticed—something that Koussevitsky would not have tolerated if they had been perceptible. He too loved to build up a dramatic conclusion to an allegro finale, an effect particularly suited to the acoustics of Symphony Hall.

Stokowski and Koussevitsky were themselves well aware of the different acoustics of their two halls. Each of them developed his technique to achieve his greatest perfection in his own hall and then strongly preferred that hall to the other's. Koussevitsky is known to have said, "The Academy of Music is good, but not nearly as good as Symphony Hall." And today Stokowski says, "Symphony Hall has good but not outstanding sound. The Academy of Music is the best concert hall in America. It has natural clear sound."

Audiences also sensed the differences that had developed in these two men's techniques. When the Philadelphia Orchestra visited Boston, there were comments about the "over-smooth, too-silky" tone. In Philadelphia, the tone of the visiting Boston Symphony Orchestra was described as "crisp, too clearly molded, and sometimes slightly imprecise." Both reactions are eminently understandable.

ACOUSTICS AND THE LISTENER

The composer, the conductor, and the performer are engaged in a complex interplay with their particular acoustical environments. But audiences too have an important role in determining the kinds of music that are acceptable in their times and consequently the types of concert halls that will be built in their communities.

Paul Henry Lang, an American musicologist, wrote in the magazine *High Fidelity* (August, 1961, pp. 26–28) on "The Bach Renascence":

It is generally accepted that Bach was totally forgotten until Mendelssohn discovered the *St. Matthew Passion* and performed it in 1829. . . . To understand whether Bach's music was properly appreciated by the rank and file of musicians [from 1700 to 1850], however, requires a glance at the historical situation.

As late as Mozart's time, musical life evolved around contemporary art. The public wanted new music and was scarcely aware of the existence of music even one generation back, except, of course, such traditional church music as Gregorian chant and Lutheran hymn. The indifference, even hostility, of today's audiences towards contemporary music was unknown to our forebears. Indeed, when Mozart prepared a few works of Handel and Bach for performance, such a return to music a couple of generations earlier than that favored by the prevailing taste was unheard of. . . . Bach was never a modern musician; when his colossal works were being composed, the style had already begun to change and by the time he reached the *Art of Fugue* and *Musical Offering* he had been left behind—there were few active musicians who could comprehend this art. . . .

With the spread of public concerts and the growth of audiences, a gradual estrangement of the public from contemporary music took place. . . . By the opening of our century neither really old nor really new music was relished or even generally known.

We began this discussion by asking, is it simply from habit that today's audiences prefer to hear music of earlier periods in acoustical environments similar to those in which they were first played? Or does each musical style in fact actually have a preferred acoustical environment?

An investigation of how the acoustical preferences of today's listeners vary with the style of the music was carried out by W. Kuhl, of the Technical Broadcasting Institute in Nuremburg, Germany. Kuhl presented 28 short excerpts of symphonic music, recorded in 20 different acoustical environments, to over 100 musicians and sound engineers. The music included samples of various styles, and the rooms varied in both size and degree of occupancy, and thus in reverberation time and clarity. Their cubic volumes varied between 70,000 and 500,000 cubic feet; acoustical measurements were made for all conditions of occupancy.

The musical excerpts, each about $2\frac{1}{2}$ minutes long, were identified to the listeners only by number. Each listener was asked to pay attention to all of the audible acoustical properties of each room: the reverberation, the recognizability of individual instrumental groups in tutti passages, the precision of the attack, and the attack tone. The listeners were asked to pay as little attention as possible to musical interpretation and minor technical defects. Each person recorded his judgment of the suitability of the room used during the recording for each sample of music by indicating "good" or "bad," and whether the reverberation time was "too short," "satisfactory," or "too long." For the recognizability of instrument groups and for quality of attack tone, he was asked to record "good" or "bad." In all, about 13,000 judgments were made on these questions.

The reverberation times preferred by the musicians and sound engineers for the various styles of music are as follows:

for a symphony in Classical style (Mozart's *Jupiter*), a little shorter than 1.5 seconds;

for a symphony in Romantic style (Brahms' *Fourth*), 2.1 seconds;

for a sample of modern music (Stravinsky's *Le Sacre du Printemps*), a little longer than 1.5 seconds.

These values of reverberation time were found not to be dependent on the cubic volumes of the rooms, and the spread of the judgments was not large. [This study is described by W. Kuhl in an article entitled "Uber Versuche zur Ermittlung der Günstigsten Nachhallzeit Grosser Musikstudios," *Acustica*, Vol. 4, pp. 618–634 (1954).]

The results of Kuhl's tests are in excellent agreement with what we have learned about the acoustical environments available during the Classical and Romantic periods.

Some contemporary musicologists believe that each age has its own way of listening to music. Perhaps we cannot expect to derive the same experience from the music of an earlier time as its contemporaries did. Certainly, most twentieth-century music has to be listened to in a manner and with an attitude far different from that demanded by any music that Bach, for example, knew. The different styles of interpretation that have become associated with differently proportioned halls may lead people who habitually listen to music in a certain hall to come to expect the musical style consonant with that hall, and this expectation may bias their attitudes toward other styles and other halls. One wonders whether listening to radio, phonograph, and television in non-reverberant living rooms, even with reverberation artificially introduced, may accustom us to demand music with high definition and low fullness of tone. If so, one can foresee a time when the music of the Romantic period will pass from the repertoires of our symphony orchestras, and new compositions will be matched to the acoustics of the living room. Concert halls, if there is still any need for them, will then be built with low ceilings shaped to guide the sound directly from the performing group to the listeners, with high intimacy, high definition, and low fullness of tone.

4

Subjective Attributes
of Musical-Acoustic Quality

Music and acoustics grew up independent of each other, and it is no surprise that they developed quite different vocabularies to describe their various concepts. Both vocabularies grew in the usual fashion of language—common words borrowed from the dictionary and shaped to a new purpose, and new words coined to fill a need, which finally grew into respected technical terms.

Because the linguistic needs of acoustics and music often overlapped, some of the same words inevitably became part of the two vocabularies. But since the purposes and interests of musicians and acousticians were different, the same words often came to have different meanings. For some words—for example, intensity and resonance—unless we know who is speaking we cannot be sure what meaning is intended.

Since acoustics is a branch of the physical sciences, it has need of a vocabulary that is precisely defined. As soon as the definitions of its terms are agreed upon by scientists, they are adopted into standards circulated by national and international bodies of scientists, in the hope that uniformity of usage will follow. On the other hand, the language of music has grown up without an academy's blessing, or stricture. As a result, many terms that are peripheral to music have become a meaningful part of the musician's vocabulary without having received special musical, as distinct from common, definition.

A third language that sets up still another barrier to easy communication between science and the arts is the aesthetic diction of the music critic. The function of the music critic is not to construe either the acoustics or the music, but rather to describe his impressions of the composition and its performance. His is a subjective language, rarely amenable to close definition; a language arbitrary and evanescent, for since words can only approximate the critic's response to his musical experience, he is constantly changing and refining his vocabulary, weeding out the words that no longer carry the impact of his impressions. Thus when a music critic describes his reaction to a new concert hall as "overbearing," "shattering," "shimmering," or "ravishing," we are without a rule by which to translate these words into specific acoustic recommendation. Because the music critic is a perceptive, experienced music listener, however, both the musician and the acoustician do well to tune their ears to his reactions.

One of the first tasks of my study of concert-hall acoustics entailed the compilation of a vocabulary of acoustical attributes related to the quality of music heard in a concert hall. With the help of musicians and music critics, I have been able to sift down the many words used to describe musical-architectural acoustics to a list of eighteen distinct, recognizable qualities and their antitheses that appear to encompass the critical variables. This collection of attributes forms a checklist against which the quality of a hall's response to musical performance can be assessed. Later in the book a scale is built around these attributes, and each attribute is assigned a weighting that represents the proportion of its contribution to the total acoustics. But first let us list and define these terms as they are most often understood by the musicians, architects, and acousticians who use them.

The first knotty problem of definition arises with the words "resonance" and "reverberation." The physical scientist generally uses "resonance" to mean the large-amplitude vibration that occurs when a body is excited in one of its normal modes of vibration by an external source having the resonance frequency of that mode. For example, the air column inside the resonator beneath a bar of a xylophone vibrates vigorously if the resonance frequency of the air column is equaled by the frequency of the vibrating bar above.

The musician uses "resonance" to describe the addition of any acoustical after-ring to a musical tone combined with an augmentation of its loudness. Thus he speaks of the resonance of a violin—even though the frequency of the vibrating string may not coincide with a resonance frequency of the violin body. Even without resonance the violin body augments the loudness of a string because it has a larger radiating surface than the string itself. And the string has its own after-ring, which might be interpreted, erroneously of course, as the after-ring of the violin body.

The scientist uses the word "reverberation" to designate the audible decay of sound in a room—the after-ring of all normal modes of vibration that were excited by the musical source. Because music played in a room with a long reverberation time is louder than that played in a dead room, a musician often uses the words reverberation and resonance interchangeably.

I am not proposing that musicians change their ways. In discussing acoustics I shall distinguish among resonance, augmentation of loudness, and reverberation. But when a musician speaks of a room or a violin as resonant, there should be no doubt of his meaning: the loudness is augmented and the after-ring of the room or instrument embellishes the music.

Some of the musical-acoustic qualities in Table 4.1 have been introduced in Chapter 2 as examples of the advantages of live halls. We shall now consider them in more detail and shall introduce the remaining attributes.

DEFINITIONS OF THE TERMS

1. Intimacy or presence

A hall that is small has visual intimacy. A hall has acoustical intimacy if music played in it sounds as though it is being played in a small hall. In the special language of the recording and broadcasting industry, an intimate hall has "presence." A listener's impression of the size of a hall is determined by the initial-time-delay gap, the interval between the sound that arrives directly at his ear and the first reflection that arrives there from the walls or ceiling. In halls that musicians describe as having intimate acoustics, the sound-reflecting surfaces are found to be so arranged that the initial-time-delay gap is small, shorter than about 20 milliseconds, 20 one-thousandths of a second. In order for a hall to be intimate, the direct sound from the performers must not be too faint relative to the reverberant sound. In the weighting of these attributes in Chapters 7 through 14, intimacy will be found to be nearly three times as important as any other one of the subjective musical-acoustic attributes that follow.

2. Liveness

A hall that is reverberant is called a live hall. A room that reflects too little sound back to the listener—for instance, one with too much sound-absorbing material—is called dead or dry. A hall is live whose cubic volume is large for the size of the audience that occupies it, and whose interior surfaces are sound-reflective. Liveness in a hall imparts fullness of tone to music.

Liveness is related primarily to the reverberation time for the middle

Table 4.1   Vocabulary of subjective attributes of musical-acoustic quality

	QUALITY		ANTITHESIS	
	Noun form	*Adjectival form*	*Noun form*	*Adjectival form*
1	intimacy, presence	intimate	lack of intimacy lack of presence	non-intimate
2	liveness, fullness of tone	live	dryness deadness	dry dead
	reverberation	reverberant	lack of reverberation	unreverberant
	resonance	resonant	dryness	dry
3	warmth	warm	lack of bass	brittle
4	loudness of the direct sound	loud direct sound	faintness . . . weakness . . .	faint . . . weak . . .
5	loudness of the reverberant sound	loud . . .	faintness . . . weakness . . .	faint . . . weak . . .
6	definition, clarity	clear	poor definition	muddy
7	brilliance	brilliant	dullness	dull
8	diffusion	diffuse	poor diffusion	non-diffuse
9	balance	balanced	imbalance	unbalanced
10	blend	blended	poor blend	unblended
11	ensemble	—	poor ensemble	—
12	response, attack	responsive	poor attack	unresponsive
13	texture	—	poor texture	—
14	no echo	echo-free anechoic	echo	with echo echoic
15	quiet	quiet	noise	noisy
16	dynamic range	—	narrow dynamic range	—
17	no distortion	undistorted	distortion	distorted
18	uniformity	uniform	non-uniformity	non-uniform

and high frequencies, those above about 500 cycles per second. A hall can sound live and still be deficient in bass. The term warmth describes the quality that results from reverberation at the low frequencies.

3. Warmth

Warmth in music is defined as liveness of the bass, or fullness of the bass tone relative to that of the mid-frequency tone. Fullness of the bass tone occurs when the reverberation time for the low frequencies (250 cycles per second and below) is somewhat longer than the reverberation time for the middle frequencies (500 to 1000 cycles per second). If the reverberation time is shorter for the low frequencies than for the middle frequencies, the sound is said to be brittle. Sometimes in a small room or studio there is so wide a gap between the acoustical resonances at the low frequencies that the augmentation of the different musical tones is noticeably uneven. If some low-frequency tones are exaggerated, the resulting uneven sound may be what is called "boomy." Boomy acoustics rarely occur in large concert halls or opera houses, unless sound-absorbing materials effective only at the high frequencies (trebles) have been used extensively on the walls and ceiling. Most concert halls that are highly regarded have a warm sound—a rich, full bass.

4. Loudness of the direct sound

Loudness is a complex attribute. Our impression of the loudness of music in a hall is made up of the loudnesses of the direct and the reverberant sound, and we shall discuss these two loudnesses separately.

In a small hall the direct sound created by the orchestra usually reaches the back rows of the audience with adequate loudness. But in a very large hall, particularly if the seats are not raked sufficiently toward the back, the loudness of the direct sound is too low by the time it reaches the distant listeners. This has been illustrated in Figure 2.4 for outdoor listening. The best halls are of limited length, and the surfaces above and on the sides of the stage are planned to project the sound evenly to the rear seats. The direct sound of an orchestra in a hall with normally raked seats is usually at its most comfortable level about 60 feet from the concertmaster.

5. Loudness of the reverberant sound

The energy in the reverberant sound is related to two variables, the intensity of the sound that does not travel directly to the listener, and the reverberation time of the hall with audience and orchestra present. In a hall with very large cubic volume and a short reverberation time, the loudness of the reverberant sound for a passage that calls for the fortissimo will be insufficient to express the composer's specification. On the other hand, if the hall is small and highly reverberant, a symphony orchestra playing a double forte passage may reach levels that cause ear tickle or at least discomfort to many listeners. Good halls achieve an adequate balance between these extremes.

Liveness, warmth, and the loudness of the direct and reverberant sounds are next in importance to acoustical intimacy, and taken together, they receive a slightly greater weighting in the computational scheme presented in the later chapters.

6. Definition or clarity

A hall is said to have definition when the sound is clear and distinct. A hall lacking in definition gives music a blurred or muddy quality. The degree of definition in a hall is a function of the pattern of interior sound-reflecting surfaces and is therefore related to the intimacy. It is also a function of the reverberation time and is therefore related to the liveness; it is a function of the distance of the listener from the performer and is therefore related to the loudness of the direct sound; and it is a function of the cubic volume of the room and is therefore related to the loudness of the reverberant sound. Thus although we may perceive it as an entity, definition is really a kind of integration of four of the five attributes just discussed and therefore is not given a separate numerical scale in the computational system that follows in later chapters.

7. Brilliance

Brilliance is defined as bright, clear, ringing sound, rich in harmonics. It comes from the relative prominence of the treble and the slowness of its

decay. It is affected by the initial-time-delay gap, the ratio of the reverberation times at high frequencies to those at middle frequencies, the distance of
the listener from the performers, and the presence in the hall of suitable
sound-reflecting surfaces. A hall that has liveness at the high frequencies,
clarity, and acoustical intimacy has brilliant sound. In other words, brilliance
is closely related to three of the six attributes discussed above and is not
given a separate numerical scale in the computational system.

8. Diffusion

Diffusion concerns the spatial orientation of the reverberant sound. The
diffusion is best when the reverberant sound seems to arrive at the listener's
ears from all directions in about equal amount. The orchestral sound is
diffused in the hall by a combination of a long reverberation time and an
abundance of irregular interior surfaces—for example, coffers in the ceiling,
niches on the walls, statues, balcony faces. Diffusion is lacking when a hall
has smooth side walls and ceiling which carry the sound directly from the
stage to the audience without encouraging cross reflections or scattering of
the sound waves. Poor diffusion may result also when the stagehouse over
the orchestra is reverberant but the rest of the hall dead. Although this kind
of reverberation is of some benefit to the music, it is not as satisfactory as
reverberation developed in the body of the hall itself.

9. Balance

Good balance entails both the balance between the sections of the
orchestra and the balance between orchestra and vocal or instrumental
soloists.

Some of the ingredients that combine to give good balance to a concert
hall are acoustic and some are musical. The stage enclosure should be
properly designed for width, depth, and height, and it should have irregularities on its inner surfaces. There should be either a partially open ceiling
or reflecting panels at the sides and over the forward part of the audience.
Beyond that, balance is in the hands of the musicians: the conductor's seating
of the sections and his control of the players.

In an opera house, both the stage design and the pit design affect the balance of singer and orchestra as well as the conductor's control of the orchestra.

10. Blend

Blend is defined as a mixing of the sounds from the various instruments of the orchestra in such a way that they seem harmonious to the listener. Blend is partly a matter of disposition of the orchestra, which should be spread neither too wide nor too deep. Blend also strongly depends on the design of the ceiling over the stage and on the presence of splayed surfaces that mix the sound before it emerges from the stage enclosure. In later chapters balance and blend are treated under one heading because both depend on the design of the sending end of the hall.

11. Ensemble (ease of hearing among performers)

Ensemble refers to the performers' ability to play in unison, that is to say, the extent to which they initiate and release their notes simultaneously so that many voices sound as one. In order to achieve good ensemble, the musicians must be able to hear their fellow performers in the orchestra. If the stage or pit is very wide and shallow, the two sides of the orchestra will not be able to hear each other and the ensemble will be poor. The stage enclosure and the reflecting surfaces at the sides and above the stage are in general responsible for carrying the sounds from the performers on one part of the stage to those on other parts.

Diffusion, balance and blend, and ensemble are next in importance to the five most significant attributes named above: intimacy, liveness, warmth, loudness of the direct sound, and loudness of the reverberant sound.

12. Immediacy of response (attack)

From the musician's standpoint, a hall should give the performers the feeling that it responds immediately to a note. Immediacy of response is related to the manner in which the first reflections from surfaces in the hall arrive back at the musician's ears. If the reflections occur too long after the note is sounded, the musician will hear them as an echo; if he hears only the reflections from the nearby walls of the stage around him, he will fail to sense the acoustics of the hall at all. Immediacy of response is thus determined by intimacy, liveness, diffusion, ensemble, and echo. Like Items 6 and 7, it has not been given a separate numerical scale in the computational system.

13. Texture

Texture is the subjective impression created in the mind of the listener by the pattern in which the sequence of sound reflections arrives at the listener's ears. For example, in some halls a number of reflections follow the initial-time-delay gap in uniform sequence, as was shown in Figure 2.14. In other halls, there is a considerable gap in time between the first and second or the second and third reflections. In still other halls, some reflections are much louder than others.

The pattern of the reflections forms a kind of a texture that is superimposed on the more gross subjective effects produced by the other attributes of acoustics.

14. Freedom from echo

Echo describes a delayed reflection sufficiently loud to annoy the listeners. It may come from ceiling surfaces that are very high or that focus sound into one part of the hall. Echo commonly results from a long high curved rear wall whose focal point is near the front of the audience or even on the stage. Echo is most likely to occur in the front seats of large halls and in halls with short reverberation time. If echo has not been avoided in the initial design of a hall, changes must be made in the reflecting surfaces after the hall is completed.

15. Freedom from noise

A concert hall must be free of extraneous noise from traffic, from adjoining halls or practice rooms, from subways, airplanes, ventilating systems, and movement of late-comers on stairways and in passageways. It is a commonplace that the first factor in good design of a hall for music is the isolation of all external noise sources from the listeners. Many a good hall has been undone by ventilating-system noise or traffic or aircraft noise.

16. Dynamic range

Dynamic range is the spread of sound levels over which music can be heard in a hall; it extends from a low level determined by the noise of an audience in a hall to the loudest levels produced by the performers. The loudest levels of the music are determined by the force of the orchestra together with the acoustical characteristics of the hall. Extraneous sources of noise should be reduced to inaudibility in the presence of normal audience noise. The loudest levels produced by the orchestra should not be great enough to cause uncomfortable ear tickle. Because loudness and noise are rated under Items 4, 5, and 15, no separate numerical scale for dynamic range is established in the computational scheme.

17. Tonal quality

Tonal quality is beauty of tone. A fine instrument has a fine tonal quality, and similarly a concert hall can have a fine tonal quality.

The tonal quality of a hall can be marred in many different ways. For example, abnormal sound absorption by certain surfaces or materials causes the loss of a band of frequencies. A rattle may occur in a metallic surface, or the metal bars in the front of an organ may ring. Sometimes there is a special kind of distortion—a rasping sound added by the hall to the orchestral music. Tonal quality is occasionally downgraded by a "flutter echo," a consequence of the unfortunate juxtaposition of reflecting surfaces so that a peculiar "buzz" may be heard in some locations.

18. Uniformity

One aspect of a good hall is uniformity of sound. Many halls have a section in which the sound is poor, for example, under a deep balcony overhang, or at the sides of the front if the hall is especially wide, or close to the stage. The sound may also suffer in certain locations where reflections produce echoes, muddiness, or lack of clarity. Some halls are said to have "dead" or "live" spots, for instance, under balconies. Here again the vocabularies of acoustics and music differ. Musicians sometimes describe as dead spots places where the music is not as clear or as live as it is in other parts of the hall. In its acoustical use, the term describes only locations at which the music is particularly weak.

Comment

This list of eighteen terms concludes the description of the principal attributes of acoustical quality in a hall intended for the performance of music. Other attributes could undoubtedly be named, and some of the eighteen included here could be discussed in combination or split even more finely and the parts discussed separately. With the terms defined here a musician would be able to describe a concert hall that he likes as one in which orchestral music is live, brilliant, warm, intimate, clear, and adequately loud. He might say that music played in the hall has good attack, the orchestra is balanced, and the performers hear each other well. And he might conclude that the hall is uniform acoustically, has no echo, and has a wide dynamic range.

5

Interviews and Measurements

At the outset of this study it was impossible to foresee what factors in concert halls would be found crucial to their acoustics for music. My first need was for a rough scale of categories into which the halls could be sorted, so that a rough approximation of "rank order" or relative merit could be ascertained. A 6-point category scale, in which the highest category was "excellent" or A$^+$, the lowest "poor" seemed to offer a sufficient number of categories to permit each hall to be placed in its appropriate niche.

My next step was to try to isolate and quantify those features of structure that the best halls have in common and, conversely, those that the poorest halls share. If this acoustic information could be correlated with musicians' assessments of the halls, that is to say, if all halls judged excellent were found to share certain properties and all those judged less pleasing turned out to be plagued by similar defects, it might be possible to formulate a set of principles of acoustic design for music that could be applied with confidence by architects and their acoustical consultants.

I had to study many aspects of many halls—halls long and short, wide and narrow, horizontal ceilings and slanted ceilings, halls with long and short reverberation times, thin-wood-paneled walls and heavy plaster or masonry, upholstered chairs and hard chairs, steeply raked floors and flat floors, halls with large and small capacities. Because there are so many variables, I should have liked to be able to study hundreds of halls, but the time required would have been unreasonable and the cost excessive. I finally limited my visits to approximately 60 halls in 20 nations. Of these halls, I was able to obtain drawings and architectural and acoustic measurements of 51. In addition, I have included three halls which I have had no opportunity to visit but for which drawings and acoustical information are available. One of these, the Neues Gewandhaus at Leipzig, is no longer standing. In all, I have been able to include in this study 54 halls located in 16 nations.

The technical data about the acoustics of a concert hall tell only a part of the story. We can learn from measurements whether the reverberation time or the initial-time-delay gap is long or short, and so on. But by themselves these data do not provide a prescription by which we can be assured of the acoustic result that is desired. Similarly, subjective evaluations of musical acoustics by artists and listeners are not adequate in themselves. Artists' evaluations suggest that small halls are better than large halls and that old halls are better liked than new halls, but here again, our practical needs are hardly satisfied by these observations. To understand the consequences of acoustic design, the acoustician must compare the dimensions, materials, and shapes of the halls, together with their acoustic measurements, with the subjective musical evaluations, and from this correlation of acoustic effort with aesthetic end, he can begin to untangle the threads of cause and effect.

Who is a valid judge of the acoustics of a hall? Certainly musicians are a first source of reliable information. I had only to listen with Leonard Bernstein, Erich Leinsdorf, Eugene Ormandy, Herbert von Karajan, and Charles Munch while music was being played, and then to hear their analysis of what we had heard to be convinced that these men hear immediately many of the effects that are introduced into the music by the acoustics. The knowledge and perception of musicians have perhaps never been adequately exploited by acoustical planners.

Eugene Ormandy said to me, "In my many years as a conductor, this is the first time anyone has come to me to ask my opinion about acoustics." The reason perhaps was that it is no easy task to know how the musician's opinion could be fitted to the architectural needs. What was needed was an analysis of the components that seemed to be responsible for the excellence of the music heard in a number of fine halls, and these halls had to be compared, detail for detail, with other less successful halls. A vocabulary of descriptive words was needed that acousticians and musicians could use, words that formed a common language, in which they could discuss their common interests.

I have tried to overcome these limitations by listening to music in many halls. In some halls I have attended more than 15 musical performances, and I have made a point of listening in at least two different parts of each hall. I have studied the effects that the shape of the hall, choice of materials, design of the stage, and many other factors have on the music. Now when I speak with musicians who are listening critically at the same time with me, my impressions and theirs generally agree.

A musician's opinion should be heeded when he expresses musical judgments, such as, "In this hall music is harsh (or muddy)," or "The sound is too weak," or "The violin tone is not brilliant," or "The sectional balance is poor." But a musician exceeds his competence when he says that a hall should be lined with thin wood or have a large attic over it, for such statements concern the details of structure, and on questions of architecture and acoustics few musicians can speak as experts.

A second valuable source of musical judgment is the music critic. Many music critics have traveled widely, particularly in their own nation. Most critics are skilled listeners, and many have learned to associate the acoustics of a hall with musical quality. They have made important contributions to my interviews.

A third source of information may be the concert-goers. Listeners are less reliable judges of acoustics, however, since many of them have listened to music in one hall all their lives. To many listeners the hall in their community seems good, partly because they have grown accustomed to it and partly because they have no basis for comparison. In one hall I sat at a location where there is an annoying echo. When I asked the occupant of a neighboring seat whether the echo bothered him, he said, "I have never heard it, and I have had this seat for 20 years." Apparently he had learned to hear only the performance.

THE INTERVIEWS WITH MUSICIANS AND CRITICS

In the course of this study I have interviewed a number of outstanding conductors and performers, most of whom have traveled extensively and played in many concert halls in many countries. Their musical roots are in the United States, Canada, Great Britain, and many countries of Europe and South America; they vary widely in age, musical preferences, and musical experience. I have interviewed nearly an equal number of professional music critics.

My technique for interviewing musicians and music critics was as follows: First I showed photographs of a number of halls and asked for the musician's detailed comments on any halls that he knew well. Musicians usually knew as many as ten or twenty, critics somewhat fewer. After he had completed his general comments, I asked him to rank-order the halls he knew best. The interviews generally lasted from one to three hours, and often they were lively and interspersed with anecdotes. Not until the questioning was completed did I discuss with any of the artists the results of the survey up to that date.

The musicians interviewed were:

Sir John Barbirolli	Erich Leinsdorf	Hermann Scherchen
Sir Adrian Boult	Igor Markevich*	Stanislaw Skrowaczewski*
Leonard Bernstein	Dimitri Mitropoulos	Izler Solomon*
Eleazar de Carvalho	Pierre Monteux	William Steinberg*
Alexander Gibson	Charles Munch	Isaac Stern
Tauno Hannikainen	Eugene Ormandy	Leopold Stokowski
Irwin Hoffman	Fritz Reiner	Bruno Walter
Herbert von Karajan	Sir Malcolm Sargent	

The music critics whom I interviewed are from the United States, Canada, Great Britain, and Germany. Their names with some identification follow:

Roger Dettmer*	Chicago *American*
Cyrus Durgin	Boston *Globe*
Alfred Frankenstein	San Francisco *Chronicle*
Albert Goldberg	Los Angeles *Times*
Paul Henry Lang	New York *Herald Tribune*
Jay Harrison	New York *Herald Tribune*
Paul Hume	Washington *Post*
Irving Kolodin	*Saturday Review*
Robert C. Marsh*	Chicago *Sun-Times*
Harold Rogers	*The Christian Science Monitor*
Max de Schauensee	Philadelphia *Bulletin*
Howard Taubman	New York *Times*
Harold Schonberg	New York *Times*
Jules Wolffers	Boston *Herald*
Thomas Archer*	Montreal *Gazette*
Eric McLean*	Montreal *Star*

* Interviewed by Russell Johnson of Bolt Beranek and Newman Inc. using the same procedures.

Colin Mason	*The Guardian*, Manchester, England
Peter Heyworth	*The Observer*, London
Frank Howes	*The Times*, London
Desmond Shawe-Taylor	*The Sunday Times*, London
Antonio Mingotti	*Abendzeitung*, Munich, Germany

The critics too are of widely diverse ages and backgrounds. Many know a number of halls. The interviews with the English and German critics were conducted by mail, and they were asked only about halls in their own countries.

In three halls (Kleinhans Hall in Buffalo, Queen Elizabeth Theatre in Vancouver, and the Alberta Jubilee Hall in Edmonton) questionnaires were distributed to many members of the audience. In a number of other halls (Royal Festival Hall in London, Aula Magna in Caracas, Kresge Auditorium in Cambridge, F. R. Mann Auditorium in Tel Aviv, and Symphony Hall in Boston) questionnaires were given to a small number of the audience who were known to have had broad listening experience.

In general, questioning an unselected group of listeners whose backgrounds and listening experiences were not known gave discouraging results. Most people evinced satisfaction with the hall that they were accustomed to or else spoke in vague generalities.

THE PHYSICAL MEASUREMENTS

For each concert hall in the series, acoustical measurements were made and technical details assembled, as follows: *(a)* reverberation times at eight frequencies with audience and orchestra present, *(b)* reverberation times at these same frequencies with an empty hall, *(c)* pulse measurements designed to show in detail the reflection pattern of sound at several positions in the hall, *(d)* dimensions of stage, pit, stage enclosure, and the hall as a whole, *(e)* the number of seats on each floor level, the number of standees permitted, and the number of boxes, and *(f)* construction of seats, and description of carpets, walls, and seating surfaces, stage and hall floors, draperies, curtains, proscenium opening, and so forth.

Much of the information was collected during my visits, since the architectural drawings were seldom sufficiently detailed. Also, I found that many halls had been modified: the seats had been changed, balconies rebuilt, stairways relocated, the stage extended or shortened. As a result, I gave great care to checking all measures, rather than assuming that the hall conformed with the existing drawings.

After the data were assembled they were sent to the halls for checking. The manager or the architect or acoustical consultant of nearly every hall returned his comments, and their corrections have been incorporated.

THE SUMMARIES AND TECHNICAL DETAILS

In Chapter 6, data assembled on the 54 halls are presented alphabetically by country, but with the halls in the United States alphabetized under *America* and placed first. For each hall there is a description and summary of the findings, the important technical data, architectural drawings, and photographs.

Some data presented in Chapter 6 are inconsistent with information in the literature; one of the differences concerns La Scala in Milan, which is usually considered to hold between 3200 and 3400 persons. Of course, this figure includes standing room and there is always a question of how many people can be crowded into the standing area of an opera house. The seating plan available at the box office shows 1185 numbered chairs and 156 boxes; both figures are accurate. One of the architects for the reconstruction tells me that eight persons can occupy a box in La Scala if it faces the stage and four if it is on a side at the front. Hence, I have assumed an average occupancy of six for each of 155 boxes and 20 for the one large box. A greater number of persons in a box as small as those in La Scala would be both physically and acoustically unsatisfactory. There are also 154 unnumbered seats in the upper rings from which the stage is visible only if one stands. I have assigned these seats to standing-room space. In sum, La Scala is a house that seats 2135 persons and is able to accommodate an unknown additional number of standees.

Particular care was taken to explore the surface materials of each hall in order to distinguish plaster from thick wood and thick wood from thin wood—materials that profoundly affect the reverberation time and warmth of a hall. Other details were also checked. For instance, the hall, the pit, and its cover in the Bayreuth Festspielhaus had to be remeasured. A balcony had been added in 1932 at the rear of the hall; deep spaces above and at the sides of the proscenium over the pit recently have been closed off to form ducts for the cooling air; and the two parts of the cover over the pit have been remodeled.

Even the house carpenter may be misinformed about some of the materials used in a building. I was told that the ceiling of the Lyric Theatre in Baltimore was of plaster, covered with canvas and painted to resemble wood. The carpenter had seen the painter at work. On observing the ceiling from below one would wager that the ceiling was wood. On close examination, I found that the ceiling was indeed of wood, but covered with canvas and again painted to resemble wood!

In discussing the individual halls I have tried to indicate clearly when I am giving the opinions of the musicians and critics interviewed, when I am giving my own opinions, and when I am giving objective descriptions.

In addition to the technical data that follow the description of each hall in Chapter 6, a number of charts are presented in Appendix 2, which give the reverberation times for full and empty halls as a function of frequency, details about the spacing of the seats, the date of completion of each hall, and additional data related to the acoustics.

The terminology used in the *Technical Details* for each hall is defined in Appendix 3.

6

The Fifty-Four Halls

POCHEÉ CODE FOR ARCHITECTURAL DRAWINGS OF CHAPTER 6

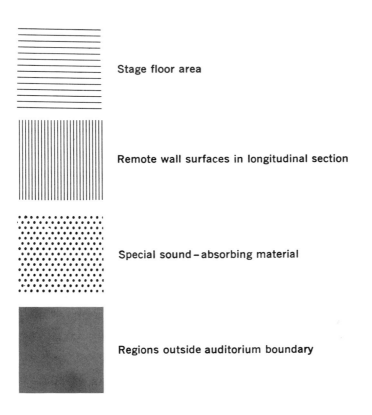

Stage floor area

Remote wall surfaces in longitudinal section

Special sound – absorbing material

Regions outside auditorium boundary

When the Lyric Theatre was opened in 1894, its success was immediate. Originally designed in a general way like the Leipzig Neues Gewandhaus (although 65 per cent wider), it has the sound of a baroque rectangular hall with side balconies. The architecture is characterized by a wide oval-topped proscenium and full-length side balconies supported by columns, beneath which are located a number of boxes. The hall is carpeted richly and hung with draperies.

Attending a concert in the Lyric Theatre is a pleasant experience. The audience is gracious, and the Theatre has charm and a feeling of southern hospitality that almost makes you expect to find a butler at intermission passing hot confections on burnished salvers.

In 1928 the rear balcony of the Lyric Theatre was enlarged from 10 to 23 rows, and the total capacity for concerts became 2616 and for opera 2456. As a result of the change the reverberation time was shortened. When the hall is used for concerts, a plywood orchestra enclosure is erected on the stage.

Five conductors who have used this hall extensively, Pierre Monteux, Charles Munch, Eugene Ormandy, Fritz Reiner, and Leopold Stokowski, rank this hall among the three best in America. One of them commented, "Of all the halls in the United States, this hall sounds best from the stage. To the conductor, the orchestra sounds as it should."

Two music critics who know the Lyric Theatre well find the sound very clear and beautiful and at the right loudness. For opera, because of its smaller size, they believe it to be superior to the Metropolitan Opera House in New York.

Although for concerts the mid-frequency reverberation time is shorter than optimum, 1.5 seconds when the theater is fully occupied, the Lyric Theatre has a clear, warm, intimate sound with good brilliance. The hall is reasonably uniform acoustically, and orchestral music played in it is adequately loud. The sound is least pleasing at the rear of the main floor. Because the sides of the hall, which are penetrated by windows and doors, are also the outside walls of the building, aircraft and loud street noises can be heard inside the hall.

BALTIMORE, LYRIC THEATRE

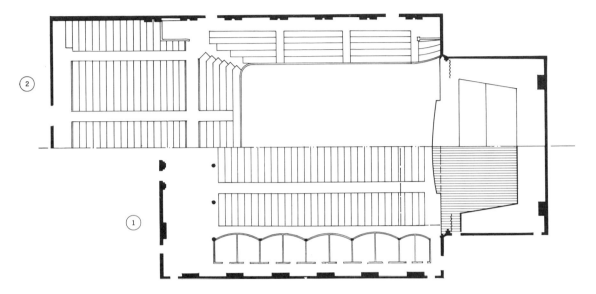

SEATING CAPACITY 2616

① 1148

② 1468

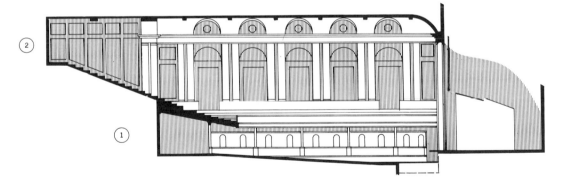

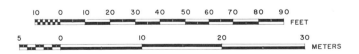

The fact that music sounds particularly good to the conductor may be due to the location of the podium. Since it stands on the apron of the stage outside the orchestra enclosure, it is well into the main hall and gives the conductor a better sense of the over-all acoustics. Also, the small stage enclosure delivers to him a well-blended sound.

The Lyric Theatre is one of the better halls of our country. Let us hope that time will preserve it from the unceasing demand for new buildings with ever-larger seating capacities.

TECHNICAL DETAILS*

Concerts

$V = 744,000$ ft^3 $T_{500-1000}$(Occup.) = 1.5 sec $S_T = 18,400$ ft^2

$N_A = 2616$ seats $S_A = 16,700$ ft^2 $S_A/N_A = 6.4$ ft^2

$t_I = 21$; 11 msec $S_O = 1690$ ft^2 $V/S_T = 40.4$ ft

Opera

$V = 720,000$ ft^3 $T_{500-1000}$(Occup.) = 1.4 sec $S_P = 2612$ ft^2

$N_A = 2456$ seats $S_A = 15,714$ ft^2 $S_T = 19,350$ ft^2

$N_T = 2456$ S_O(Pit) = 1024 ft^2 $S_A/N_T = 6.4$ ft^2

$t_I = 21$; 11 msec S_{OF}(Pit) = 1088 ft^2 $V/S_T = 37.2$ ft

* The terminology and symbols are explained in Appendix 3.

ARCHITECTURAL AND STRUCTURAL DETAILS

Uses: 35% for orchestra, 25% for speech, 5% for opera, 5% for ballet, 30% for other. *Ceiling:* ¾-in. tongue-and-groove boards, covered with cloth and painted. *Walls:* plaster on wood lath in the older part, and plaster on gypsum lath in the newer part; the partitions between the boxes at the sides of the main floor are two layers of painted canvas on a 1-in. wooden frame; balcony fronts are open-mesh cast iron. *Floors:* main floor and older part of balcony are of wood; addition is concrete. *Stage floor:* built-up wooden frame construction. *Stage height:* 51.5 in. above floor at front row of seats. *Carpet:* carpet with sponge rubber underpad, 4.5 ft wide on two center aisles on main floor and 2.25 ft wide on two side aisles; 2150 sq ft of carpet at rear of main floor seating space; carpet in large cross aisle and in ten short aisles of the balcony; no carpet on upper four aisles or at rear of balcony. *Added absorptive materials:* velvet draperies, hung with 100% fold, cover about 1200 sq ft of wall space; damask masking curtain in proscenium. *Seating:* the hall was reseated after the photograph was taken. Main floor seats: backrests have cloth-upholstered fronts and metal rears; seat bottoms have artificial leather tops and metal undersides; armrests are of wood. Balcony seats: same, except backrests are of wood, not upholstered. *Orchestra enclosure:* walls, ¼-in. plywood on light wooden framing. Ceiling, painted linen canvas.

References: Drawings and photographs, courtesy of William D. Crump, managing director of the Lyric Theatre. All data verified by the author during visits. *Architect:* T. Henry Randall.

The Indiana University Auditorium is an extremely large modern hall. Not only does it contain 3788 seats, but it is also very wide, with an impressive vaulted ceiling, and grilled penetrations on the two side walls. Close inspection reveals large areas of sound-absorbing material on the ceiling and side walls. The auditorium has a large stagehouse with a conventional proscenium opening. The rear of the hall can be closed off by a great curtain, which reduces the number of seats to 1200. The Metropolitan Opera Company of New York has performed many times in the Auditorium. It is used for all types of musical events as well as a variety of other functions.

The reverberation time in the Auditorium is short for orchestral music but excellent for opera. In operatic productions the singing voice projects well, and the balance between the singers and the pit orchestra is satisfactory in most locations in the hall. The balance is less satisfactory at the sides of the front half of the main floor. There the singing voice drops in level, and the instruments at the end of the pit nearer the listener become too loud. In the pit the brass and percussion tend to dominate the strings.

Throughout most of the hall one hears little reverberation. Near the front and on the stage there is a special kind of liveness due to reflections from the rear wall of the main floor, the balcony front, the solid surfaces projecting back from the edges of the large grilles on the side walls, and the lighting coves in the ceiling. Singers say that the Auditorium supports their voices well. Conductors in the pit report that the ensemble is satisfactory and the orchestra easy to control. The low ceiling provides adequate short-time-delay reflections on the main floor, with the result that the hall sounds more like one that seats far fewer than 3800 people. Listening conditions in the seats deep under the overhang of the balcony are relatively poor, as are those in the last few rows of the upper balcony.

For orchestral music the intimacy rating and the reverberation time are low. As a result, concert music is lacking in liveness and, in most of the hall, is not sufficiently loud.

BLOOMINGTON, INDIANA UNIVERSITY AUDITORIUM

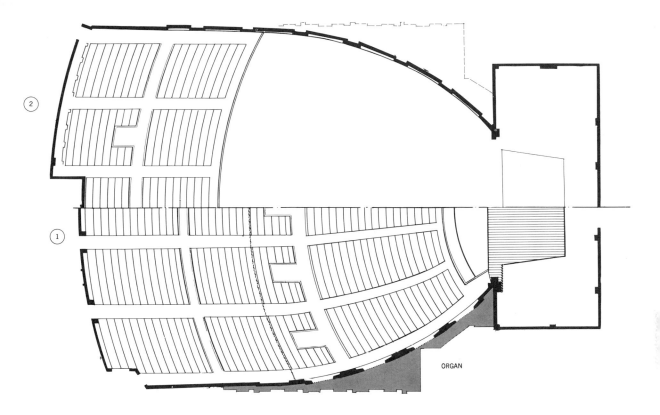

②

①

SEATING CAPACITY 3788

① 2620

② 1168

ORGAN

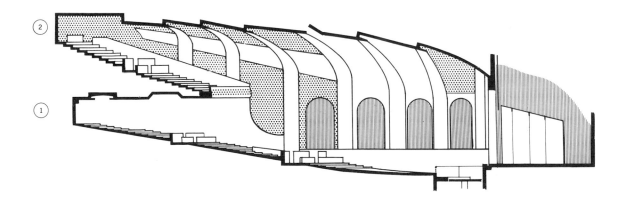

②

①

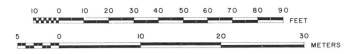

10 0 10 20 30 40 50 60 70 80 90
FEET

5 0 10 20 30
METERS

TECHNICAL DETAILS*

Concerts

$V = 950,000$ ft^3	$T_{500-1000}$(Occup.) $= 1.5$ sec	$S_T = 28,240$ ft^2
$N_A = 3788$ seats	$S_A = 26,240$ ft^2	$S_A/N_A = 7.0$ ft^2
$t_I = 40;\ 10$ msec	$S_O = 2000$ ft^2	$V/S_T = 33.6$ ft

Opera

$V = 902,000$ ft^3	$T_{500-1000}$(Occup.) $= 1.4$ sec	$S_P = 1652$ ft^2
$N_A = 3718$ seats	$S_A = 25,740$ ft^2	$S_T = 28,270$ ft^2
$N_T = 3718$	S_O(Pit) $= 878$ ft^2	$S_A/N_T = 6.9$ ft^2
$t_I = 40;\ 10$ msec	S_{OF}(Pit) $= 878$ ft^2	$V/S_T = 31.9$ ft

* The terminology is explained in Appendix 3.

ARCHITECTURAL AND STRUCTURAL DETAILS

Uses: music, drama, dance, lectures, and student assemblies; opera is presented each year. *Ceiling and side walls:* plaster on metal lath or masonry. *Floors:* concrete. *Stage floor:* wood. *Pit:* concrete and wood sides; a canvas hanging is used on the rail when pit is enlarged for full orchestra. *Stage height:* 42 in. above floor level at first row of seats. *Orchestra enclosure:* heavy canvas with many coats of paint on light framing. Openings in ceiling for border lights. *Carpets:* on all aisles. *Absorptive material:* all ceiling sections except the second and third sections from the front are covered with perforated cane acoustic tile; two-thirds of the side walls are covered with another porous material called "Spongeacoustic"; the organ pipes are located on the left side behind three of the grilles; the other five grilles in the hall cover sound-absorbing material; almost the only hard surfaces on the side walls are below the dado. *Seating:* seats are fully upholstered.

References: Drawings courtesy of L. L. Davis, manager of the Auditorium; photographs courtesy of *Musical America* and Indiana University. All data verified by the author during visits. *Architect:* A. M. Strauss. *Associate architect:* Eggers and Higgins.

Boston
SYMPHONY HALL

Symphony Hall, built in 1900 to replace the old Music Hall, is known as the first hall designed on scientifically derived principles of acoustics. It is rectangular in shape with a high, horizontal, coffered ceiling and two wrap-around balconies. On entering the hall, one encounters two strong architectural features: the stage with its back wall devoted to a row of gilded organ pipes, and the upper walls with their niches, in front of which stand replicas of Greek and Roman statues. The combination of shades of gray and cream paint, gilded balcony fronts, red-plush balcony rails, black leather seats, and red carpets would place this hall architecturally in the middle of the nineteenth century, although it was built fifty years later. In some ways it is reminiscent of the Leipzig Neues Gewandhaus; nevertheless it is quite different, primarily because it seats 2631 people compared with 1560 for the Gewandhaus. During May and June each year, tables are installed on the main floor for "Pops" concerts and the capacity is reduced to 2345.

The sound in Symphony Hall is clear, live, warm, brilliant, and loud, without being overly loud. The hall responds immediately to an orchestra's efforts. The orchestral tone is balanced, and the ensemble is excellent.

Bruno Walter said, "This is a fine hall, a very good hall. Even the first time that I conducted there, I was struck by its acoustics. It seems to be very live. It is the most noble of American concert halls."

Herbert von Karajan, in comparing this hall with the Grosser Musikvereinssaal in Vienna, which is often cited as the world's best, said, "The Boston hall is superb acoustically. For much music, it is even better than the Vienna hall because of its slightly lower reverberation time."

Sir Adrian Boult wrote, "The ideal concert hall is obviously that into which you make a not very pleasant sound and the audience receives something that is quite beautiful. I maintain that this really can happen in Boston Symphony Hall; it is our ideal."

With one exception, the conductors who were polled rated this hall as the best in America and one of the three best in the world, with such encomiums as: "one of the world's greatest halls," "when this hall is fully occupied the sound is just right—divine," "an excellent hall, there is none better."

BOSTON, SYMPHONY HALL

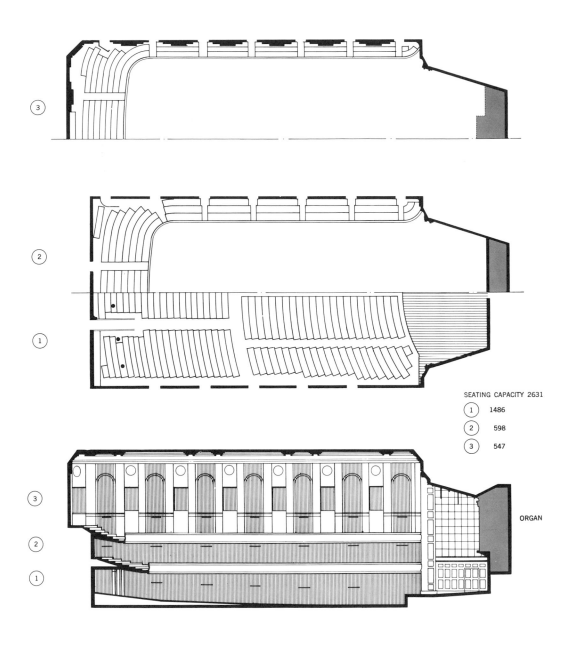

SEATING CAPACITY 2631

① 1486

② 598

③ 547

ORGAN

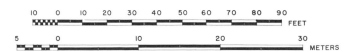

10 0 10 20 30 40 50 60 70 80 90
FEET

5 0 10 20 30
METERS

Concert violinists and pianists seem to like Symphony Hall very much, particularly the immediacy of its response.

Ten of the thirteen American and Canadian music critics interviewed who know this hall rate it among the best in the world: "The sound is excellent; the hall has full reverberance; the orchestra is in good balance unless one is too near the stage on the main floor." "This hall is wonderful; it has the right loudness; music played in it is clear and clean." "Extremely favorable. One of the best halls I have ever been in." "I would certainly put it in the very top rank."

There are a few negative features in Symphony Hall, as there are in every hall. The seats in rear corners under the overhangs of the balconies are shielded from the reverberant sound of the upper hall, and the reflected sound that reaches these seats from the soffits of the side balconies is somewhat unnatural. In the centers of the side balconies, echoes from the corners of the rear wall can be heard when staccato trumpet notes are played. Both these blemishes involve very few seats.

In my experience, only the Grosser Musikvereinssaal in Vienna, the Concertgebouw in Amsterdam, St. Andrew's Hall in Glasgow, and the Stadt-Casino in Basel have the same growth of crescendo and quality of reverberation as Symphony Hall. It is a rewarding experience to listen to music there.

How did an architectural design so appropriate for music come to be chosen? Let's look at the record. When a city proposes to replace a concert hall that is well liked, much public discussion is generated. Those who have made a weekly pilgrimage to the old hall for two score years or more are deeply influenced by their memories and they naturally object to any change. Some patrons may fear that the acoustics of the new hall will not be as satisfactory as those of the old.

Boston accomplished the transition by choosing a design that is nearly a reproduction of the former hall: "Laying aside with regret Mr. McKim's beautiful design after the Greek theatre, they adopted the shape of hall which had of late been in vogue because successful." There were only two important changes from the old hall, an increase in length of 40 feet and the elimination of a 33-foot-high canopy over the orchestra which leaves the ceiling over the stage about 43 feet high.

Wallace C. Sabine, the acoustical consultant, wrote in 1900:

While several plans were cursorily examined, the real discussion was based on only two buildings—the present [old] Boston Music Hall and the Leipzig Gewandhaus; one was familiar to all and immediately accessible, the other familiar to a number of those in consultation. . . . the Leipzig Gewandhaus . . . was so small as to be debarred from serving directly. . . . The old hall approaches more nearly the new in seating capacity, and, moreover, it is a more familiar standard. . . . In respect to loudness, I do not think that the new hall will, on the whole, be at a disadvantage in comparison with the old. . . . In respect to reverberation or residual sound, the two halls will be very nearly the same, the materials of the walls being the same.

Boston's leading music critic of the day, William Foster Apthorp of the Boston *Evening Transcript*, wrote on the day following the first concert:

But I must own that, to me, the first impression was disappointing. The opening measures of the "Euryanthe" sounded terribly tame. Everything was clean cut and distinct. The tone was beautifully smooth, and so to speak, highly polished; but it had no life, there was nothing commanding and compelling about it.

Apthorp, undoubtedly seated on the main floor in the front half of the hall, was noticing the change—the lack of a low canopy over the orchestra, which would have enhanced the short-time-delay reflections at his seat. His observations add weight to my own belief that a canopy like the one at Tanglewood in Lenox, Massachusetts, would further improve the intimacy and brilliance of the sound in the front half of the main floor.

If I seem to be overcritical of Symphony Hall, let me emphasize my complete agreement with the late Rudolph Elie, Jr., music critic for the Boston *Herald*, who wrote in 1950, "It is very clear to me now, that Symphony Hall is the most acoustically beautiful hall in the United States. It is to the orchestra what a Stradivarius is to the great violinist in providing a sound box of the utmost brilliance and sensitivity."

TECHNICAL DETAILS FOR CONCERTS*

$V = 662{,}000$ ft^3	$T_{500-1000}$(Occup.) $= 1.8$ sec	$S_T = 16{,}600$ ft^2
$N_A = 2631$ seats	$S_A = 15{,}000$ ft^2	$S_A/N_A = 5.7$ ft^2
$t_I = 15; 7$ msec	$S_O = 1600$ ft^2	$V/S_T = 39.9$ ft

* The terminology is explained in Appendix 3.

ARCHITECTURAL AND STRUCTURAL DETAILS

Uses: 50% for orchestra, 10% for soloists, 10% for organ and glee club, 10% for recordings, 10% for jazz concerts, and 10% for other. *Ceilings:* ¾-in. plaster on metal screen; 15% of the ceiling is ventilation grilles, each with about 40% open area. *Walls:* 30% plaster on metal lath, 50% on masonry backing, 20% is ½-in.- to 1-in.-thick wood, including the stage walls; balcony fronts are an open-pattern cast iron. *Floors:* the main floor is a flat concrete slab finished with wood; during the winter concert season, a sloping floor is installed (see drawing) constructed of ¾-in. boards on 4 x 4 in. framing members, supported on angle irons; the air space beneath the floor varies from zero at the front to 5 ft at the rear of the hall; the balcony floors are wood over concrete. *Carpets:* on main aisles downstairs, with no underpad. *Stage enclosure:* most of the enclosure, including the ceiling, is wood paneling in sections about 3 ft square; the frames of the panels are about 1 in. thick and 6 in. wide; the centers of the panels are about ½ in. thick; on the side walls, these panels are mounted on ¾-in. furring fastened to terra-cotta block; from the stage floor up to a height of about 14 ft from the floor, the paneling is about 1 in. thick. *Stage floor:* part of the stage, starting 23 ft from the rear, permanently slopes upward toward the rear at the rate of ⅜ in. per foot; all the stage is 1½-in. wooden planks over large air space with ¾-in. flooring on top; wood box platforms ranging in height from 3 in. near the conductor to 12 in. at the rear and side edges of the stage raise the rows of the orchestra. *Stage height:* 54 in. above floor level at first row of seats. *Seating:* the front and rear of the backrests and the top of the seat-bottoms are leather over hair; the underseat and the arms are of solid wood.

References: H. E. Johnson, *Symphony Hall, Boston,* Little, Brown and Company, Boston, 1950. Drawings and photographs courtesy of the Boston Symphony Orchestra, Thomas D. Perry, Jr., manager. Details verified by author during visits. *Architect:* McKim, Mead and White.

One of the architectural gems of America is the Kleinhans Music Hall in Buffalo, which was dedicated in 1940. Well-proportioned lines and a primavera wood interior give an immediate feeling of intimacy, warmth, and comfort. The Kleinhans Hall, which has 2839 seats, is one of only five or six important halls for music built between 1900 and 1950. The center-line profile of Kleinhans is typical of many of the modern halls that have been built since 1940, Ford, Tel Aviv, Alberta Jubilee. The seats are luxuri-ously upholstered and widely spaced. The balcony is enormous, yet it leaves one with the feeling of intimate space. Buffalo audiences are proud of the hall and they find no fault with its acoustical qualities.

Two of my colleagues at M.I.T., R. H. Bolt and J. A. Kessler, distributed questionnaires to most of the audience at a summer concert in 1950. The program included music by Gershwin and Kurt Weill. The answers to the questionnaires indicated that the loudness, brilliance, and liveness of music played in the hall were considered very good by over 80 per cent of the audience. Nearly 60 per cent thought the definition to be good to excellent, and the remaining 40 per cent found it good. Nearly 75 per cent said they were aware of no extraneous noise. The audience at this particular concert was not a typical symphony audience, since more than 70 per cent were under 30 years of age. Concert-goers of long experience were in the minority. In addition, the musical program for the test concert was stronger in brass and weaker in string tone than is usual for more serious music. Obviously one cannot extend these results to anticipate the reactions of a sophisticated musical audience.

Within a year after its inauguration, Kleinhans was catapulted into a prickly bed of acoustical controversy. On Friday, May 16, 1941, the Buffalo *Evening News* reported an acoustical study by a local professor of physics. Using data taken in the empty hall, the physicist showed that the hall has much lower reverberation at all frequencies than is generally believed desir-able. He concluded that, "The overall deadness of the Kleinhans Music Hall and the extra deadness at the low and the very high frequencies usually are noticed even more by the performers than the audience. . . . [It is] more

BUFFALO, KLEINHANS MUSIC HALL

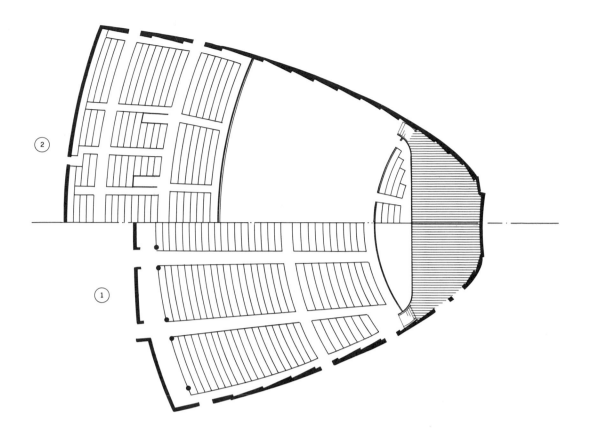

SEATING CAPACITY 2839

(1) 1575

(2) 1264

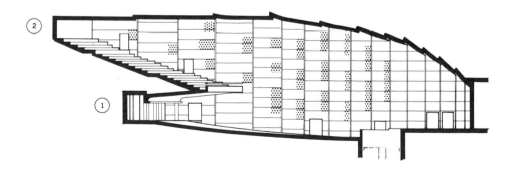

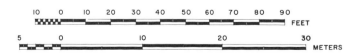

objectionable to single performers than to large groups such as a large orchestra." Leopold Stokowski also spoke out in 1941 about the deadness of the hall.

I have on several occasions attended concerts in the Kleinhans Music Hall. The hall unquestionably lacks liveness, but contrary to the newspaper report, the brilliance of the string tone is excellent, particularly on the main floor, and the sound is warm with rich, full bass. In certain parts of the main floor, the sound takes on a reverberant character. This reverberation is not the usual "ring" of a hall as a whole, but is composed of reflections from the curved vertical and horizontal sections of the stage enclosure. This can be classified as "stage liveness" rather than "hall liveness." The conductor can by his technique and the arrangement of the orchestra achieve good sectional balance. Music comes through clearly and faithfully, but with a lack of the desirable support from room reverberation. There is no intruding noise from any source. Listening to music there is rather like listening to a very fine FM-stereophonic reproducing system in a carpeted living room. The lack of support from reverberation also means that the sound is not as loud as it is in Symphony Hall, Boston, for example, nor are the fortissimos as impressive. For speech and for highly articulated music, this hall is excellent.

Izler Solomon said, "I conducted there for many years. The acoustics are good, perhaps not quite as good on the stage as on the main floor of the auditorium."

Eight musicians who are familiar with this hall mentioned its deadness. A concert violinist said that on stage the sound is quite good. He feels a sense of immediacy and support. None of the music critics interviewed knew the hall well.

TECHNICAL DETAILS FOR CONCERTS[*]

$V = 644{,}000 \text{ ft}^3$ $T_{500-1000}(\text{Occup.}) = 1.32 \text{ sec}$ $S_T = 23{,}200 \text{ ft}^2$

$N_A = 2839 \text{ seats}$ $S_A = 21{,}000 \text{ ft}^2$ $S_A/N_A = 7.4 \text{ ft}^2$

$t_I = 32; 12 \text{ msec}$ $S_O = 2200 \text{ ft}^2$ $V/S_T = 27.8 \text{ ft}$

[*] The terminology is explained in Appendix 3.

In summary, music played in this hall is clear and warm, but deficient in liveness and loudness, compared to Boston's Symphony Hall or New York's Carnegie Hall.

ARCHITECTURAL AND STRUCTURAL DETAILS

Uses: orchestra, soloists, glee club, and lectures. *Ceiling:* ¾-in. painted plaster. *Side walls:* ¾-in. plaster on metal lath on which is pasted a linen cloth over which is cemented 1/16-in. flexible wooden sheets. *Rear walls:* ¾-in. plaster on metal lath on which is cemented a heavy woven monk's cloth. *Floors:* concrete. *Stage enclosure:* the orchestra enclosure is permanent and is made of ¾-in. plywood irregularly supported on 2 x 2 in. furring strips held, in turn, by a hollow-tile structure. Lighting coves overhead open to a high attic and permit air to filter out. *Stage floor:* 1⅛-in. wooden planks on ¾-in. subfloor over a large air space. *Stage height:* 42 in. above floor level at first row of seats. *Added absorptive material:* on each wall are located ten vertical strips of thin, perforated asbestos, backed in places by patches of sound-absorbing material. *Carpets:* the main floor seating area and aisles are fully carpeted. *Seating:* both the front and the rear of the backrests are upholstered in hard-weave cloth; likewise the tops of the seat-bottoms. The armrests are of wood. The seat-bottoms are solid.

References: Drawings and photographs courtesy of Kleinhans Music Hall Management, Inc., the late Winifred E. Corey, director, and Stanley C. Podd, architect. Some information from Buffalo *Evening News,* May 16 and June 20, 1941. Details verified by the author during visits. *Architect:* Eliel Saarinen and F. J. and W. A. Kidd.

Kresge Auditorium is a many-purposed campus auditorium of 1238 seats. To enter the auditorium, one must first climb the steps of one of the four entrances at the rear cross aisle. The first elements to be seen are the white acoustic "clouds" and the gray spherical-shaped ceiling at a height of 44 feet. After a few more steps the free-standing organ is fully exposed on a gallery at the right of the stage and the rich wood of the side and stage walls comes into view. Finally, attention is drawn to the multicolored seats and the fan-shaped seating plan.

The architectural concept of an exposed domed ceiling presented difficult acoustical problems during the design stages. Domed ceilings cause focusing of sound and are notoriously bad for acoustics. Without properly placed sound-reflecting panels, a hall of this shape would be unusable for music and unsatisfactory for speech. Bolt Beranek and Newman Inc. as the acoustical consultants collaborated with the architect in the design of suspended plaster panels to minimize the undesirable consequences of the dome geometry while at the same time preserving the appearance of a dome. The large curved rear wall is finished with sound-absorbing material to control focused echoes from that surface. These measures produced acoustics satisfactory for many types of music and for speech.

Judged in the light of the goals set by the architect and the owner, the acoustical results have been quite successful. For recitals and for small musical ensembles, the hall is among the best in the United States. When a full symphony orchestra performs, the sound is at times too loud, but this is not unexpected in a relatively small auditorium. Also, because of its relatively small cubic volume, Kresge Auditorium is not sufficiently reverberant for symphonic music of the Romantic style. The low ceiling over the stage and the particular shape and location of the forward reflecting panels cause some imbalance among the sections of the orchestra. Organ music of the cathedral type played in Kresge frequently receives unfavorable comment because the reverberation time is much less than optimum for that kind of music.

An objective evaluation of the acoustics was made in 1959 by Pro-

CAMBRIDGE, KRESGE AUDITORIUM

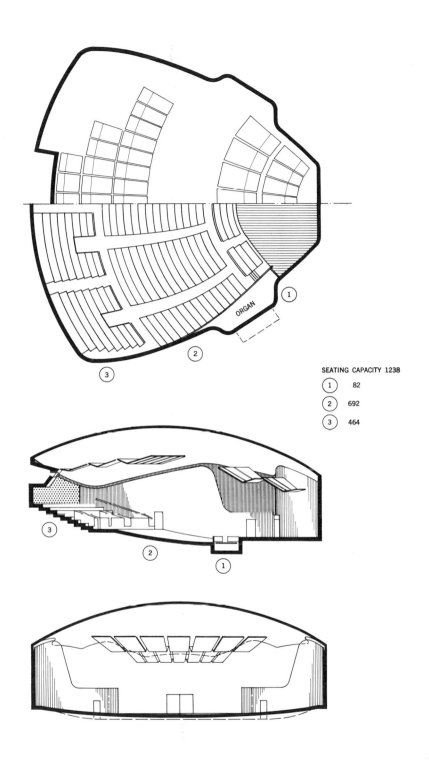

ORGAN

SEATING CAPACITY 1238

① 82
② 692
③ 464

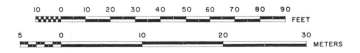

| 10 | 0 | 10 | 20 | 30 | 40 | 50 | 60 | 70 | 80 | 90 | FEET |

| 5 | 0 | 10 | 20 | 30 | METERS |

fessor Klaus Liepmann, Director of Music at the Massachusetts Institute of Technology:

The hall was designed for various purposes including drama, opera, operettas, and a most diversified number of concerts: orchestra, chorus, solo recitals, organ recitals, and chamber music. As far as music is concerned, I can say that the Kresge Hall has proved ideal in many respects. The tone is clear and clean, and while the reverberation period might seem somewhat short for the repertoire of the Romantics when they employ a big orchestra, this very clarity turns out to be a decided advantage when it comes to solo recitals, chamber music, and music of the Baroque. The favorable impression of the writer has been shared enthusiastically by Dr. Charles Munch whenever he conducts the Boston Symphony in Kresge, and by various outstanding organists, notably André Marchal of Paris, when they play the organ in Kresge.

The professional music critics who know this hall best are those in Boston. In general they agree with Professor Liepmann that for chamber groups, soloists, and piano the hall is superb. Some reviews follow:

The Christian Science Monitor, Boston, May 3, 1955, Jules Wolffers, writing of a chamber music concert:

One has never heard the true beauty of the lower instruments, in particular, so well projected. A passage for violas, cellos, and double basses, as only one example, was free of all the fuzziness usually associated with these instruments. The effect was all the more remarkable considering the few players involved at the moment—some ten in all. The flute comes through with utmost beauty and the other woodwinds are also heard to fine advantage. . . .

Boston *Herald*, December 16, 1956, O.C.M.:

Yesterday afternoon, in Kresge Auditorium at M.I.T., E. Power Biggs gave an organ recital. . . . Kresge, as we all know by now, is the handsome building with the famous acoustics. It may seem a trifle startling that the designs of the musical mind of another day should be heard in a structure that so strikingly bespeaks the scientific intellect of our own times. But the fact is that the two do not conflict; they dramatize and complement one another. . . .

Most organists point out that the reverberation time is too low for many compositions written for cathedral-sized spaces. Some organists accept the challenge of the "dry" acoustics and take pleasure in playing the Holtkamp organ.

The Boston Symphony Orchestra performs in Kresge Auditorium at least once a year. At a conference that I attended in August 1959, Charles Munch, the conductor, said that he is much pleased with the sound on the stage of Kresge, except that fortissimo passages for a full 105-piece orchestra are somewhat too loud. T. D. Perry, the manager of the orchestra, commented that the balance among sections of the orchestra is different in different parts of the hall.

Izler Solomon said, "I found the hall very exciting. It is very alive and I like the quality. With a small orchestral group and chorus it is very charming."

The acoustical results described here have been achieved in a hall that was designed for small musical ensembles, lectures, convocations, and drama. The basic problem posed by the dome-shaped roof, namely, the focusing of the sound, has been largely solved. A different arrangement of the panels over the stage could undoubtedly improve the sectional balance for large orchestra, but not without some difficulty in achieving an architectural solution as visually satisfying as the present one.

TECHNICAL DETAILS FOR CONCERTS*

$V = 354,000 \text{ ft}^3$ $\quad$ $T_{500-1000}(\text{Occup.}) = 1.47 \text{ sec}$ $\quad$ $S_T = 10,500 \text{ ft}^2$

$N_A = 1238 \text{ seats}$ $\quad$ $S_A = 9280 \text{ ft}^2$ $\quad$ $S_A/N_A = 7.5 \text{ ft}^2$

$t_I = 15; 10 \text{ msec}$ $\quad$ $S_O = 1270 \text{ ft}^2$ $\quad$ $V/S_T = 33.6$

* The terminology is explained in Appendix 3.

ARCHITECTURAL AND STRUCTURAL DETAILS

Uses: 50% for lectures and drama, 15% for organ, 5% for orchestra, 18% for chamber music and operetta, 12% for soloists and glee club. *Ceilings:* 3½-in. to 5½-in. concrete shell; the hanging sound-reflecting panels are 1-in. plaster on wire lath. *Side walls and stage enclosure:* wooden paneling, about ½ in. thick on ¾-in. wooden furring. *Rear wall:* glass fiber absorbing material, about 6 in. deep, faced with woven plastic fabric and narrow wooden slats, 6 in. on center. *Floors:* concrete. *Stage floor:* 2-in. laminated wood floated on glass fiberboard over concrete. *Stage height:* 32 in. above floor level at first row of seats. *Carpet:* none. *Added absorptive material:* varying amounts have been placed on top of the reflecting panels to reduce the reverberation time for speech, and to dampen panel resonances. *Seating:* front of backrest and top of seat-bottoms are upholstered, undersides of seat-bottom and rear of backrest are of solid metal.

References: Drawings courtesy of Eero Saarinen and Associates. Photographs courtesy of Massachusetts Institute of Technology Photographic Service. Details verified by author during visits. *Architect:* Eero Saarinen and Associates.

Chicago, with its Orchestra Hall, Civic Opera House, Auditorium, and Arie Crown Theatre, has more large halls for music than any other American city. The Arie Crown Theatre, which has 5081 seats, is the largest and newest of the four. Opened in May 1961, with performances of *Aida, Martha, Turandot,* and *La Traviata* by the Metropolitan Opera Company of New York, it has received a favorable press and enthusiastic support from the opera lovers of Chicago.

It is difficult to realize the full size of this hall. If the Academy of Music in Philadelphia, which seats 2984, were placed along one side at the rear of the main floor of the Arie Crown, it would not extend beyond the center aisle, and the front row of seats of the Academy would fall on about the twelfth row of the Arie Crown Theatre. The two halls are about the same height, but aside from that they are worlds apart. The Academy is a delicate, old-world music box with a white and gold interior and a tiny proscenium, only 48 feet wide. The Arie Crown Theatre is bold, painted a deep salmon red, with a large proscenium whose width can be varied from 40 to 85 feet. Circular "shields" on the front side walls conceal openings behind which the loudspeakers for an electronic organ may someday be placed. But despite its size the Theatre is dwarfed by the building that houses it, the large McCormick Place Convention and Exposition Center, which measures approximately 1100 by 400 feet.

The Arie Crown Theatre is not intended primarily for music; it is an excellent all-purpose auditorium. A dominant feature is a transparent cloth screen that billows above the orchestra pit and conceals multichannel stereophonic loudspeakers. The placement of this system precludes any reflecting surfaces, such as hanging panels, in the vicinity of the stage, and thus deprives the hall of the short-time-delay reflections essential for acoustical intimacy and adequate loudness. For these reasons, the sound system is necessary for many types of performing groups. At this writing, no orchestra enclosure has been provided for placement on the stage, and some concerts have been presented with the performing body seated over the orchestra pit with a steel curtain lowered behind the performers. The result is not bad,

CHICAGO, ARIE CROWN THEATRE, McCORMICK PLACE

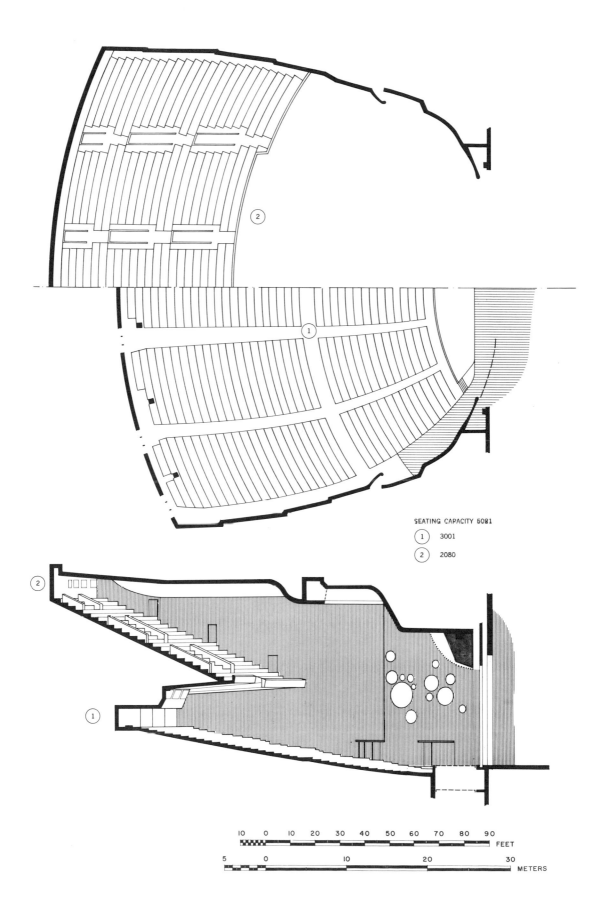

SEATING CAPACITY 5081

(1) 3001

(2) 2080

10 0 10 20 30 40 50 60 70 80 90 FEET

5 0 10 20 30 METERS

although the long initial-time-delay gap, as well as some lack of balance and blend at seats on the main floor, detract somewhat from the musical quality.

Excerpts from articles by Chicago music critics during the opening week of performances by the Metropolitan Opera Company are of interest.

Robert C. Marsh of the Chicago *Sun Times* commented in his review:

The thing that impresses you quickly is the ease with which voices carry across the orchestra into the theater. I had seats up front, and later in the evening I tried a pair in the back. In both locations there was a greater sense of contact with the singers than I had ever experienced in the Chicago Civic Opera House.

Roger Dettmer of the Chicago *American* wrote in *Musical America* (July, 1961):

No Chicago theater now in use transmits the singing voice so faithfully. There is clarity and carrying power aplenty without distortion. Natural balances prevail, though the closer up front one goes, the more stereophonic the orchestra becomes. The hall features sufficient and pleasing reverberation, even when full, and there was no overhang or echo in any of the several widely scattered locations tested.

Claudia Cassidy, commenting on the *Dancers of Bali,* wrote:

The show carries in the big house, and the music shimmers even more beautifully at a distance. . . .

My own impression of the Arie Crown Theatre is that it could be significantly improved for music if a canopy of the type used at Tanglewood in Lenox, Massachusetts, were hung over the orchestra pit and the forward part of the auditorium. Such an addition would make this a first-class concert hall for its size. A canopy of this type would also be beneficial to opera. If it were installed permanently, however, drastic changes would have to be made in the sound system.

With the present architectural design and stereophonic sound system, the next best solution for concerts would be a deep enclosure on the stage. Although this arrangement would put a wider separation between the orchestra and the audience, the balance and blend of the music, the short-time-delay reflections, and the orchestra ensemble would be satisfactory. This type of enclosure was recommended by Bolt Beranek and Newman Inc., the acoustical consultants, as part of the original design, and the plan still is appropriate.

TECHNICAL DETAILS*

Concerts

$V = 1{,}291{,}000$ ft^3	$T_{500-1000}(\text{Occup.}) = 1.7$ sec†	$S_T = 35{,}100$ ft^2
$N_A = 5081$ seats	$S_A = 33{,}100$ ft^2	$S_A/N_A = 6.5$ ft^2
$t_I = 36;\ 14$ msec	$S_O = 2000$ ft^2	$V/S_T = 36.8$ ft

Opera

$V = 1{,}283{,}800$ ft^3	$T_{500-1000}(\text{Occup.}) = 1.5$ sec	$S_P = 3520$ ft^2
$N_A = 5081$ seats	$S_A = 33{,}100$ ft^2	$S_T = 37{,}590$ ft^2
$N_T = 5081$	$S_O(\text{Pit}) = 970$ ft^2	$S_A/N_T = 6.5$ ft^2
$t_I = 36;\ 14$ msec	$S_{OF}(\text{Pit}) = 1130$ ft^2	$V/S_T = 34.2$ ft

* The terminology is explained in Appendix 3.
† Estimated.

ARCHITECTURAL AND STRUCTURAL DETAILS

Uses: general purpose. *Ceiling:* ¾-in. plaster on metal lath; same on under-balcony surface. *Side and rear walls:* ¾-in. plaster on metal lath. *Main floor:* concrete. *Stage floor:* linoleum on wood over 2-in. air space. *Stage height:* 30 in. above the floor at the first row of seats. *Carpets:* aisles fully carpeted; strips of carpet between rows. *Added absorptive material:* both rear walls and balcony rail, 1-in. glass fiberboard in front of 2-in. air space with open-weave Saran fabric facing. *Seating:* fully upholstered with solid backsides; underseat solid.

References: Drawings from architect. Details verified by personal visits. Photographs courtesy of E. J. Lee, general manager of the theater. *Architect:* Alfred Shaw. *Consulting architect:* Edward Stone and John **Root.**

This oddly shaped hall was primarily the design of Chicago's musical giant, Theodore Thomas, who conducted the Chicago Symphony Orchestra from 1891 until 1905. Its acoustics, when fully occupied, are dry and clear—the antithesis of those in Chicago's abandoned Auditorium where the Orchestra had performed previously. But let us read the story of its beginnings from the publications that followed the hall's dedication. Charles Edward Russell wrote [*The American Orchestra and Theodore Thomas*, Doubleday, Page and Company, Garden City, New York, 1927, pp. 292–301]:

From the beginning Theodore Thomas had known that the Auditorium was not the place for orchestral concerts. It was so big that to fill it with sound he was obliged to employ a stress all out of keeping with his ideas and purposes, a stress that obliterated the finer points he wished the public to seize and assimilate. The stage was so ill adapted to an orchestra's use that he regarded it as hopeless. In the season of 1903-1904 he told me that he had tried thirteen different arrangements . . . all that his years of studies in acoustics could suggest . . . and none of them had proved tolerable. . . . Nothing would prevent what was to his ears a deadly mishmash of sound where his passion was for clarity and sweet reasonableness.

But the public was fond of the Auditorium, which was a beautiful place, admirably adapted to spectacles, operas, and public meetings. . . . If the Chicago public was ever to reach that stage of musical perception and development he had hoped for it, he must have a hall where he could show veritable effects. . . . He announced that other quarters must be had for the orchestra or he would leave it.

Daniel H. Burnham was the architect . . . he put into practice every suggestion that Mr. Thomas had made. The exceptions were small and unimportant. . . . The hall was dedicated on December 14, 1904. . . . About the building. It was so different from the Auditorium; everything sounded so strange in it. . . . The orchestra in the Auditorium and the orchestra in the new orchestral hall were different machines. The new hall had hardly a third of the depth of the old and its acoustics were so perfect that the slightest whisper on the stage was audible at the back of the upper gallery. For thirteen years the orchestra had been accustomed to play so it could make itself heard in the great hollow of the Auditorium. . . . [In Orchestra Hall] the sound was so clear that problems of technique and blend, not noticed before, appeared. Thomas felt that with adequate trial in a short

CHICAGO, ORCHESTRA HALL

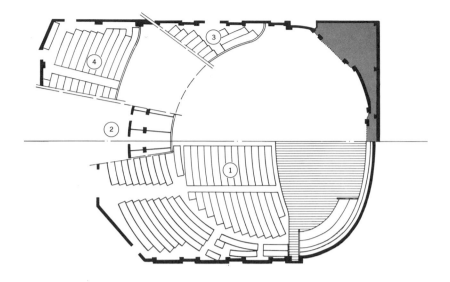

SEATING CAPACITY 2582

1.   1001
2.   138
3.   929
4.   514

ORGAN

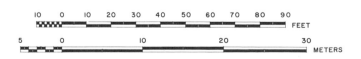

10 0 10 20 30 40 50 60 70 80 90
FEET

5 0 10 20 30
METERS

time all the apparent harshness of the orchestra in its new quarters would be smoothed away. Thomas [probably] felt that Chicago . . . might have known that he would not stumble at the summit and crisis of his art. . . . [But, nevertheless,] the cry arose that after all the labor and sacrifice the new hall was a failure . . . a part of the press used it industriously.

Theodore Thomas himself wrote [George P. Upton, *Theodore Thomas, A Musical Autobiography*, Vol. I, A. C. McClury and Co., Chicago, 1905, p. 102]:

Another obstacle the Association had to contend against was the lack of a building suitable for orchestral purposes. The only hall in which our concerts could be given was the Auditorium—an immense theatre, with a seating capacity of four or five thousand, which had been erected . . . for opera festivals, political conventions and other large popular gatherings. The great size of this theatre called for the largest possible orchestra, but even then it was often ineffective, notwithstanding the remarkable acoustic properties of the building.

Mrs. Theodore Thomas wrote, after Mr. Thomas's death on January 4, 1905 [*ibid.*, pp. 110–111]:

But unfortunately an adverse criticism of the new hall appeared, which he feared would injure its reputation unless immediately counteracted, and this made him feel, all too keenly, the necessity of adjusting the orchestra to its new surroundings in the shortest possible time, in order that the fine acoustics which he knew the hall possessed, *and with which he was perfectly satisfied*, might be made apparent to the world also, without delay.

I have attended many concerts in Orchestra Hall and have found that, when all its seats are occupied, its acoustics are very dry and the reverberation time is short. I am told that the curved stage ceiling and the nearly circular rear stage wall cause an imbalance of sound at the conductor's podium and a blend of orchestral tones that is not the best. The musicians complain that they do not hear other sections of the orchestra in proper balance. In a misdirected effort to control these effects, the domed ceiling over the stage has been covered with acoustic plaster. At various times, conductors have experimented with draperies hung on the stage walls.

Because the seats in the balcony are not upholstered, the hall is quite reverberant when empty. Its reverberance, together with the excellence of the

Chicago Symphony Orchestra under its conductor, Fritz Reiner, have made the empty hall a favorite for orchestral recordings.

Holders of season tickets to the symphony concerts say that it is difficult to hear under the boxes and under the upper balcony. It is also difficult to hear in the boxes unless one is seated at the front. In my opinion, the best seats are in the first three rows of the lower balcony and toward the rear of the upper balcony.

Of the musicians and conductors interviewed who know this hall well, all but one expressed dissatisfaction with the acoustics. They agree that with an audience the hall is too dead and they all think that the stage is too wide and too shallow. All of them remark on the difficulties of hearing the various departments of the orchestra in proper balance. One Midwestern conductor said, "Playing in the orchestra, I found myself completely isolated. Conducting, I was the last person to hear any discrepancy. The stage is too wide and shallow. The brass-string balance as heard in the hall depends on the conductor and the work being performed. But the brass never have to force."

Roger Dettmer of the *Chicago American* said during an interview: "In my opinion, the best seats are on the main floor, between rows K and N, center. Other people maintain that the sound is better in the front balcony and in the gallery. In the gallery, there's a greater blending, but the sound is very intense—it travels upward from the orchestra and hits you with a terrific impact.

"When the hall is half empty, the reverberation is high; when the hall is full, there is almost none. You hardly ever get a warm sound, but it is bright. The music tends to be without bass support, even though there are nine double basses."

Robert Marsh of the Chicago *Sun-Times* reports that, "Towards the rear center of the main floor there are about 100 seats in which the sound equals the best in this country. In the rear of the first balcony and under the balcony on the main floor, the sound is pretty dreadful. Without audience the hall is too reverberant, like an old barrel."

Other music critics whom I consulted responded with statements like: "It is a bad hall. It is as dead as they come. There is something about the stage end that destroys the quality of the music."

Several years ago, the firm of Bolt Beranek and Newman Inc. was engaged by a Chicago architect to suggest revisions that would improve the acoustics. They concluded that there was no practical way to make this a first-class hall although several steps could be taken to improve it. The greatest improvement would be gained if it were possible to lengthen the auditorium, thus permitting the construction of a new stage and a major redesign of the ceiling. By this means the performing end of the hall could be improved and the reverberation time increased. But such drastic reconstruction is apparently impossible, because the stage end of the hall abuts a public alley and Chicago building codes prevent its being closed. At present, I am told that the owners are exploring the possibility of replacing Orchestra Hall with a new hall.

TECHNICAL DETAILS FOR CONCERTS[*]

$V = 536,000 \text{ ft}^3$	$T_{500-1000}(\text{Occup.}) = 1.3 \text{ sec}†$	$S_T = 20,000 \text{ ft}^2$
$N_A = 2582$ seats	$S_A = 18,000 \text{ ft}^2$	$S_A/N_A = 7.0 \text{ ft}^2$
$t_I = 40; 24$ msec	$S_O = 2000 \text{ ft}^2$	$V/S_T = 26.8 \text{ ft}$

[*] The terminology is explained in Appendix 3.
† Estimated.

ARCHITECTURAL AND STRUCTURAL DETAILS

Uses: orchestra, soloists, and lectures. *Ceiling:* 1-in. plaster on metal lath. *Walls:* 1-in. plaster on metal lath. *Floors:* concrete. *Stage floor:* wood on concrete. *Stage height:* 43 in. above floor at first row of seats. *Stage enclosure:* domed ceiling is covered with painted acoustic plaster; side walls are 1-in. plaster on metal lath. *Carpets:* on all aisles, except uppermost balcony. *Added absorptive material:* 250 sq ft of drapery on rear wall of main floor. *Seating:* main floor and boxes fully upholstered in cloth; first balcony wood, not upholstered.

References: Drawings and photographs from Shaw, Metz and Associates. References supplied by Seymour Raven, manager of the Chicago Symphony Orchestra. Details verified by author during visits. *Architect:* D. H. Burnham.

Severance Hall was built in 1930 during the period when most American acousticians adhered to the philosophy expressed by F. R. Watson in his book *Acoustics of Buildings* [John Wiley and Sons, Inc., New York, 1923]:

> Some years ago . . . the author was led to two conclusions: First, that practically all the acoustic defects in auditoriums are due to reflected sound; and second, that speakers and musicians are aided by nearby reflecting surfaces. . . . These two conclusions logically and unexpectedly suggested the outdoor theater, which has practically no reflected sound and which is generally commended for its good acoustics, particularly when it is equipped with a stage that has reflecting surfaces. From this conception, to obtain ideal acoustic conditions in an indoor auditorium, it would be necessary to follow two rules: (1) Provide a stage with suitable reflecting surfaces so that performers can "hear themselves." (2) Design the auditorium for listening so that the reflected sound will be reduced to be comparable with outdoor conditions.

Severance Hall, which seats 1890, was designed to meet these standards, and they were fulfilled by means of a low ceiling, elegant chairs, thick carpets, and extensive draperies. The body of the hall is acoustically dead. But unfortunately the live stage enclosure that Watson postulated was weakened by openings that gave into the stagehouse for theatrical performance, and by the organ grilles.

In 1958, a program of modification was undertaken at the instigation of George Szell, conductor of the Cleveland Orchestra. Most of the draperies and carpets were removed, and a better stage enclosure was installed. The reverberation time of the hall increased noticeably. The improvement brought about by these changes has been greatly appreciated by Cleveland audiences. Since the installation of the new stage enclosure, there have been further experiments toward achieving a satisfactory orchestral balance. On two occasions when I attended concerts in Cleveland, I found that the Orchestra was pulled forward away from the rear of the enclosure and carpets were added under the heavier instruments. It is possible that the installation of suitable reflecting panels over the front of the audience would effect further improvements in the quality of the sound heard on the main floor and at the

CLEVELAND, SEVERANCE HALL

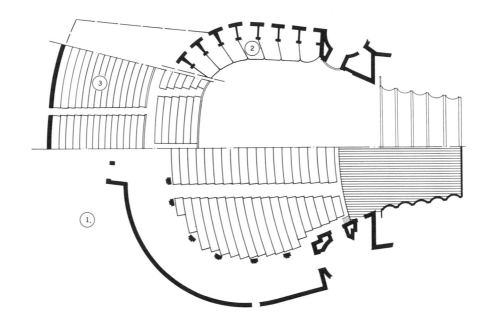

1.

SEATING CAPACITY 1890

1 782

2 170

3 938

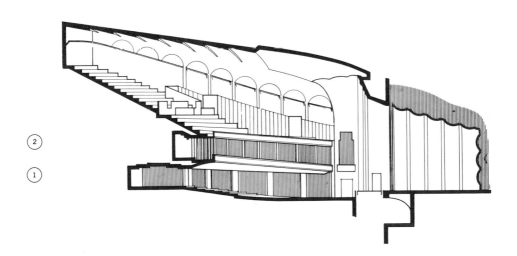

2

1

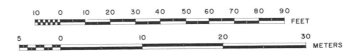

10 0 10 20 30 40 50 60 70 80 90
FEET

5 0 10 20 30
METERS

sides of the balcony. The enthusiasm with which the 1958 changes have been received demonstrates, as we shall see elsewhere, that the acoustical philosophy of the years 1920 to 1935 does not conform with the present-day desires of most musicians and experienced listeners.

Stanislaw Skrowaczewski when interviewed said that he had conducted in this hall recently and found the acoustics very good.

Robert Marsh of the Chicago *Sun-Times* said, "For me, Severance Hall now has just about the right reverberation period. I don't like terribly reverberant halls. The sound in Severance is very uniform. There is a little damping under the balcony overhang. The sound is so beautifully integrated as it comes through the proscenium that, even if you are sitting far over on the left-hand side, you get just as good a sense of presence from the basses and cellos as you do from the violins that are much closer to you. Severance is not an extremely bright hall, although one does not have any feeling of loss of high frequency."

TECHNICAL DETAILS FOR CONCERTS*

$V = 554{,}000 \text{ ft}^3$ $T_{500-1000}(\text{Occup.}) = 1.7 \text{ sec}$ $S_T = 15{,}000 \text{ ft}^2$

$N_A = 1890 \text{ seats}$ $S_A = 13{,}000 \text{ ft}^2$ $S_A/N_A = 6.9 \text{ ft}^2$

$t_I = 20; 13 \text{ msec}$ $S_O = 2000 \text{ ft}^2$ $V/S_T = 36.9 \text{ ft}$

* The terminology is explained in Appendix 3.

ARCHITECTURAL AND STRUCTURAL DETAILS

Uses: almost entirely musical with emphasis on symphonic music. *Ceiling:* plaster on wire lath. *Walls:* plaster, except for doors and space dividers. *Floors:* concrete covered with vinyl tile. *Stage floor:* wood over air space. *Stage height:* about 27 in. above floor level at front row of seats. *Carpets:* none. *Seating:* front of the backrests, top of seat-bottoms and armrests are upholstered; rear of backrests are plywood and bottom of seats are metal with four ⅞-in. diameter holes. *Orchestra enclosure:* surface on interior of stage is ⅛-in. plywood glued to ⅞-in. softwood core, on the back of which another layer of ¼-in. plywood is attached; the lower 9 ft of the plywood wall sections (above the stage floor) are filled with sand (approximately 5 in. thick).

References: R. S. Shankland and E. A. Flynn, *Journal of the Acoustical Society of America,* **31,** 866–871 (July 1959), and H. J. Ormestad, R. S. Shankland, and A. H. Benade, *Journal of the Acoustical Society of America,* **32,** 371–375 (March 1960); photographs courtesy of A. Beverly Barksdale, manager, Cleveland Orchestra. Details verified by author during visit. *Architect:* Walter and Weeks.

During the first two years of its existence, the Ford Auditorium was one of the most controversial halls of the American musical world. The low, flat ceiling and the broad fan shape, combined with smooth side walls, produced a reverberation time shorter than optimum for music and a lack of sound diffusion. The hall seats 2926 persons.

Little is known of the original goals set for the acoustical design of this hall. It is not even known whether any acoustical advice was followed, since the acoustical consultant died before the auditorium was completed, and so far as is known he left no written reports. In any event, when during the construction of the Auditorium the Detroit Symphony Orchestra considered becoming the principal tenant, its administrators wondered whether the acoustics would be adequate for symphonic music. Although the construction of the hall was well under way, the orchestra sought a review of the design by Bolt Beranek and Newman Inc. After reviewing the drawings, Bolt Beranek and Newman concluded that for orchestral music the ceiling was too low and its shape was not the best, and there appeared to be no plans for a stage enclosure. Obviously at so late a date the basic shape and the height of the hall could not be altered. It was recommended that a heavy orchestra enclosure be constructed, that acoustic diffusing elements be added, and that the location of the organ be changed. These recommendations had not been followed when the hall was opened, although a shallow plywood and canvas shell was provided and a small portative organ was purchased for placement directly on the stage inside it.

After a year's use and considerable adverse comment by some visiting music critics, the orchestra management engaged Bolt Beranek and Newman to design the present stage enclosure, which was completed in the spring of 1959. At this point a new difficulty appeared. The increase in liveness and loudness of the orchestral music brought out a ringing sound of 580 cycles per second (near D) clearly audible in the hall. The source of the ringing turned out to be the overhead organ grille which is constructed of hollow aluminum tubes, each 6 feet long and 2 inches square. At this writ-

DETROIT, HENRY AND EDSEL FORD AUDITORIUM

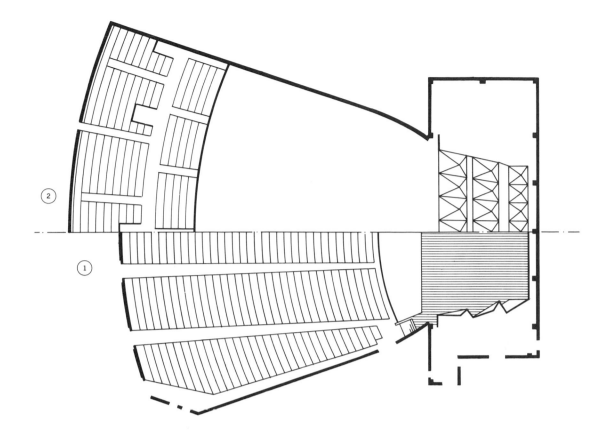

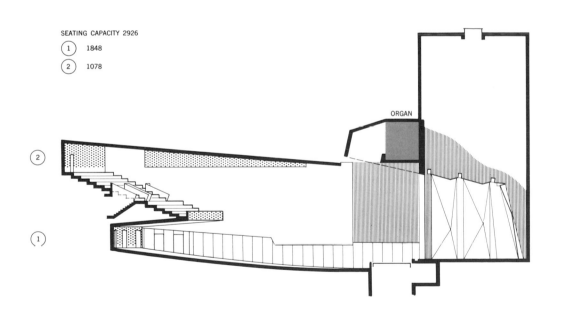

SEATING CAPACITY 2926

1 1848

2 1078

ORGAN

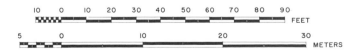

10 0 10 20 30 40 50 60 70 80 90 FEET

5 0 10 20 30 METERS

ing the ringing sound has not been eliminated, but the management of the orchestra has received recommendations for correction.

The new orchestra enclosure has met with enthusiasm, and the criticism of the lack of liveness in the hall has abated. Some additional changes could be made in the hall to provide adequate short-time-delay reflections. If these changes were added to the enclosure that is already successfully in service, the acoustics of this hall would equal many of the auditoriums in this country. The Ford Auditorium will never be classed with the greatest concert halls, however, because of its relatively low reverberation time. Only an increase in cubic volume could accomplish that end.

In November 1959, Howard Harrington, the manager of the Detroit Symphony Orchestra, wrote to me:

> The shell was completed this past spring and has been used for approximately 75 concerts. We have found that it has vastly improved the auditorium, and our audience which had been extremely critical of the auditorium before the construction of the shell now seems almost entirely satisfied with the new sound. Our conductor, Paul Paray, feels that the major problems have been eliminated.
>
> I think you would also be interested to know that several of the leading American organists who have played on the Aeolian-Skinner organ installed in the auditorium have found that the shell adds tremendously to the effectiveness of the organ. Virgil Fox when he played here with the orchestra told me he was amazed at what had been accomplished.

TECHNICAL DETAILS*

Concerts

$V = 676{,}000 \text{ ft}^3$ $T_{500-1000}(\text{Occup.}) = 1.55 \text{ sec}$ $S_T = 22{,}100 \text{ ft}^2$

$N_A = 2926 \text{ seats}$ $S_A = 19{,}900 \text{ ft}^2$ $S_A/N_A = 6.8 \text{ ft}^2$

$t_I = 28; 6 \text{ msec}$ $S_O = 2200 \text{ ft}^2$ $V/S_T = 30.6 \text{ ft}$

Opera

$V = 630{,}000 \text{ ft}^2$ $T_{500-1000}(\text{Occup.}) = 1.45 \text{ sec}$ $S_P = 1300 \text{ ft}^2$

$N_A = 2926 \text{ seats}$ $S_A = 19{,}900 \text{ ft}^2$ $S_T = 22{,}170 \text{ ft}^2$

$N_T = 2926$ $S_O(\text{Pit}) = 970 \text{ ft}^2$ $S_A/N_T = 6.8 \text{ ft}^2$

$t_I = 28; 6 \text{ msec}$ $S_{OF}(\text{Pit}) = 1050 \text{ ft}^2$ $V/S_T = 28.4 \text{ ft}$

* The terminology is explained in Appendix 3.

ARCHITECTURAL AND STRUCTURAL DETAILS

Uses: all purpose. *Ceiling:* ¾-in. plaster on metal lath. *Side walls:* up to an average height of 8 ft, the side walls are ¾-in. plywood on furring strips; upper side walls are 1-in. plaster on metal lath. *Rear walls and balcony face:* perforated metal facing over 3-in. mineral wool. *Floors:* concrete. *Original stage enclosure:* canvas ceiling; rear and side walls were ¼-in. plywood; the top 40% of the proscenium opening and a 6-ft border on each side were heavy velour hangings; the rear wall of the enclosure was 15 ft back of the proscenium opening and was about 70 ft wide; the canvas ceiling was about 22 ft above the stage floor. *Present stage enclosure:* ½-in. braced plywood; about 20% of the enclosure is ⅛-in. plywood, without bracing, to facilitate easy removal for changes if desired. *Stage floor:* wooden planks over large air space. *Stage height:* 48 in. above floor level at first row of seats. *Carpets:* in aisles and vomitories. *Added absorptive material:* upper edge of each side wall has about 250 sq ft of perforated metal facing over 3-in. mineral wool. *Seating:* top of seat-bottom and front and rear of backrest and double armrests are upholstered with hard-weave mohair; underside of seat-bottom is solid.

References: Plans from Detroit Symphony Orchestra, Howard Harrington, manager. Details verified during visits by the author. *Architect for the interior:* Crane, Kiehler and Kellogg.

Lafayette, Indiana
PURDUE UNIVERSITY
HALL OF MUSIC

On entering the main floor of the Edward C. Elliott Hall of Music at Purdue University, one is impressed immediately by the large number of seats—6107 in all—and the great width of the hall—170 feet under the first balcony. One of Europe's traditional 900 to 1400 seat concert halls could be enclosed in a rear corner of this auditorium, and its presence would scarcely be noticed. Since the hall is used for speeches, jazz concerts, and drama, as well as for symphonic music, too long a reverberation time would not have been acceptable. The sheer enormousness of the hall required the use of much sound-absorbing material to keep the reverberation time in check. For most performances, other than grand opera and symphony orchestra, electronic sound amplification is used.

A Chicago music critic who was interviewed said, "I've heard the Metropolitan Opera at Purdue. It's like attending a performance at a football field. Everything seems to be so remote, and the sound is so vague that there is no sense of an ensemble performance."

The opera *Die Fledermaus* was being presented in English by the Metropolitan Opera the night I was there. Except at seats far under the balconies and at the rear of the second balcony, the intelligibility of the spoken lines was satisfactory. Also, I found that the balance between the pit orchestra, which holds about 70 musicians, and the artists on stage was good.

The great cubic volume of the hall and the relatively high ceiling, which is half covered with sound-absorbing material, gives the sound an "outdoor" character. As it would outdoors, the loudness drops off toward the rear of the hall and is very low in the upper reaches of the balcony. This hall is an example of the design philosophy that was advocated by many acousticians in the period 1920 to 1935, which has been discussed in the section on Cleveland's Severance Hall. Compared with other large halls designed for all-purpose use, the Hall of Music must be viewed as a success. Music is clear and rich in bass and, in spite of its "outdoor" aspect, there is noticeable liveness.

LAFAYETTE, INDIANA, PURDUE UNIVERSITY HALL OF MUSIC

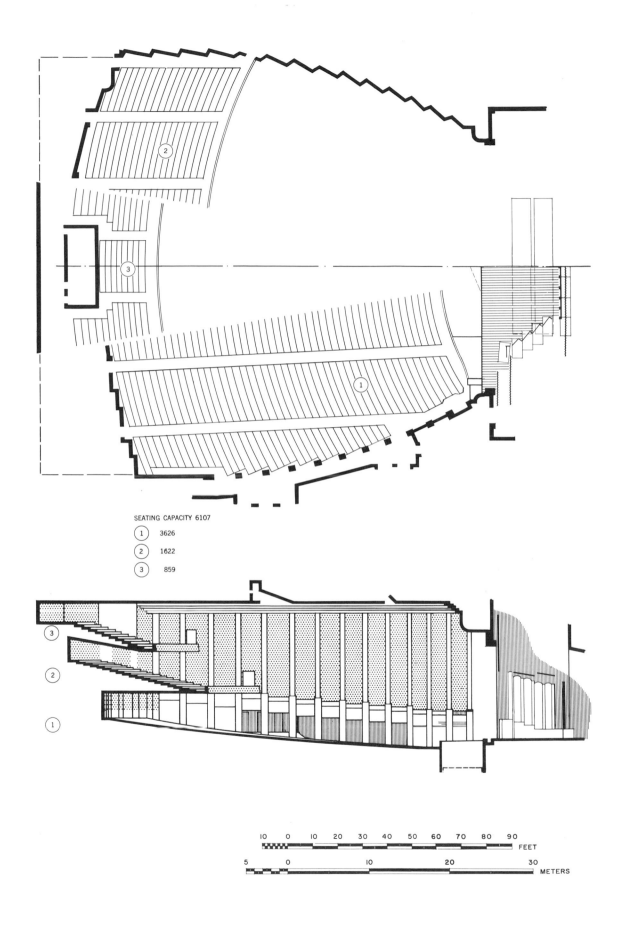

SEATING CAPACITY 6107

(1) 3626

(2) 1622

(3) 859

10 0 10 20 30 40 50 60 70 80 90
FEET

5 0 10 20 30
METERS

TECHNICAL DETAILS*

Concerts

$V = 1,320,000$ ft^3 $T_{500-1000}$(Occup.) $= 1.6$ sec $S_T = 39,500$ ft^2

$N_A = 6107$ seats $S_A = 37,200$ ft^2 $S_A/N_A = 6.1$ ft^2

$t_I = 45; 6$ msec $S_O = 2300$ ft^2 $V/S_T = 33.4$ ft

Opera

$V = 1,270,000$ ft^3 $T_{500-1000}$(Occup.) $= 1.45$ sec $S_P = 3626$ ft^2

$N_A = 6107$ seats $S_A = 37,210$ ft^2 $S_T = 41,680$ ft^2

$N_T = 6107$ S_O(Pit) $= 840$ ft^2 $S_A/N_T = 6.1$ ft^2

$t_I = 45; 6$ msec S_{OF}(Pit) $= 840$ ft^2 $V/S_T = 30.5$ ft

* The terminology is explained in Appendix 3.

ARCHITECTURAL AND STRUCTURAL DETAILS

Uses: general purpose, occasional opera and concert. *Ceiling:* half of the ceiling is bare plaster; the other half is 8-ft strips of ⅝-in. sound-absorbing material spaced 8 ft apart, extending the length of the hall; the soffits of the balconies are of plaster. *Side walls:* the surfaces facing the stage are plaster; the surfaces not facing the stage are covered with sound-absorbing material identical to that on the ceiling. *Rear walls:* the rear walls of the balconies are perforated asbestos board, with mineral-wool sound-absorption backing. *Balcony faces:* covered in the same manner as the rear walls. *Floors:* concrete. *Stage floor:* wood over air space. *Stage height:* 25 in. above the level of the floor at the front row of seats. *Stage enclosure:* side walls are ¼-in. plywood on 1 x 3 in. framing. Ceiling is painted canvas. *Carpets:* in aisles and cross aisles. *Added absorptive material:* see ceiling and side walls above. *Seating:* front of the backrests and the top of the seats are upholstered; rear of the backrest and the underseats are solid metal. *Pit:* walls are solid; floor is of wood.

References: Drawings courtesy of Walter Scholer and Associates; photographs courtesy of *Opera News* and Brown Bros. Stage enclosure details furnished by J. W. Ditamore, director of the hall. Other details verified by author during visit. *Architect:* Walter Scholer.

Tanglewood, where the Boston Symphony Orchestra's Music Shed is located, is an incredibly beautiful estate in the Berkshire Hills of Massachusetts. During the summer season music lovers are attracted to Tanglewood from great distances. The Music Shed at Tanglewood now boasts a unique position among concert halls. It is the only place that houses a very large audience, 6000 listeners, under acoustical conditions that rival the best in America. And an additional 6000 people seated on the lawns outside can enjoy the music that issues from the partly open sides of the Music Shed. Even though the sides of the Shed are open to the lawn to a height of about 15 feet, Tanglewood behaves like an enclosed hall—the open areas are equivalent acoustically to steeply raked seating at the outer edges of the hall.

The Tanglewood Music Shed was not always as satisfactory as it is today. Before 1959, the Boston music critics seldom visited the hall. Harold Rogers of the *Christian Science Monitor* said, "My predecessor told me that the Tanglewood Music Shed did not have the quality of a good indoor hall. On my first visit, I agreed with him."

The management of the Boston Symphony Orchestra recognized the deficiencies in acoustical quality and authorized an acoustical study by Bolt Beranek and Newman Inc. in 1954. In 1958 the acoustical consultants, working with the architect, completed the design of the orchestra enclosure and the acoustic canopy that now covers the front third of the hall. The construction was completed in July 1959 and the results have been well received. Both musicians and music critics have expressed enthusiasm.

Isaac Stern said to me after the 1959 season, "The new orchestra enclosure in the Tanglewood Music Shed is one of the most fantastically successful efforts to create brilliant, ringing sound with wonderful definition, despite the enormous size of this hall. It is particularly successful in providing an equal sound value wherever one sits. On stage there is a wonderfully live quality, and yet complete clarity for balancing with a large orchestra."

At the end of the summer season of 1959, Charles Munch wrote, "The new canopy has solved all the old problems of disproportion among the various elements of the orchestra. The greatest benefit has come to the

LENOX, MASSACHUSETTS, TANGLEWOOD MUSIC SHED

strings and especially the violins which now can be heard in the Shed with as much brilliance and clarity as in the best concert halls."

Pierre Monteux said in 1959, "What has been done is absolutely marvelous. Last year I could not hear the violins. This year the sound is marvelous."

Eric McLean wrote in the *Montreal Star* (1960):

But the effect of the new shell and canopy on the music is almost uncanny. A full, well-blended, yet detailed sound is projected to the furthermost benches of the Shed, and although it begins to deteriorate outside the Shed, orchestra tuttis can be heard with surprising clarity over an area many times the size of the Shed.

Most people, on first hearing, are convinced that an elaborate system of electrical amplification has been installed, but in actual fact there is not a single speaker in the hall.

Thomas D. Perry, Jr., Manager of the Boston Symphony Orchestra, wrote to me in 1959: "The results are, quite simply, superb. The sound is acknowledged by the conductors, soloists, players, public and press to be noticeably improved over what was already felt to be a remarkably good hall—and when you can get such an acknowledgment in a field so subtle as acoustical design, you have virtually wrought a miracle."

Two critics wrote in the New York *Times* at different times in 1959:

It was instructive to note how fine the acoustics were, thanks to the new stage shell which was installed this year.

The new sound does bring the winds forward and is evenly distributed all around.

Cyrus Durgin of the Boston *Globe* wrote (1960):

To state what happened tonight in artistic terms, this was one night, one concert in a thousand. The sound, the playing, the music all were total glory and sheer magnificence. . . . Not to detract from the achievement of the musicians, one must add that the new dark-gray, acoustic stage shell has greatly improved the sound in Tanglewood's Music Shed. The difference is extraordinary.

The acoustics of the completed hall corroborates our predictions. The Tanglewood Music Shed's canopy and enclosure are the first application of the early results of this six-year program of studies. The low ceiling (almost 50 per cent open) produces the necessary short-time-delay reflections in the

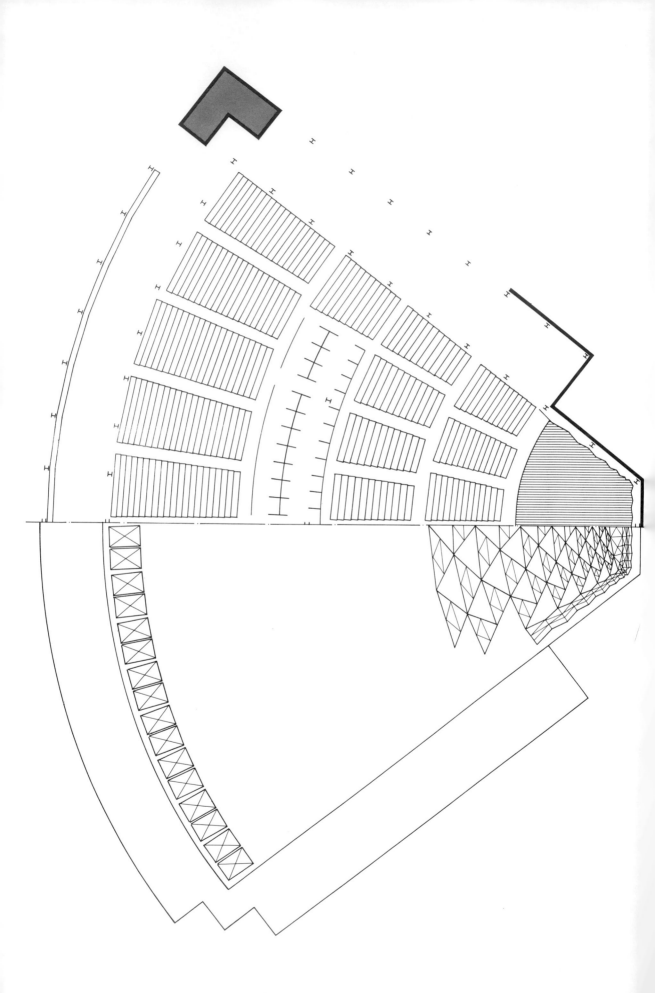

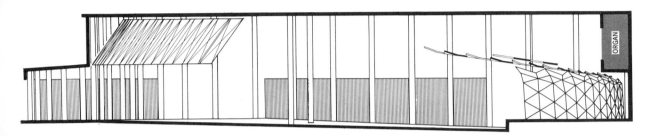

SEATING CAPACITY 6000

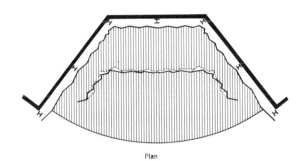

Plan

Chamber music screen

Elevation

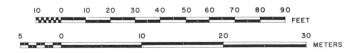

front of the hall, yet leaves the upper volume of the hall available for reverberation.

In addition to the necessary short-time-delay reflections the canopy contributes to excellent sectional balance for a large orchestra, improved clarity inside the Music Shed, and louder sound for the 6000 people seated on the lawns.

The enthusiastic comments recorded above gloss over several problems that still linger in a hall of this size. The very wide fan-shaped plan and the consequent width at the front of the stage provide little side wall reinforcement to music played in the center of the stage. Thus in this hall the piano, whose sound is deflected from radiating upward by its cover, does not carry as well as do the strings, whose sound does radiate upward. Also, the two sides of the hall are somewhat unsymmetrical musically, because the stage wall behind the first violins reflects their sound better to one side of the hall than the other. This is, of course, equally true for the instruments on the other side of the stage. In a narrow, rectangular hall, these difficulties can be avoided. On the other hand, to attempt to provide music for 6000 to 12,000 listeners in a narrow rectangular hall would require such a long room that the sound at the rear would be too weak and the orchestra would be barely in sight.

A chamber-music enclosure was constructed for the stage in 1960. It is an irregular curved screen forming an enclosure 60 feet wide and 14 feet high, which decreases the size of the large stage and enhances the direct sound to the audience. An area 28 x 6 feet at the center has been made sound-absorbent in order to diminish the loudness of the timpani, which are placed in front of it. Audiences of 4000 to 6000 people now attend performances of Bach and Mozart symphonies played by a small orchestra which had previously performed in a 1000-seat theater nearby.

Eugene Ormandy (1962) said to me, "This year and also a year ago I sat in boxes at the center of the Shed and was amazed at the fine quality of the sound. The acoustical enclosure is wonderful. The brass is somewhat predominant in the large orchestra, though the conductor should be able to control it. With the chamber-music enclosure, the sound is very intimate. One can genuinely enjoy Bach there; it does not sound like a large hall."

TECHNICAL DETAILS FOR CONCERTS[*]

$V = 1,500,000 \text{ ft}^3$ $T_{500-1000}(\text{Occup.}) = 2.05 \text{ sec}$ $S_T = 33,000 \text{ ft}^2$

$N_A = 6000 \text{ seats}$ $S_A = 30,800 \text{ ft}^2$ $S_A/N_A = 5.1 \text{ ft}^2$

$t_I = 19; 12 \text{ msec}$ $S_O = 2200 \text{ ft}^2$ $V/S_T = 45.5 \text{ ft}$

[*] The terminology is explained in Appendix 3.

ARCHITECTURAL AND STRUCTURAL DETAILS

Uses: symphony orchestra, chamber orchestra and choral music. *Ceiling:* 2-in. wooden planks. *Side and rear walls:* upper part of the side walls is ¾-in. painted fiberboard; lower part is open to enable people to listen to concerts on the lawn outdoors. *Stage enclosure:* ⅜-in. to ⅝-in. plywood with modulations in shape and randomly braced; the canopy is suspended on steel cables from the roof and consists of a series of non-planar triangular plywood panels, ⅜-in. to ⅝-in. thick, connected tip-to-tip. *Stage floor:* wood over large air space. *Stage height:* 33 in. above floor at front of row of seats. *Floor:* packed dirt. *Seating:* plain metal folding chairs without upholstery; seats in the boxes are canvas sling type.

References: F. R. Johnson, L. L. Beranek, R. B. Newman, R. H. Bolt, and D. L. Klepper, "Orchestra Enclosure and Canopy for the Tanglewood Music Shed," *Journal of the Acoustical Society of America,* **33,** 475–481 (April 1961). Drawings from the architect, Eero Saarinen and Associates. Photographs, courtesy of the manager of the Boston Symphony Orchestra, T. D. Perry, Jr. Details confirmed by the author during visits. *Architect:* Joseph Franz, engineer, from preliminary design of Eliel Saarinen. In 1937, Saarinen consented to the use of his original drawings with such changes as were necessitated by the financial resources of the Berkshire Festival Corporation. He withdrew as architect and took no part in the revisions. The architects for the 1959 orchestra enclosure and canopy and the 1960 chamber-music enclosure were Eero Saarinen and Associates for whom Warren Platner was designer-in-charge.

"The Finest Music of All Comes to Carnegie Hall." This couplet, which was heard on American radios in the heyday of broadcasting, was literally true. Any concert artist or symphony orchestra that aspired to world-wide fame appeared in Carnegie Hall sooner or later. When plans were revealed in 1960 to demolish this famous structure to make room for an office building, musicians and music lovers rose to its defense, and pushed through the legislation that made it possible for the City of New York to buy Carnegie Hall and lease it to a non-profit association to operate. Under the leadership of Isaac Stern, Carnegie Hall is flourishing today.

Just how good is Carnegie Hall acoustically? Fortunately, most of my interviews with conductors, musicians, and music critics were carried out before Carnegie Hall was "saved." Presumably each of my informants spoke without emotion since at that time it seemed to be accepted that New York's concert music would be played in the Lincoln Center Philharmonic Hall.

The conductors who were interviewed were unanimous in saying that the hall is "good," but that it does not rank with the best in the world. The comments that follow are typical of those made by the ten conductors who rated Carnegie Hall:

"Carnegie Hall is only 'good' to 'fair.' From the podium there is a slightly damped feeling—especially on climaxes. This hall responds to small Mozart orchestras well."

"I would call it a medium-quality hall acoustically. In some ways it is better than the Philadelphia Academy of Music, but it ranks below Boston Symphony Hall."

"This hall is good without an audience, but it is not so good with an audience. It is better than Philadelphia, but worse than Boston."

"In Carnegie Hall the music is clear as a bell. It has excellent high-frequency brilliance, but the middle and low-frequency brilliance is not the best. There is a lack of body in the sound. The hall is extremely directional; when one is 'out of the focus' of the stage, on either side at any level, the quality drops off rapidly."

"This hall should have more lows and just a little less of the extreme

NEW YORK, CARNEGIE HALL

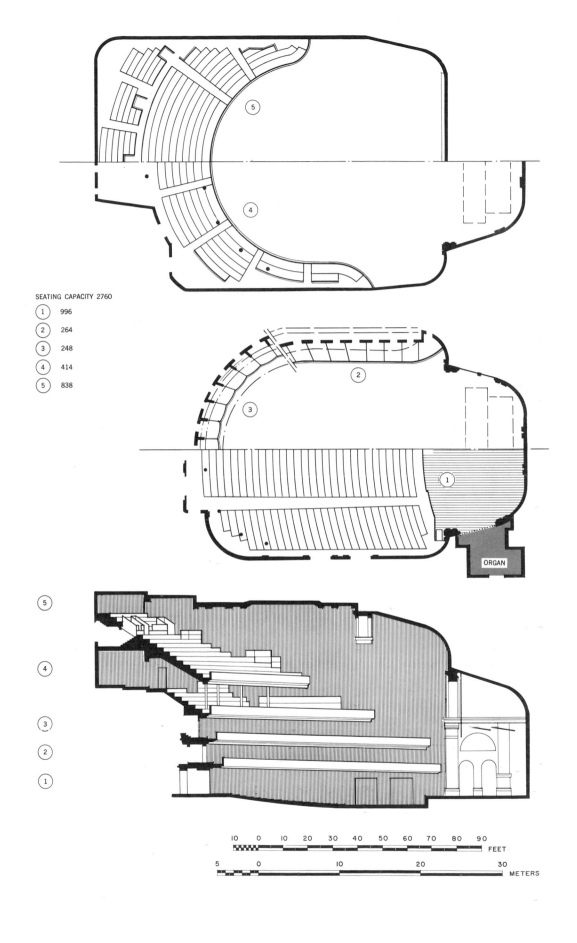

SEATING CAPACITY 2760

1 996
2 264
3 248
4 414
5 838

ORGAN

10 0 10 20 30 40 50 60 70 80 90
FEET

5 0 10 20 30
METERS

highs. In certain seats the sound is very weak. The stage needs a better canopy."

As we all know, our feeling for a hall, like our feeling for a well-loved person, can be great without requiring perfection. In 1959, before he knew of the part he would play in its rescue, Isaac Stern expressed his love for Carnegie Hall when he said to me, "It is so hard to be truly objective about this hall. I have so many pleasant memories of it, starting from my very first performance there. There are so many psychological connotations. I love this hall. I like its spaciousness. I like the high stage because it is helpful to a violinist to have the audience 'below' him and not above, as in Royal Festival Hall, eyeing him as though he were under a dissecting microscope."

Alfred Frankenstein, music critic of the San Francisco *Chronicle*, rated the psychological factors as almost equal in importance to the actual acoustical qualities when he said, "I am sure that any hall that is venerated for the great music, great orchestras, and great artists that have played there has a much better chance of being called a great hall. For example, 'Carnegie Hall is Carnegie Hall.'"

Irving Kolodin, music critic for the *Saturday Review*, said to me in December 1960: "I have a fondness for this hall. Because of many years of listening there, I use it as a criterion by which to judge other halls. It is not a liability to any performance, except perhaps for choral groups where the small size of the stage results in a distorted seating plan for the orchestra. Carnegie Hall lets the orchestra be itself. It doesn't impose its personality on it. Whether from Europe or Philadelphia, an orchestra always sounds with its own style. Carnegie is probably a hall for listeners."

A music critic from Chicago could view Carnegie Hall dispassionately, "I'm one who does not think highly of Carnegie Hall. I certainly do not care for the top balcony, where the sound is not loud enough. On the main floor, it is better but not extremely good. The tonal balance in the hall is quite good. The balance between strings and brass is strongly dependent on the arrangement of the orchestra. The brass, if placed on center, is very bright."

Only one music critic that I interviewed rated Carnegie Hall above Symphony Hall in Boston. The other music critics' judgments can perhaps be summarized by one who has attended concerts in Carnegie weekly for over 25 years. In his words, "It has good acoustics, but it is not really sublime. The sound is better in the upper galleries than on the main floor, because on the main floor the sound goes over your head. The string tone is not brilliant, but it is satisfactory. The hall has a mellow sound. It is good, but not great."

One music critic who knows well the three important halls in the eastern part of the United States compared them as follows: "Carnegie Hall is nearer to Symphony Hall in Boston in acoustical quality than the Philadelphia Academy of Music or the Royal Festival Hall. In the top balcony, the sound is beautifully blended, as is true in many halls. Boston has more brilliance on the string tones, but Carnegie has a better blend. The brass and woodwinds are about the same in Carnegie and Boston."

I have attended perhaps 50 concerts in Carnegie Hall. I am impressed by the excellence of the sound in many parts of the hall and by the imperfections in others. Carnegie does not have the liveness of Symphony Hall in Boston. Nor does it bring forth the rich tone of the violas and cellos as the Academy of Music in Philadelphia does. Subway noise is most troublesome during quiet passages, particularly on the right-hand side. Some echoes are audible in parts of the hall. Yet it is a comfortable hall in which one can easily relax and concentrate on the music. Carnegie's most obvious feature is its ability to remain in the background—it seems to urge you to pay attention only to the performance. And most of us feel, as Isaac Stern does, that sentiment, love, and history are an integral part of music—and in these qualities, Carnegie Hall surpasses every other hall in America.

TECHNICAL DETAILS FOR CONCERTS[*]

V = 857,000 ft^3	$T_{500-1000}$(Occup.) = 1.7 sec	S_T = 21,360 ft^2
N_A = 2760 seats	S_A = 19,160 ft^2	S_A/N_A = 6.9 ft^2
t_I = 23; 16 msec	S_O = 2200 ft^2	V/S_T = 40.0 ft

* The terminology is explained in Appendix 3.

ARCHITECTURAL AND STRUCTURAL DETAILS

Uses: 60% orchestra, 10% soloists, 2% chorus, 3% jazz, 25% other. *Ceiling:* 1-in. plaster on wire lath, 10% open for ventilation. *Walls:* ¾-in.

plaster on wire lath with a small air space between the plaster and the solid backing. Beneath the first tier of boxes, the walls are plaster on solid backing. Balcony fronts are plaster. *Floors:* wooden flooring on sleepers over concrete. *Carpets:* on main floor, carpeting in aisles and 18-in. runner between rows; in boxes (levels 1 and 2), full carpeting; on upper two levels (3 and 4), carpet in aisles. *Stage enclosure:* walls of stage are plaster on wire lath; just prior to 1960, thin nylon draperies 30 ft high were hung on either side of stage; in front of these draperies there were three folding screens, each with two panels. Each panel is made of ¼-in. plywood on 9-ft-high by 4-ft-wide frames of 2 x 2 in. wood. Above the stage there are two frames, each about 6 ft wide and 40 ft long, sloped forward about 20°; painted canvas is stretched over the frames. *Stage floor:* wood on sleepers over concrete. *Stage height:* 48 in. above the floor at the front row of seats. *Seating:* top of seat-bottoms covered with velour over hair padding over springs; under-side solid; velour cloth over thin hair padding on front of seat backs; in boxes, simple chairs with leather over thin hair padding on top of seat-bottoms. *Added absorption:* heavy velour masking curtain in the proscenium.

References: Plans from Harrison and Abramovitz, architects; photographs from Carnegie Hall. Details verified by author during visits. *Architect:* William B. Tuthill.

New York
GRACE RAINEY ROGERS
AUDITORIUM

In 1954, when the directors of the Metropolitan Museum of Art undertook extensive changes in one wing, they decided on the complete renovation of the old lecture auditorium. This auditorium, which has 708 seats, is used for music, lectures, and cinema. The interior is finished with Korina plywood which helps achieve a pleasant appearance. The hall is small and narrower at the front and rear than in the middle. The entire design had to be worked out within the confines of the existing structural steel of the old building, which to a large extent determined its basic shape and size.

Conductors and musicians speak favorably of the Grace Rainey Rogers Auditorium. Leopold Stokowski wrote in 1957: "Recently I conducted a concert in the Grace Rainey Rogers Auditorium. It was a joy to make music in a place where the acoustical conditions have been created with such skill and deep understanding of what music requires in an enclosed space."

Izler Solomon said, "I like this hall. On the stage with a chamber group of sixteen musicians, I was able to get a full concept of the sound of the instruments, definitions and balance. There is little difference with the hall empty and the hall full." Violinists say it is a good hall to play in.

Emanuel Winternitz, Curator of Musical Collections at the Metropolitan Museum of Art, wrote in 1955: "Since the auditorium was finished I have heard and organized quite a number of musical events there for various ensembles, including wind groups, strings, mixed orchestras, vocal ensembles, as well as performances on the reconstruction of a baroque organ which we now have on stage. I have also heard several lectures and symposia there and had a chance to lecture myself. As you of course know, the ideal demands of various instruments and of the speaking voice are not quite identical. In view of this and also of the fact that the auditorium is to be used constantly for lectures and for music, I find it an excellent compromise between these requirements and have heard many favorable reactions to the acoustics."

New York music critics have been divided in their opinions. About half of them concur with the comments of one: "This is a very satisfactory hall to listen in. For a sonata or solo instrument the shading is very delicate.

NEW YORK, GRACE RAINEY ROGERS AUDITORIUM

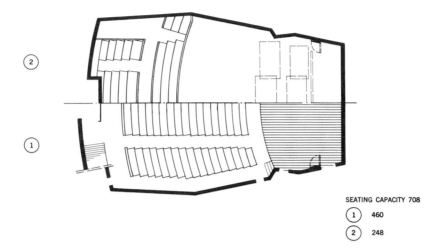

SEATING CAPACITY 708

(1) 460

(2) 248

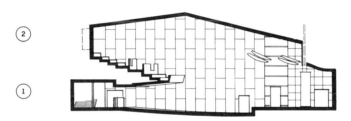

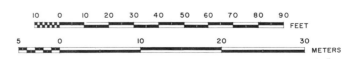

10   0   10   20   30   40   50   60   70   80   90
FEET

5   0   10   20   30
METERS

A string quartet there is marvelous. Once I heard a full symphony orchestra there. On some of the loud passages the hall was uncomfortably loud. A chamber orchestra is very good." Other music critics agree with the statement, "This hall is not as pleasant as it should be on the main floor—there the music is a little cold and the hall seems overly reverberant. In the balcony, the sound is more intimate and the reverberation seems about right for early music and for the music of the Baroque and Classical Periods."

Irving Kolodin, music critic for the *Saturday Review,* said: "I think a hall has to be used for a while to develop a reputation for itself. An older group of listeners tends to like a hall that it has grown accustomed to. When these people go to a new hall they remember the old one as 'good.' A new hall has to be used for a while and a younger element mixed in before the new hall becomes accepted. From my seat in the balcony Grace Rainey Rogers is one of the louder halls. It sounds as though one is in the middle of the performance. I have not decided whether I like it or not. More listening will be required."

In my opinion music played in the Grace Rainey Rogers Auditorium sounds very good in the balcony, although for a large performing group it is somewhat too loud in fortissimo passages. The sound on the main floor is not quite as good because of the shape of the ceiling, which reflects sound primarily into the balcony. The thin plywood paneling reduces somewhat the loudness of the lower frequencies and tends to give the sound a slightly thinner and less warm aspect.

TECHNICAL DETAILS FOR CONCERTS*

$V = 193{,}600 \text{ ft}^3$	$T_{500-1000}(\text{Occup.}) = 1.15 \text{ sec}$	$S_T = 6900 \text{ ft}^2$
$N_A = 708 \text{ seats}$	$S_A = 5300 \text{ ft}^2$	$S_A/N_A = 7.5 \text{ ft}^2$
$t_I = 15; 13 \text{ msec}$	$S_O = 1600 \text{ ft}^2$	$V/S_T = 28.1$

* The terminology is explained in Appendix 3.

ARCHITECTURAL AND STRUCTURAL DETAILS

Uses: general purpose. *Ceiling:* ¼-in. plywood with 2 x 3 in. randomly spaced wood bracing, bolted through 3-in. wood spacers to a suspended ½-in. plaster ceiling. *Walls:* on sides and on rear stage, ¼-in. plywood on free-standing 3 x 4 in. studs supported 6 in. from solid wall. Panels are braced randomly with 2 x 2 in. wood. On rear wall, plywood is perforated with 1-in. glass fiber blanket backing. The steel lift partition is a perforated motion picture screen. *Floors:* cork tile on concrete. *Stage canopy:* $\frac{3}{8}$-in. plywood on $\frac{3}{4}$-in. plywood ribs, 24 in. on center. *Stage floor:* maple wood finish over wooden subfloor over 2-in. air space. *Stage height:* 30 in. above floor at front row of seats. *Carpet:* on entire floor outside of seating area. *Added absorptive material:* drapery on stage in front of lift partition. *Seating:* upholstered in fabric without perforated bottoms.

References: Drawings and details from architect; photographs from Metropolitan Museum of Art. All details verified by author during visits. *Architect:* Voorhees, Walker, Foley and Smith.

The renowned Metropolitan Opera Association of New York regularly features on its roster some of the world's finest singers. Its pit orchestra is among the finest in this country. Its home, the Metropolitan Opera House, has a tradition carefully nurtured by a proud New York Society and by the nation-wide audience devoted to its Saturday afternoon radio broadcasts.

Its 3639 seats make the "Met" one of the largest houses used exclusively for opera in the world. It is characterized by an Italian-style horseshoe shape, with five rings above the main floor. The ceiling is high and horizontal except at the edges where it curves downward. The baroque décor adds to the beauty of the house and also to its acoustical quality.

The sound is distributed quite evenly to all the seats throughout the house, except those under the ring of boxes on the main floor and those located near the stage in the upper two rings. The best seats are those directly opposite the stage in the upper four rings. Even in the rear of the upper balcony, which is 160 feet from the stage, the sound is excellent.

Several factors contribute to the generally good acoustics in spite of the large size of the Met. One is its horizontal flat ceiling, with shallow irregularities on the surface which provide sound diffusion. Another is the large fronts or faces on the boxes and on the three rings above them. The side faces of the balcony reflect sounds into the seats near the rear of the house. The acoustics are benefited also by the large apron on the stage in front of the singers. This apron reflects the voices of the singers into the upper four levels; some of this sound would otherwise be lost by absorption in the pit.

There are, however, at least three acoustical limitations at the Met. First and most important is its size. Its cubic volume is nearly twice that of the Teatro Alla Scala in Milan, the Théatre de l'Opéra in Paris, the Festspielhaus in Bayreuth, or the Staatsoper in Vienna, and it is nearly half again as great as that of the Academy of Music in Philadelphia. To sound as loud as they do in the European theaters just named, singers at the Met have to produce about twice as much acoustic power. Second, there are inadequate reflecting surfaces for producing short-time-delay reflections on the main floor. Hence the music there is not as intimate, or brilliant, or loud

NEW YORK, METROPOLITAN OPERA HOUSE

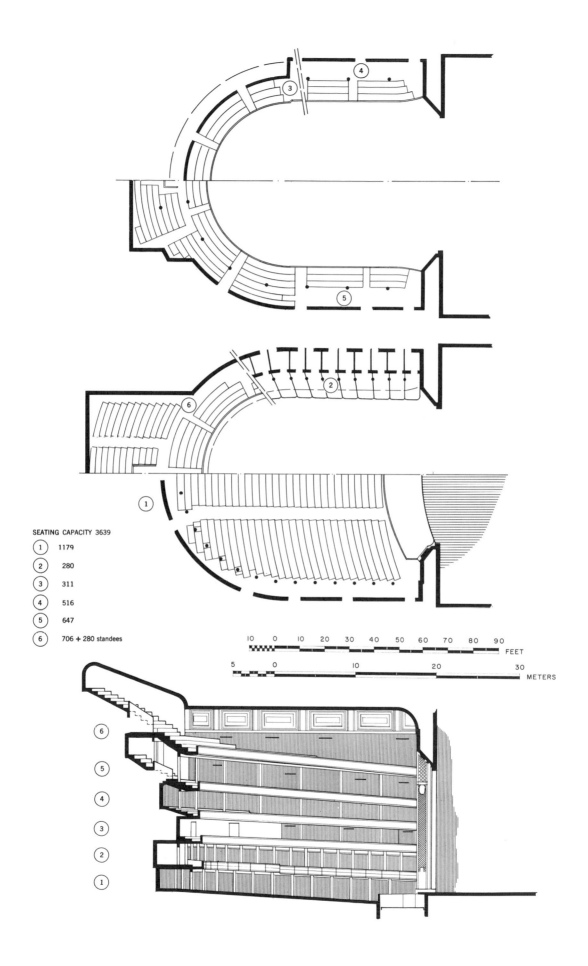

SEATING CAPACITY 3639

1. 1179
2. 280
3. 311
4. 516
5. 647
6. 706 + 280 standees

as it might be. Third, the reverberation time is low, and the hall has a "dead" feel to it.

Singers experience some difficulty in performing at the Met, particularly when they have had little experience with its characteristics. There is an absence of "house return," that is to say, reflections that return to the stage from surfaces in the house. Conductors generally dislike the pit. Its width, measured from the first rows of the audience to the stage, is not great enough, and it is very long. As Fritz Reiner stated the problem, "The pit extends from 39th Street to 40th Street and the conductor has no control over the orchestra. The two ends of the orchestra cannot hear each other." Conductors agree that the Met's pit should be made wider to provide for one more row of musicians.

Four opera conductors who were interviewed rated the Metropolitan as "good," but less satisfactory than the opera houses of Philadelphia, Milan, Vienna, or Paris.

Almost every music critic interviewed has heard opera performed at the Met. Their judgments covered a wide range of opinion, as can be seen in the following quotations:

"I have sat in many places and have been surprised by the over-all quality of the sound at the Met. Of course, in the rear of the boxes and at the rear corners under the boxes on the main floor, the sound is muffled."

"The Met is pretty good. In spite of its size, I think it is very satisfactory. A Mozart opera can be done there without losing its intimacy."

"The acoustics in this house are variable, depending upon where you sit. In the rear of the house, the acoustics are excellent in all the rings and galleries above the level of the boxes. The sides are unsatisfactory acoustically. On the main floor, the balance is not good and the quality is not the best."

"This is a peculiar house. The singers seem to fight like mad to fill the huge auditorium. The orchestra sounds good in relation to the singer, but the voices have to fight to get over it. Surprisingly, the orchestra sounds smaller than it looks. It is incongruous on the main floor to find this thin orchestral sound, and still the singers seem to fight to get over it."

"I don't consider this a prize exhibit. It eats up sound to a greater extent than any other house in the world. It takes a huge voice to get through to the audience, although a small well trained voice does seem to get through. The main floor is much less good than the two rings above the boxes; it has a deader sound to it. The Met is undistinguished acoustically."

"I despise the Metropolitan Opera House everywhere except in the top balcony. It has very poor acoustics. The main floor is entirely unsatisfactory acoustically no matter where you are listening from."

On opening-day in 1883 the music reviews were mixed. The New York *Daily Tribune* said,

The new house was shown to be not only satisfactory, but really admirable in its acoustic properties.

The New York *Times* stated,

Much disappointment was caused by the comparative failure of the acoustic properties of the auditorium. Much of the brilliancy of tone which should have been produced by the band was dulled, even to those spectators seated in the most desirable parts of the parquet, and in the upper rows of the boxes and the balcony only the high voices were distinctly heard.

Part of the difficulty of the opening performance of *Faust* was the relatively small number of strings, only 23 violins and 8 violas, in the pit orchestra. The lack of brilliancy of orchestral tone that the critics found on the main floor is understandable: the short-time-delay reflections into the main floor are inadequate. But it is not clear why the reviewer could not hear the low-pitched voices distinctly in the upper part of the house. Perhaps he listened from only the rear of the boxes or the rear of the rings. Or perhaps the particular voices on that occasion were too small for so large a house.

TECHNICAL DETAILS FOR OPERA[*]

$V = 690,000$ ft^3	$T_{500-1000}(\text{Occup.}) = 1.2$ sec	$S_P = 2700$ ft^2
$N_A = 3639$ seats	$S_A = 24,050$ ft^2	$S_T = 27,730$ ft^2
$N_T = 3779$	$S_O(\text{Pit}) = 980$ ft^2	$S_A/N_T = 6.4$ ft^2
$t_I = 22; 18$ msec	$S_{OF}(\text{Pit}) = 1,130$ ft^2	$V/S_T = 24.9$ ft

* The terminology is explained in Appendix 3.

ARCHITECTURAL AND STRUCTURAL DETAILS

Uses: opera, some ballet, and orchestra. *Ceiling:* plaster, ornamented. *Walls:* plaster on solid backing; doors are of wood with glass windows; the rear wall of the boxes is covered with velvet fabric; the rear one-third of each box is separated from an adjacent box by a wooden partition covered with fabric; the front (faces) of all boxes and rings are of plaster. Doors are wood and glass. *Floors:* wood. *Pit:* wooden floor with linoleum and wood sides; part of the railing of the pit above the audience floor level is louvered. *Carpet:* 100% carpet, entire house. *Seating:* fully upholstered, solid underseats. Boxes have upholstered movable chairs.

References: Drawings courtesy Harrison and Abramovitz, architects. Photographs and other details courtesy Herman E. Krawitz, technical and business administrator, Metropolitan Opera Association. Details verified by author during visits. *Architect:* Josiah C. Cady.

The oldest theater discussed in this book, and one with an enviable reputation, is the Academy of Music in Philadelphia, which was opened in 1857. Venerated for a century of fine concerts and operas, beautiful and intimate, this hall and the Philadelphia Orchestra mean to America the best in music. Philadelphia music-goers will tolerate no word of unfavorable criticism. The Academy is unquestionably the finest opera house in the United States. It ranks among the best concert halls.

In the middle of the nineteenth century, there were no symphony orchestras to speak of in the United States, and recitals were given only by an occasional traveling virtuoso, often supported by lesser luminaries in an endless program. Grand opera, however, was immensely popular and enjoyed unique prestige from Rome to St. Petersburg, from Paris and Berlin to New York. The Academy of Music was built for the express purpose of housing performances of opera on a scale enjoyed in the European capitals. In fact, the architects used the Teatro Alla Scala in Milan as their model.

With a cubic volume only 40 per cent greater than that of the Vienna Staatsoper, the Academy nevertheless holds 70 per cent more people. The hall is sometimes called the "big squeeze"; each of its 2984 seats is allotted only 5.5 square feet, including aisles, as compared to 7.5 square feet in Vienna in the 1955 reconstruction, or 6.6 square feet in the Metropolitan Opera House, which was built in 1883. Obviously, either the standards of comfort and safety were lower in those days or people were smaller.

The famous dry well beneath its main floor, has already been mentioned in Chapter 1 as an example of acoustical mythology.

Conductors of opera rate the Academy excellent—except that the orchestra pit is too small. For orchestral concerts, the sentiment is mixed. One of the two conductors interviewed who knew the hall well said, "Perhaps the Academy of Music is the third best hall in the world. The middle frequencies are full and warm. The high frequencies are not overly strong but are in satisfactory proportion to the middles. The lows are good in relation to the middles. There is a natural sound." The other conductor observed, "The acoustics are a little dry. It is a very old hall—really an Italian style

PHILADELPHIA, ACADEMY OF MUSIC

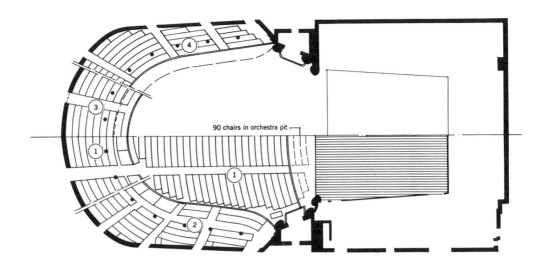

90 chairs in orchestra pit

SEATING CAPACITY 2836 to 2984

(1) Concerts 1295; Small pit 1205; Large pit 1147

(2) 540

(3) 577

(4) 572

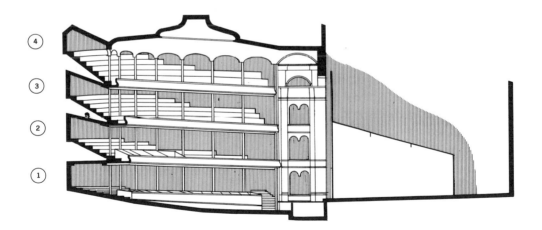

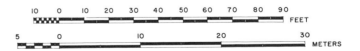

FEET

METERS

opera house. It has a dark, mellow sound. Its best feature is the intimate relationship between audience and orchestra." Fritz Reiner remarked, "The Academy has very good acoustics although somewhat dry. It is like an Italian opera house." Pierre Monteux said, "This hall is too dry; the tone stops instantly. The sound should have a more flattering carry-over." Herbert von Karajan remarked, "There is good orchestral balance, but the sound is too small. One doesn't get full power from the climaxes. The orchestra pit is too small for present-day orchestras."

According to Isaac Stern, "The sound in the Academy is true. There is a feeling of clarity and power. But on stage the artist does not get the support that he does in Carnegie and Boston. The hall is not very live."

Every music critic who has heard opera in the Academy of Music agrees that it is an excellent opera house. For concerts, many people like the Academy but some are less enthusiastic. Cyrus Durgin of the Boston *Globe* said, "The sound in Philadelphia is beautifully blended. There is not as much brilliance there as in Boston; the sound is sort of velvety. I enjoyed this hall right away; it is more intimate than Carnegie." Howard Taubman of the New York *Times* said, "Compared with Carnegie and Boston, it is the most mellow, the warmest. It is not as reverberant as the other two, but there are elements other than reverberation in the picture. The Philadelphia Orchestra has a glorious brilliant tone. The orchestra-conductor combination is an integrated unit. Ormandy produces good sound; he can overcome the acoustical deficiencies of a hall." Irving Kolodin of the *Saturday Review* commented, "The sound is warm, resonant, pleasing and not overly defined. I like the music there." Eric McLean of the Montreal *Star* said, "This hall seems to have no reverberation. Yet my complaint is not that the hall is too dead, but that the impact of the sound is not as great as I would expect. I expected that the tremendous Philadelphia string section would produce a really rich string sound. I expected it to come through with more body to it." Another out-of-town critic said, "My impression of the Academy was favorable and pleasant, but it is not in the same class as Boston. The hall is not live enough."

My own judgment is that orchestral music, when played in this hall by the Philadelphia Orchestra under Eugene Ormandy, is very fine. Ormandy has learned to overcome some of the weaknesses of the hall by demanding a silkier, more sustained tone from his strings. The sound in the hall is clean, clear, and intimate. The orchestra is in good balance, except that the double basses are not as strong as I would like, owing largely to the thin wood of the orchestra enclosure. The hall does not reverberate after a chordal climax. The balance of violins against cellos is good. The orchestra sounds as though it were playing in a drawing room: a quality of intimacy is imparted to the audience. Taken all in all, it is a hall in which Americans can justly take pride.

TECHNICAL DETAILS*

Concerts

$V = 555,000$ ft^3 $T_{500-1000}$(Occup.) $= 1.4$ sec $S_T = 18,700$ ft^2

$N_A = 2984$ seats $S_A = 16,700$ ft^2 $S_A/N_A = 5.6$ ft^2

$t_I = 19$; 10 msec $S_O = 2000$ ft^2 $V/S_T = 29.7$ ft

Opera

$V = 533,000$ ft^3 $T_{500-1000}$(Occup.) $= 1.35$ sec $S_P = 2401$ ft^2

$N_A = 2836$ seats $S_A = 15,700$ ft^2 $S_T = 18,740$ ft^2

$N_T = 2836$ S_O(Pit) $= 640$ ft^2 $S_A/N_T = 5.5$ ft^2

$t_I = 19$; 10 msec S_{OF}(Pit) $= 690$ ft^2 (approx.) $V/S_T = 28.4$ ft

* The terminology is explained in Appendix 3.

ARCHITECTURAL AND STRUCTURAL DETAILS

Uses: orchestra, opera, chorus, chamber orchestra, soloists. *Ceiling:* plaster on wood lath on flat surfaces; plaster on wire screen on curved surfaces. *Walls:* wooden boards, ⅜ x 3 in., nailed to wooden framing; with the passage of time they have shrunk and separated; the boards are covered with a heavy burlap glued in place; behind the boards, the air space averages 1 ft in depth. *Floors:* two layers of ⅜-in. boards on joists. *Stage enclosure:* the side walls and ceiling are mostly ³⁄₁₆-in. plywood panels with almost no bracing other than at the edges. The rear wall and rear 8 ft of each side wall are painted canvas. *Stage floor:* two layers of wood on joists. The subfloor is 2 x 6 in. tongue-and-groove fir and the top floor is ²⁵⁄₃₂-in. tongue-and-groove maple and yellow pine. *Stage height:* 52 in. above the floor level at the front row. *Carpets:* 3–4 ft wide in aisles on main floor and first ring; 1-ft strips under seats; no carpets on top ring. *Seating:* mohair cloth upholstery on tops of seat-bottoms and fronts of backrests; underseats and rear of backrests are solid. In the top ring, the seats are not upholstered.

References: Drawings, seating details, photographs, and stage enclosure details from Harold T. Mason, manager of the Academy of Music. Details verified by author during visits. *Architects:* Napoleon E. H. C. Le Brun and Gustavus Runge.

New theaters in America no longer exhibit the expensive handwork that went into the Eastman Theatre. Built in 1923, it embodies fabrics, metals, and decorations of a quality found in the royal palaces of old. It contains 3347 large comfortable seats. One is aware immediately on entering the hall of the huge volume of nearly 900,000 cubic feet.

Two conductors who were interviewed have expressed their opinions about Eastman Theatre. One who has conducted there often since its early days is dissatisfied with the hall. He considers that the hall sounds dry and has an empty feeling, probably because of its width. He once recommended to the management that they remove all the draperies and take up all the carpets. The other conductor said, "The hall is fairly good for concerts, and yet the music does not come off right. There is not a noble sound, it is a bit harsh. The Eastman Theatre does nothing to the sound. It is not in the class of Carnegie."

The high ceiling and wide, splayed side walls direct sound primarily to the rear of the hall. Hence the main difficulty with the acoustics is the largeness of the initial-time-delay gap at seats on the main floor. This gives the music heard there a harshness and a lack of clarity. The sound is somewhat better in the upper balcony. According to a regular Rochester concertgoer, there is difficulty in hearing only in the center part of the main floor. The rear part of the upper balcony he finds perfect, probably because the initial-time-delay gap there is relatively short.

The Metropolitan Opera Association has often performed in the Eastman Theatre during its annual tour. Since the orchestra may contain as many as 85 to 100 pieces, depending on the opera presented, it uses the full pit, half of which is recessed under the stage. The singers on stage can hear only the musicians at the open edge of the pit. It is also impossible for the musicians in most of the pit to hear what is happening on the stage or even to attain balance among the sections of the orchestra. The conductor hears something completely different from what he would hear in an open pit. To a listener in the rear of the hall the instruments back under the stage sound as though they were in another room.

ROCHESTER, NEW YORK, EASTMAN THEATRE

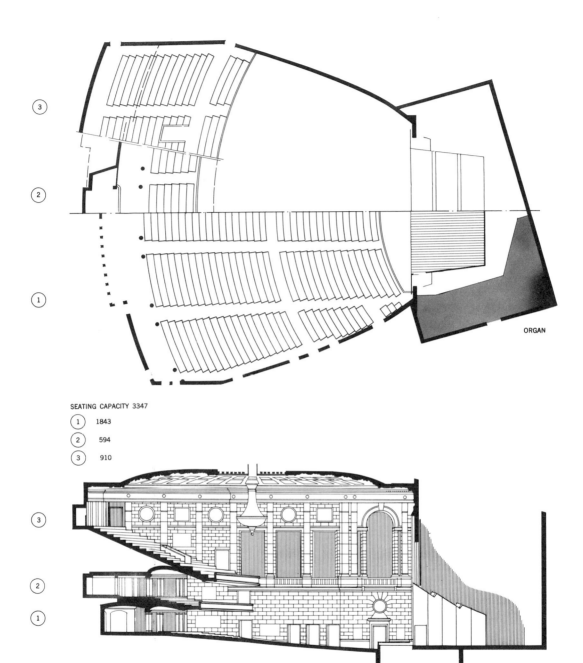

ORGAN

SEATING CAPACITY 3347

1. 1843
2. 594
3. 910

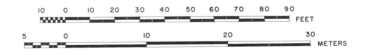

TECHNICAL DETAILS[*]

Concerts

$V = 900,000 \text{ ft}^3$	$T_{500-1000}(\text{Occup.}) = 1.75 \text{ sec}$	$S_T = 22,730 \text{ ft}^2$
$N_A = 3347 \text{ seats}$	$S_A = 20,530 \text{ ft}^2$	$S_A/N_A = 6.1 \text{ ft}^2$
$t_I = 55; 31 \text{ msec}$	$S_O = 2200 \text{ ft}^2$	$V/S_T = 39.6 \text{ ft}$

Opera

$V = 846,500 \text{ ft}^3$	$T_{500-1000}(\text{Occup.}) = 1.65 \text{ sec}$	$S_P = 2752 \text{ ft}^2$
$N_A = 3347 \text{ seats}$	$S_A = 20,530 \text{ ft}^2$	$S_T = 24,050 \text{ ft}^2$
$N_T = 3347$	$S_O(\text{Pit}) = 770 \text{ ft}^2$	$S_A/N_T = 6.1 \text{ ft}^2$
$t_I = 55; 31 \text{ msec}$	$S_{OF}(\text{Pit}) = 1750 \text{ ft}^2$	$V/S_T = 35.2 \text{ ft}$

[*] The terminology is explained in Appendix 3.

ARCHITECTURAL AND STRUCTURAL DETAILS

Uses: general purpose. *Ceiling:* plaster. *Side walls:* plaster, approximately 50% covered with sound-absorbing materials that have been heavily painted. *Rear walls and balcony fronts:* covered with sound-absorbing materials, heavily painted. *Floors:* concrete. *Stage enclosure for orchestra:* painted canvas. *Stage floor:* wood. *Stage height:* 42 in. above the floor at the first row of seats. *Carpets:* on all floors. *Seating:* fully upholstered both sides of backrest; underseat is solid. *Pit:* half-recessed under stage; the floor is of wood; the walls are concrete; the railing is asbestos board.

References: Drawings from the *American Architect*, February 1923. Photographs courtesy of Ansel Adams, Eastman Kodak Company. Stage and seating details from J. M. Young, general superintendent. Details verified by the author during a visit. *Architect:* Gordon E. Kaelber. *Associate architect:* McKim, Mead and White.

Newly sand-blasted and scrubbed to within a micron of its pristine cleanliness, the War Memorial Opera House surpasses New York's Metropolitan Opera House in beauty of exterior and lobbies. Its interior is reminiscent of the Eastman Theatre in Rochester and other theaters built in the early 1930's. Yet it has a dignity and beauty that exceed that of many contemporary halls, partly because the architect eschewed adornments and confined the design to simple lines, a high ceiling, and a majestic proscenium.

Recently I attended two performances, the world premier of *Blood Moon* by Norman Dello Joio, and *Nabucco* by Verdi. The long thin pit gave the conductor trouble with ensemble, but the timbre was satisfactory throughout the house. The singers were easy to hear above the orchestra, although they seemed to force their voices. Most pleasant was the general liveness, greater than that of the Metropolitan Opera House, La Scala, or the Staatsoper in Vienna. I had access to seats in four parts of the house during the two operas. In the front of the house (the 15th row near the left aisle of the main floor), the reverberation tended to interfere with intelligibility of opera sung in English. But the hard materials of the interior also gave warmth to the music, and a fullness of bass not found in many European houses.

The shallow dome presents no acoustical problem, because the very large chandelier beneath it effectively diffuses the sound. G. Albert Lansburgh, one of the architects for the San Francisco Opera, tells me that the dome is treated with acoustic plaster. He also says that there are good sight lines to all 3252 seats.

In moving about the hall, I found the sound best in the forward parts of the two balconies, probably because of reflections from the side walls and ceiling. Sound penetrates well to the rear of the balconies, which have relatively wide mouths and favorable side-wall reflections. On the main floor, the instruments at the end of the pit nearest the listener dominate. In the balconies the balance is good.

Seven conductors who have had experience in the San Francisco Opera House were interviewed. Each rated it good for either orchestra or opera from the positions of both the conductor and the listeners. For concerts, all

SAN FRANCISCO, WAR MEMORIAL OPERA HOUSE

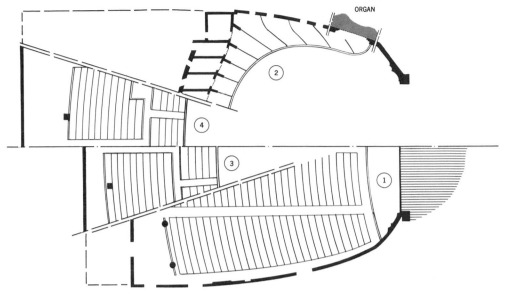

ORGAN

② 2

④ 4

③ 3

① 1

SEATING CAPACITY 3252

① 1   1300

② 2   192

③ 3   852

④ 4   908 + 300 standees

④ 4

③ 3

② 2

① 1

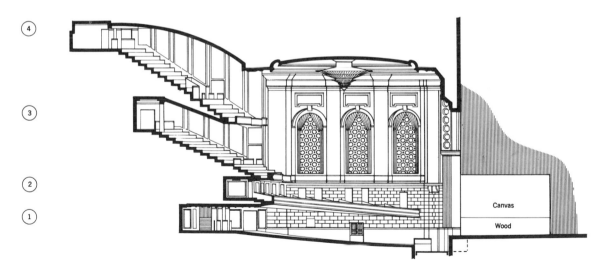

Canvas

Wood

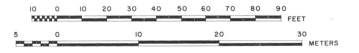

10 0 10 20 30 40 50 60 70 80 90
FEET

5   0   10   20   30
METERS

the conductors placed the hall below Boston, Carnegie, and Philadelphia, and for opera about equal to New York's Metropolitan. Several of them remarked that the audience hears much better in the balcony than on the main floor. One violinist thought the hall "has good reverberation for the violin . . . wonderful sound in the middle boxes and in the balcony."

A number of music critics know the San Francisco Opera House well. All those I interviewed thought it better for opera than for symphony. A comment by a music critic who attends many performances there every year is typical: "The sound on the main floor of this hall is fair, but not good. The sound in the top balcony is superb. The sides of the floor and the side boxes are poor acoustically. The loudness is satisfactory everywhere. For concerts, the hall is not in the same class with Boston and Carnegie."

As is true of all wide halls with high ceilings, the initial-time-delay gap is somewhat too long for the listeners on the main floor. The ceiling supplies these first reflections to the fronts of the balconies and the side walls supply their first reflections to the rear of the balconies. Still, for its size and the comfort of its seating, this house is acoustically quite satisfactory.

TECHNICAL DETAILS*

Concerts

$V = 771{,}000$ ft^3 $T_{500-1000}$(Occup.) $= 1.7$ sec† $S_T = 23{,}340$ ft^2

$N_A = 3252$ seats $S_A = 21{,}240$ ft^2 $S_A/N_A = 6.5$ ft^2

$t_I = 51; 30$ msec $S_O = 2100$ ft^2 $V/S_T = 33.0$ ft

Opera

$V = 738{,}600$ ft^3 $T_{500-1000}$(Occup.) $= 1.6$ sec† $S_P = 2430$ ft^2

$N_A = 3252$ seats $S_A = 21{,}240$ ft^2 $S_T = 25{,}430$ ft^2

$N_T = 3402$ S_O(Pit) $= 760$ ft^2 $S_A/N_T = 6.5$ ft^2

$t_I = 51; 30$ msec S_{OF}(Pit) $= 1075$ ft^2 $V/S_T = 29.0$ ft

* The terminology is explained in Appendix 3.
† Estimated.

ARCHITECTURAL AND STRUCTURAL DETAILS

Uses: concerts, opera, general purpose. *Ceiling:* plaster except for center domed section which architect says is acoustic plaster. *Walls:* plaster with some wood trim. *Floors:* entire floor area carpeted except in upper part of top balcony where carpet is only in aisles. *Stage:* wood over air space. *Pit:* wooden floor on elevator; wooden rear and front walls with 1 ft of velvet covering over an open railing. *Stage height:* 40 in. above floor level at first row of seats. *Added absorptive materials:* velvet draperies, about 1 ft high above rails of cross aisles. *Seating:* main floor, fully upholstered with four holes 1 in. in diameter in underseat; balcony, same but with hard backs. *Orchestra enclosure:* canvas throughout except that ¼-in. plywood covers the bottom part of the walls, extending upward 10 ft from the floor.

References: B. J. S. Cahill, "The San Francisco War Memorial Group," *The Architect and Engineer,* **111,** 11–44, 59 (November 1932); photographs courtesy of *Musical America* and *Opera News. Details* verified by the author during a visit. *Architect:* Arthur Brown, Jr. *Collaborating architect:* G. Albert Lansburgh.

The Teatro Colón is one of the most beautiful large opera houses in the world. With 2487 seats, it is larger than most of the famous opera houses in Europe but smaller than the Metropolitan Opera House. It has been very successful since its dedication in 1908.

Irving Kolodin, music critic for the *Saturday Review* wrote (1960):

> No city anywhere has a finer home for opera than the Colón of Buenos Aires . . . gratifying the ear with a rich blend of sound. . . . The Colón has the reputation of being a singer's theater, and it was confirmed by the judgment of Carlos Cillario as he merged his excellent orchestra and chorus in resonant fullness with the principals. . . . A good disposition of the orchestra for these particular surroundings—woodwinds at the conductor's left, violins at the right, and heavy brass beyond them—plays its part in the superior sound produced.

Mr. Kolodin commented to me after his return to the United States: "It is my belief that the ceiling over the pit and the large panels at either side, penetrated by a few boxes, somehow project the sound better into the house. This architecture gives the sound a clarity and a projection that isn't found at the Met."

Many soloists consider the Teatro Colón the best hall of any they have played in, from the point of view of the performer. The stage has a small, intimate enclosure for solo performances. A soloist who has played in this setting feels that every note, "even the faintest, reaches the most distant listener with clear, loud, shimmering sound."

In 1949 I spent an academic term as visiting professor in the University of Buenos Aires. I attended the opera several times and had the opportunity to listen on all six levels in the theater.

For opera, the Colón is not as good as the Staatsoper in Vienna or La Scala in Milan. It is, on the whole, better than the Metropolitan Opera House, particularly on the main floor, because the main floor is narrower and because the large surfaces on either side of the proscenium provide short initial-time-delay gaps. The aspect of the house that pleases soloists is the well-defined reflections of the correct intensity back to the stage from

BUENOS AIRES, TEATRO COLÓN

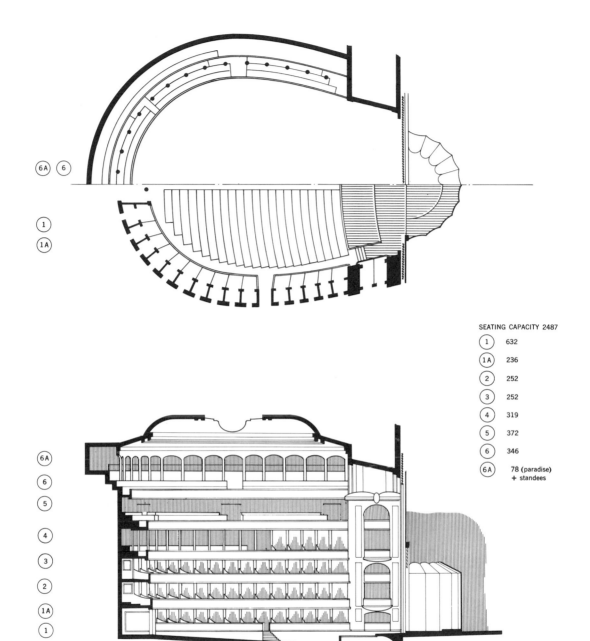

SEATING CAPACITY 2487

(1)	632
(1A)	236
(2)	252
(3)	252
(4)	319
(5)	372
(6)	346
(6A)	78 (paradise) + standees

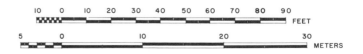

10 0 10 20 30 40 50 60 70 80 90
FEET

5 0 10 20 30
METERS

the ceiling and the balcony faces. These reflections give the performer a feeling of "immediacy."

The ceiling does not have the best shape for reflecting sounds effectively into the main floor and the first two or three rings above it. Regular opera-goers in Buenos Aires say that the best seats for opera are in the top two galleries. In moving from one level to another, I found that it is only in the top two or three galleries that the violin tone (from the pit orchestra) comes through with its full quality. This is directly attributable to reflections from the main ceiling.

I found the sound of the pit orchestra muffled on the main floor. Most of the floor of the pit was as much as 10 feet below the rail at the edge of the pit. This means that the violins are shielded from the audience on the main floor; and because of the unfavorable shape of the ceiling, the violin tone is not reflected well into the main floor and the first two rings above it. Mr. Kolodin's remarks about the panels at the sides of the proscenium are well taken. These panels do help to project the singers' voices and to balance them better with the orchestra. Designers of opera houses would do well to pay particular attention to the details of construction near the proscenium arch of the Teatro Colón.

TECHNICAL DETAILS*

Concerts

$V = 760{,}000$ ft^3 $T_{500-1000}$(Occup.) $= 1.8$ sec† $S_T = 21{,}200$ ft^2

$N_A = 2487$ seats $S_A = 19{,}000$ ft^2 $S_A/N_A = 7.6$ ft^2

$t_I = 19; 13$ msec $S_O = 2200$ ft^2 $V/S_T = 35.8$ ft

Opera

$V = 726{,}300$ ft^3 $T_{500-1000}$(Occup.) $= 1.7$ sec† $S_P = 3402$ ft^2

$N_A = 2487$ seats $S_A = 19{,}000$ ft^2 $S_T = 23{,}080$ ft^2

$N_T = 2787$ S_O(Pit) $= 675$ ft^2 $S_A/N_T = 6.8$ ft^2

$t_I = 19; 13$ msec S_{OF}(Pit) $= 2050$ ft^2 $V/S_T = 31.5$ ft

* The terminology is explained in Appendix 3.
† Estimated.

ARCHITECTURAL AND STRUCTURAL DETAILS

Uses: opera, recitals, conferences. *Ceilings:* plaster on metal lath. *Walls:* plaster, including balcony fronts. *Floors:* wood, carpet in aisles. *Seating:* fully upholstered. *Stage floor:* wood over air space. Surface inclines at rate of 3 in. in 100 in. *Orchestra pit:* floor and side walls made of wood. *Orchestra enclosure:* wooden side walls. Pit is raised to form a forestage.

References: Architect's drawings (made from the building in 1930) were obtained from the opera administration; photographs from Burri, Magnum. Details verified by author during visits. *Architect:* Victor Meano.

On July 26, 1960, the new Salzburg Festspielhaus, with 2158 seats, was opened. It was a musical and social occasion, attracting diplomats, industrialists, and artists. The architectural contrast with the former Festspielhaus is great. The old house resembled a shoe box—with side balconies barely 40 feet apart. In contrast, the new Festspielhaus has a width of nearly 112 feet between the faces of the side balcony boxes, and on the main floor the width approaches 124 feet! It will be a long time before the feeling of hugeness, both visual and acoustical, of this great width will be overcome.

Expectations ran high for the acoustics of the new house. Those who sit in the balcony are not disappointed. On the main floor, the comments are not as favorable. Let us look at some of the early reviews:

Everett Helm wrote in *Musical America:*

It is hard to imagine Mozart being staged in the new Festspielhaus. It is certainly not the ideal setting for Mozart's operas, all of which—some more than others—demand a certain intimacy for their ideal presentation. One can reduce the size of the stage, to be sure, but not that of the Auditorium. . . . Suffice it to say that it seemed to me rather cold, pompous and gaudy. The acoustics of the auditorium, however, seemed to be excellent— at least from where I sat in the balcony. At times I found them even too good—that is to say, the loud passages were somewhat harsh. The pianissimo passages were superb.

Time magazine reported, "the new hall's acoustics were fine—clean and clear, but not too dry . . ."

After hearing one opera, Rudolf Klein wrote for *The Christian Science Monitor:*

The very first scene made it abundantly clear that this new theatre has acoustical qualities probably unsurpassed by any other house in Europe at this time. The orchestral part, usually rather thickly flowing, was transparent, and the singers effortlessly wove the tapestry of sound. Even when they were at the rear of the stage, one understood every word.

Joseph Wechsberg wrote:

The great surprise of the evening were the acoustics that surpassed even the expectations of the optimists. . . . The Festspielhaus has a "modern" sound with a short reverberation time, which gives some old-fashioned listeners sometimes an uncomfortable feeling of too much bright-

SALZBURG, NEUES FESTSPIELHAUS

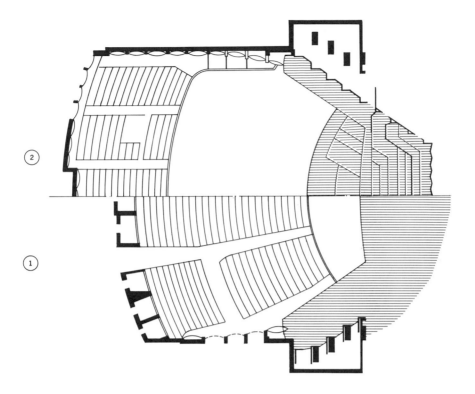

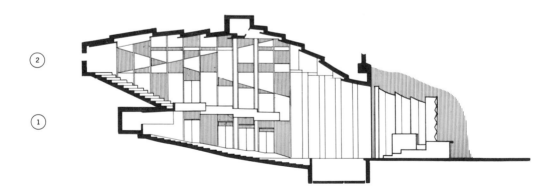

SEATING CAPACITY 2158

①	Main floor	1289
	Boxes	71
②	Balcony	762
	Boxes	36

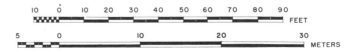

ness and brilliancy, but you can't expect them to build a 1960 house with "soft" 1860 sound.

One has only to look at the drawings to see that for opera the sound will not be as good on the main floor as in the balcony. The singers' voices are efficiently projected into the balcony by the upward-sloping ceiling. The side walls also project the voices efficiently toward the balcony and into the back corners of the main floor. On the other hand, the pit orchestra is projected by the ceiling to the rear half of the main floor, and by the side walls to the rear half of the main floor and to the boxes. The result is that, on the main floor and in the boxes, the orchestra is loud compared to the voices. In the balcony, the singers' voices are in better balance with the orchestra, but there, during loud passages, the music is somewhat too loud.

The lack of intimacy for Mozart, which is the chief complaint against the new hall, is most severely felt at the seats on the main floor where the initial-time-delay gap for the voices on stage is relatively large. It is the lack of acoustical intimacy resulting from the great width of 112 feet that causes the "modern" sound of which Wechsberg speaks, or the "harsh" sound described by Helm, in contrast to "the 'soft' 1860 sound" of a house like the Philadelphia Academy of Music, whose width is only 54 feet between balcony faces.

Actually a hall of 2100 seats is not large by American standards. The Metropolitan Opera House, which is 65 feet wide between balcony faces, is used for Mozart's operas, and it seats over 3600 people. The Philadelphia Academy of Music, which is judged by most listeners to be adequately intimate for Mozart, has nearly 3000 seats.

The materials of the hall are excellent from an acoustical standpoint. The walls and ceiling are of vibration-damped plaster, on reeds. Since the plaster and wood panels on the side walls are over 1½ in. thick, they do not absorb the lower registers of the orchestra. The sound is warm, and in the balcony it is also intimate, clear, and brilliant. The reverberation, while ideally suited to non-Wagnerian opera, is too low for concert music of the Romantic style. Antonio Mingotti writes, "For opera and classical concerts this hall is 'very good' to 'excellent.' For oratorios, and for the concert music of Strauss and Bruckner it is only 'fair' to 'good.' "

TECHNICAL DETAILS*

Concerts

$V = 547{,}500$ ft^3	$T_{500-1000}$(Occup.) $= 1.5$ sec	$S_T = 16{,}900$ ft^2
$N_A = 2158$ seats	$S_A = 14{,}800$ ft^2	$S_A/N_A = 6.9$ ft^2
$t_I = 23$; 14 msec	$S_O = 2100$ ft^2	$V/S_T = 32.4$ ft

Opera

$V = 495{,}000$ ft^3	$T_{500-1000}$(Occup.) $= 1.45$ sec	$S_P = 2100$ ft^2
$N_A = 2158$ seats	$S_A = 14{,}100$ ft^2	$S_T = 17{,}000$ ft^2
$N_T = 2158$	S_O(Pit) $= 800$ ft^2	$S_A/N_A = 6.5$ ft^2
$t_I = 23$; 14 msec	S_{OF}(Pit) $= 950$ ft^2	$V/S_T = 29.1$ ft

* The terminology is explained in Appendix 3.

ARCHITECTURAL AND STRUCTURAL DETAILS

Uses: opera, concerts, and drama. *Ceiling:* the sloped part at the front of the hall is 1½ to 2 in. of plaster on reeds, constructed as follows: ³⁄₁₆-in. to ⁵⁄₁₆-in. round iron rods underneath; two crosswise layers of marsh reed mats next, covered with a thin wire mesh (rabbit fence); next, a grid of ³⁄₁₆-in. round iron rods; covering all this is a layer of rough and fine lime plaster finished with a smooth layer of pure-alabaster plaster; the horizontal part of the ceiling is similar to the front part except that there is a concrete layer on top that can be walked on; the exposed surface is painted. *Side walls:* concave, curved sections extend from floor to ceiling; the radius of curvature is 9 ft and the depth of a curved sector at the center is 8 in.; the steel structure is formed to this shape; fastened to the steel structure is the same 1½-in. to 2-in. plaster on reeds as detailed above; finally, cemented to the gypsum areas is a finish-wood layer about ¹⁄₁₆ in. thick; in front of the concave sections are convex trapezoidal or rectangular curved panels of irregular size about 1½ in. thick, consisting of ⁵⁄₃₂-in. dense wood-fiber sheets on both sides of a core consisting of softwood studs; in the lens-shaped cavities between the convex panels and the concave gypsum walls are the indirect side-wall lighting and the sound reinforcement system. *Rear walls:* on the main floor there are boxes; on the upper floor there are convex wooden panels about 6 ft wide and bowed out about 10 in. at the center. *Floors:* the floor is made of wooden panels supported above the concrete floor by steel angles and U-shaped standards; cork linoleum is cemented to the wood floor in the seat rows and on the steps of the aisles; return air is drawn through openings in the wood floor into the plenum underneath. *Stage floor:* wood. *Stage height:* 35½ in. above the floor at the first row of seats. *Carpets:* the two main aisles and the cross aisles on the main floor are carpeted; the boxes are carpeted. *Orchestra pit:* the floor is 2-in.-thick wood over a deep air space; the side walls are made of wooden wainscoting; sections can be removed so that sound-absorbing materials can be added; at times sound-absorbing materials are used near the timpani. *Seating:* only the seat cushions and part of the armrests are upholstered; the backrest and underseat are solid.

References: Acoustical details from G. A. Schwaiger, Technical University, Vienna. All drawings, photographs, and remaining details courtesy of the architect. Details verified by the author during a visit. *Architect:* Clemens Holzmeister.

The "Grosse Saal der Gesellschaft der Musikfreunde in Wien," abbreviated "Grosser Musikvereinssaal" was opened during the reign of Kaiser Franz Josef I on January 5, 1870, by the Gesellschaft der Musikfreunde (Society of Friends of Music). The great organ was completed in 1871.

Without doubt, the pulse of any orchestra conductor quickens when he first conducts in this famous hall. The tradition of the Vienna Philharmonic, the parade of famous conductors, and the fine music played there make this the Mecca of the old halls of Europe.

On entering this hall, one is impressed with its age. The creaking floor and the much-worn wooden risers for the orchestra on the stage confirm this impression. The busy side walls are made irregular by over forty high windows, twenty doors above the balcony, and thirty-two tall, gilded buxom female statues beneath the balcony. In the daytime, the coffered and ornamented ceiling stands out, but at night the ten mammoth crystal chandeliers dominate. And everywhere are gilt, ornamentation, and statuettes.

The Viennese believe that the acoustics of their famous hall are influenced by the design of its lining materials: gypsum plaster, wood, and gilt. But these three materials are not equally effective. A thin layer of gold leaf on an impervious surface does not change its acoustical properties one whit. Exclusive of the floor, less than 15 per cent of the interior surfaces of the Grosser Musikvereinssaal is of wood. Wood is used only for the doors, for some paneling around the stage, and for trim. The other surfaces are constructed of plaster on brick or, on the ceiling and balcony fronts, plaster on wooden lath. The hall is, therefore, primarily made of plaster and this material is primarily responsible for setting its acoustical quality. This is also true of Symphony Hall in Boston. Most of the best-liked halls are lined with either plaster or *thick* wood.

The real reasons for the superior acoustics of the hall are its relatively small size (its volume is 530,000 cubic feet and it contains 1680 seats), its narrow 65-foot width, its rectangular shape, its high ceiling with resulting high reverberation time (which is slightly over 2 seconds at mid-frequencies, when the hall is fully occupied), the irregular interior surfaces, and its

VIENNA, GROSSER MUSIKVEREINSSAAL

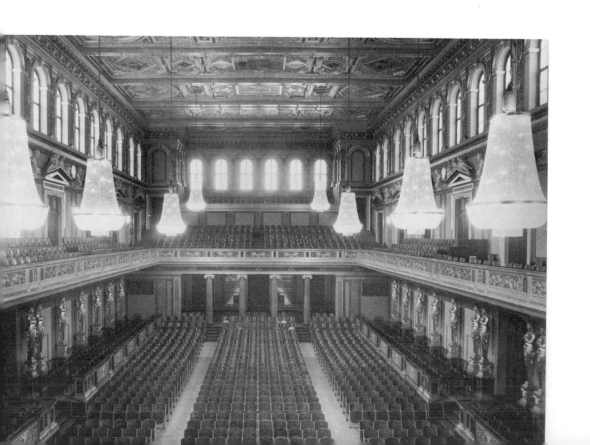

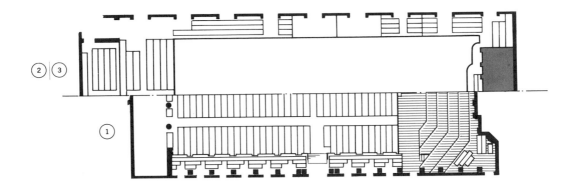

SEATING CAPACITY 1680

① 1032
② 548
③ 100 + 320 standees

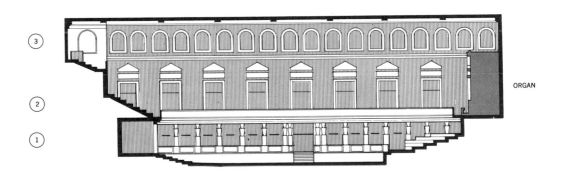

ORGAN

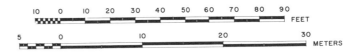

interior finish, which is primarily of plaster. Any hall built today with these characteristics would be an excellent hall for orchestral music, especially for music of the Romantic and late Classical periods.

Bruno Walter stated the position of most conductors who know intimately the Grosser Musikvereinssaal: "This is certainly the finest hall in the world. It has beauty of sound and power. The first time I conducted there, in 1897, was an unforgettable experience. I had not realized that music could be so beautiful. It is the best hall I know of."

Herbert von Karajan, who is thoroughly familiar with Vienna's great hall, adds detail, "The sound in this hall is very full. It is rich in bass and good for high strings. One shortcoming is that the technical attack of instruments—bows and lips—gets lost. Instruments that do not sound precisely in time merge. Also successive notes tend to merge into each other. It has characteristics the opposite of a recording studio. This is a highly imaginative hall; it gives the conductor inspiration. There is too much difference in the sound for rehearsing and the sound with audience. With no audience this is not the best hall for gramophone recordings of music."

All the music critics interviewed who knew this hall well considered it a very fine hall. In acoustical quality it is similar to Symphony Hall in Boston. Most of the critics felt that the clarity or definition is better than in the Amsterdam Concertgebouw. My own experience in this hall supports the music critics' judgment and I rank it acoustically among the best of the halls described in this book.

TECHNICAL DETAILS FOR CONCERTS*

$V = 530,000$ ft^3 $T_{500-1000}$(Occup.) $= 2.05$ sec $S_T = 12,000$ ft^2
$N_A = 1680$ seats $S_A = 10,600$ ft^2 $S_A/N_A = 6.3$ ft^2
$t_I = 12; 9$ msec $S_O = 1400$ ft^2 $V/S_T = 44.2$ ft

* The terminology is explained in Appendix 3.

ARCHITECTURAL AND STRUCTURAL DETAILS

Uses: concerts. *Ceiling:* plaster on spruce wood. *Side and rear walls:* plaster on brick, except around the stage, where walls are of wood; doors are of wood; balcony fronts are plaster on wood. *Floors:* wood. *Stage floor:* wooden risers over wooden stage. *Stage height:* 39 in. above floor level.

Added absorptive material: 200 sq ft of draperies over front of railing on side loges. *Seating:* on main floor and side balconies all are of wood, except that top of seat-bottoms are of cloth over 4 in. of upholstering; rear balcony seats, plywood.

References: Personal communications from G. A. Schwaiger, Technical University of Vienna, G. Skalar of the Austrian Broadcasting Co., V. L. Jordan of Copenhagen, Lothar Cremer, Technical University of Berlin, and F. Bruckmayer, Staatliche Physikalisch-Technische Versuchanstalt für Wärme und Schalltechnik, Vienna. Details verified by author during visits. Photographs and some details courtesy of Sekretariat, Gesellschaft der Musikfreunde in Wien. *Architect:* Theophil Ritter von Hansen.

In contrast with the Grosser Musikvereinssaal, the main hall of the Staatsoper is modern in design. Bombed during the war and rededicated in 1955, it has the same architectural shape as the original house of 1869. Today the absence of baroque decoration and gilded statues suggests efficiency and affluent dignity. There are three tiers of boxes, a central box for dignitaries, and two upper galleries. The interior is dominated by red plush, and the decoration is mainly white with gold. There is a large torus-shaped crystal chandelier against the ceiling.

The whole Staatsoper is a tremendous building. The auditorium occupies a relatively small space in the center. To Americans accustomed to opera houses with 3000 to 6000 seats, a house of 1658 seats seems miniature! And in 1960 excellent seats in the Staatsoper could be bought for under $5.00 and the most distant balcony seats for less than $1.00. Such low prices for tickets are possible only through government subsidy.

The conductors who know the rebuilt Staatsoper are unanimous in their opinion that the house has good sound, although some say that the orchestra does not get the "lift" from the house that it does in La Scala.

Bruno Walter said, "The Staatsoper is the most alive of all opera halls. It has the greatest splendor. It is much better than New York and better than La Scala. The orchestra does not overpower the singers."

I judge the sound of the Staatsoper excellent. One year I attended four consecutive performances with the privilege of sitting in any part of the house. On the last evening I sat in the orchestra pit through an entire act. In the galleries the house sounds similar to New York's Metropolitan, but the sound is louder because of the smaller cubic volume. On the main floor the sound is greatly superior to that on the main floor of the Met; it is louder, more intimate, and beautifully clear and brilliant.

Since the Staatsoper is only 64 feet wide, the initial-time-delay gap is short, which accounts in large part for the superior sound on the main floor.

The auditorium itself is not very live. The liveness heard during a performance comes primarily from the stagehouse, which is large, hard, and quite reverberant. The canvas backdrop, called the cyclorama in

VIENNA, STAATSOPER

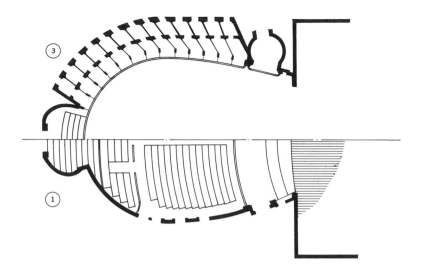

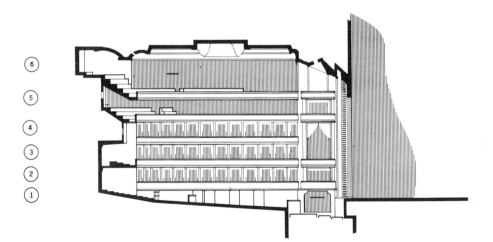

SEATING CAPACITY 1658

1 467
2 174
3 210
4 156
5 309
6 342 + 550 standees

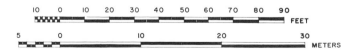

theatrical circles, is thick, heavily painted, and does not absorb high-frequency sounds. The sets are built so very high that few teaser curtains are necessary. As of 1960 more than half the sets were made of wood rather than canvas. This means that the voice is not absorbed in the sets but is reflected into the audience. No other opera house of my acquaintance has such a live stage; a singer can be heard even when his back is turned to the audience.

At the ends of the pit, behind the horns, trombones, and percussion, there are entrance chambers, small rooms open to the pit. The walls of the chamber are partly covered with sound-absorbing material to diminish the loudness of the brass and percussion, with the result that they are in good balance with the strings. The double basses are lined up against the hard wall of the pit on the stage side, which increases their loudness. Some conductors at the Staatsoper encourage the trumpets and trombones to aim the bells of their instruments down, behind the players in front of them. The pit is adequately large for nearly all operatic orchestras. Viennese opera-goers say that the orchestra often dominates the singers, but that is partly occasioned by the opera and partly in the hands of the conductor.

I rate the auditoriums of the Vienna Staatsoper and La Scala about equal, but the wooden sets and live stagehouse give the Staatsoper an over-all advantage, at least from the standpoint of the audience.

TECHNICAL DETAILS FOR OPERA[*]

$V = 376,600 \text{ ft}^3$	$T_{500-1000}(\text{Occup.}) = 1.3 \text{ sec}$	$S_P = 1720 \text{ ft}^2$
$N_A = 1658 \text{ seats}$	$S_A = 12,850 \text{ ft}^2$	$S_T = 15,720 \text{ ft}^2$
$N_T = 1938$	$S_O(\text{Pit}) = 1150 \text{ ft}^2$	$S_A/N_T = 6.6 \text{ ft}^2$
$t_I = 15; 6 \text{ msec}$	$S_{OF}(\text{Pit}) = 1150 \text{ ft}^2$	$V/S_T = 24.0 \text{ ft}$

[*] The terminology is explained in Appendix 3.

ARCHITECTURAL AND STRUCTURAL DETAILS

Uses: opera. *Ceiling:* plaster. *Walls:* in the top galleries the walls were of slotted wood backed by sound-absorbing material, installed in 1955; after trial, these sound-absorbing surfaces were covered with Plexiglas; faces of the rings are of wood; in the balcony beneath the gallery, the walls are of brocade over plywood with ¼-in. air space between them; in the boxes the walls are of tightly stretched brocade on wood. On main floor, walls are ½-in. wood. *Floors:* in the gallery and balcony, the floors consist of carpet over underpad; the main floor has linoleum over concrete with carpet in the aisles; the main-floor standing room is of wood. *Pit:* on the pit floor are 3-in. planks; the pit walls are of ¾-in. wood; there are small rooms at the end of each pit, with some sound-absorbing draperies inside; sound-absorbing material, covered by a thin layer of plastic material, extends 8 ft from the ends of the pit toward the center on both the stage and the audience sides; in September 1959, the floor of the pit was 30 in. below the house floor at the front. *Stage height:* 41 in. above the floor at first row of seats. *Seating:* in the balcony and galleries the seats are of solid wood except that the fronts of the backrests are thinly upholstered; the boxes have simple chairs with upholstered seats; on the main floor the seats are of solid wood except that the front of the backrests is covered with 1-in. upholstering.

References: Plans, details and photographs courtesy of Andre von Mattoni, Staatsoper. Some details from G. A. Schwaiger, Technical University, Vienna. Details confirmed by the author during visits. *Architect:* August Siccard von Siccardsburg and Eduard van der Null. (The reconstruction was in many hands.)

Brussels
PALAIS DES
BEAUX-ARTS

The Palais des Beaux-Arts ranks as one of the better concert halls with both conductors and listeners. The side walls are of plaster on brick. The ceiling is plaster on metal lath. All the surfaces are painted an old ivory, relieved only by dark balcony railings and horizontal gold stripes. The Palais des Beaux-Arts is a relatively new hall, opened in 1929. The coves in the ceiling, designed to permit recessing of the lights, sweep around in flowing curves and tie the hall together aesthetically. There is no stagehouse.

My first introduction to the Palais des Beaux-Arts was at a concert that followed close upon a week of listening to music in the Royal Festival Hall in London. The richness of the bass and the quality of the violin tone in the Palais were stunning in contrast to the Festival Hall. I sat in the first rise of seats at the rear of the main floor, about six seats to one side of the center line. Because of the narrowness of the hall, only 70 to 80 feet, the initial-time-delay gap at my seat was about 25 milliseconds, and I was only 60 feet from the stage. The hall gave a feeling of acoustical intimacy that focused attention on the performance. The most striking aspect of the acoustics was the warmth produced by the full, rich bass. Even with only one double bass playing, the loudness at low frequencies was impressive. The sound is not quite as good in the front half of the main floor, owing to the greater initial-time-delay gap.

The Palais des Beaux-Arts was not at first on the list of halls about which I conducted interviews; consequently most of the conductors and music critics were not asked about it. Stanislaw Skrowaczewski said, "The acoustical conditions are excellent both for the conductor and the listeners in the hall. The balance is very good."

F. Winckel [*Der Monat*, February 1957, p. 77] reports that he sent a letter to a number of European conductors before 1945 asking them to name their favorite hall anywhere in the world. The answers mentioned the Palais about as often as the Grosser Musikvereinssaal in Vienna, Symphony Hall in Boston, or the Concertgebouw in Amsterdam. My own evidence, obtained recently by questioning informally a number of well-known musicians, is that the hall has a very good reputation from both their standpoint and that of

BRUSSELS, PALAIS DES BEAUX-ARTS

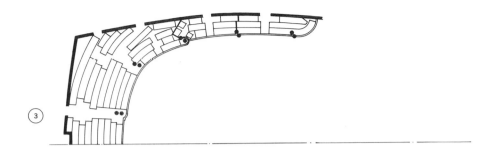

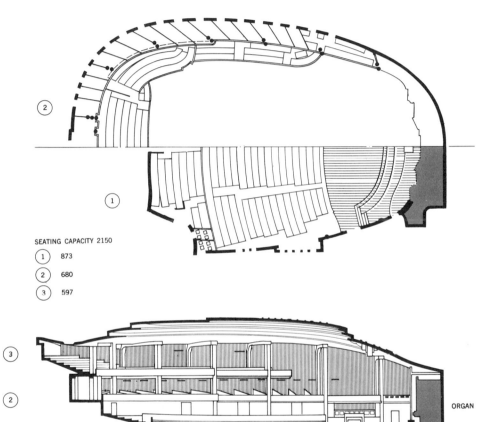

SEATING CAPACITY 2150

① 873

② 680

③ 597

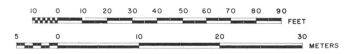

ORGAN

10 0 10 20 30 40 50 60 70 80 90
FEET

5 0 10 20 30
METERS

the regular concert-goers. However, it is not as live as the three halls just mentioned and rates below them for music of the Romantic period.

TECHNICAL DETAILS FOR CONCERTS*

$V = 442{,}000 \text{ ft}^3$ $T_{500-1000}(\text{Occup.}) = 1.42 \text{ sec}$ $S_T = 16{,}000 \text{ ft}^2$

$N_A = 2150 \text{ seats}$ $S_A = 14{,}000 \text{ ft}^2$ $S_A/N_A = 6.5 \text{ ft}^2$

$t_I = 23; 4 \text{ msec}$ $S_O = 2000 \text{ ft}^2$ $V/S_T = 27.6 \text{ ft}$

* The terminology is explained in Appendix 3.

ARCHITECTURAL AND STRUCTURAL DETAILS

Uses: 45% for orchestra, 30% for motion pictures, 8% for ballet, and 17% for theater and conferences. *Ceiling:* 75% is plaster on metal lath, 20% is thick glass on heavy metal frames, and 5% is lighting fixtures. *Walls:* plaster on brick, painted; columns are plaster on concrete. *Floors:* on main floor pine wood on 3-in. wooden sleepers resting on concrete; on upper floors, wood cemented directly to concrete. *Stage floor:* wood parquet on wood boards, supported by concrete posts and wood beams; the air space beneath varies between 4 in. and 5 ft. *Stage height:* 36½ in. above the floor at the first row of seats. *Carpets:* on main floor, in boxes, and in balconies. *Seating:* front of backrest and top of seat-bottom upholstered.

References: Drawings, plans, photographs, and details courtesy of P. Janlet, director general of the hall. Some details from A. C. Raes, Brussels. Details verified by the author during visits. *Architect:* Baron Victor Horta.

Edmonton and Calgary
ALBERTA JUBILEE
AUDITORIUMS

The architectural resemblance between these twin halls and the Kleinhans Hall in Buffalo, New York, is striking. All three have low ceilings, and about the same lateral dimensions and number of seats. The size alone of the fan-shaped seating area in the Edmonton and Calgary Halls creates a sense of splendor to which the structurally unbroken lines of the inward-leaning side walls contribute.

The Jubilee Halls were built from the same plans, at the same time, from identical materials, and were dedicated on the same day by public officials who flew from one hall to the other. A pre-dedication concert was held in Edmonton, to which a group of musicians and acousticians was invited. Since none of the critics or conductors whom I interviewed had been in either of the Jubilee halls, the principal source for evaluation is the comments of those of us who attended the first concert.

Some of the acousticians found the reverberation time (liveness) satisfactory, some found it too low. Most of them thought the low-frequency response weak and the violins somewhat lacking in brilliance. All of them thought the plastic orchestra shell, used during the test concert, harmful to the warmth of the music.

The musicians at the test concert felt that the sound was not vital, not live enough. They agreed that low frequencies were seriously lacking. They all found the definition or clarity good to excellent.

The professional musicians and acousticians in the audience expressed the following opinions: 86 per cent thought the Jubilee Halls equal to the Royal Festival Hall in London; 55 per cent thought them equal to the Metropolitan Opera House in New York.

Geoffrey Waddington, director of music of the Canadian Broadcasting Company, said: "This hall is quite dead, with a pronounced lack of low frequencies, but there are no major faults."

Arnold Walter, who is on the faculty of music at the University of Toronto, commented: "The sound was never sufficiently vital—not bright enough. Low frequencies are definitely lacking."

My own comments recorded at the time were in part: "Reverberation

EDMONTON AND CALGARY, ALBERTA JUBILEE AUDITORIUMS

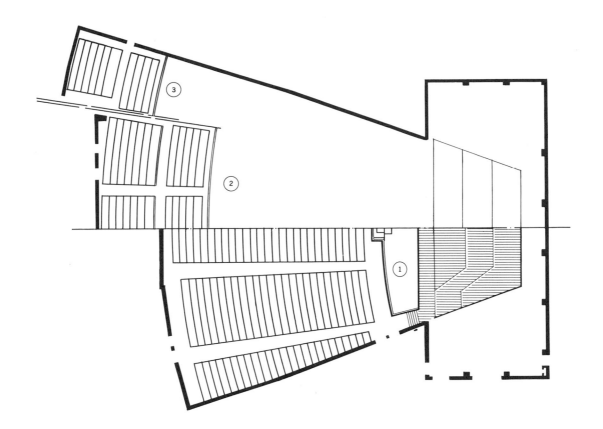

SEATING CAPACITY 2731

(1)   1268
(2)   806
(3)   657

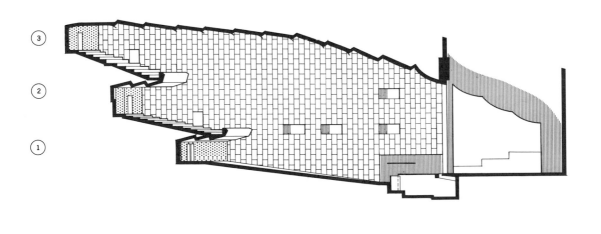

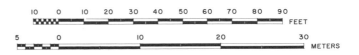

is a very satisfying and wonderful thing. However, one can get pleasure out of a hall that does not take such an active part in the performance. The reverberation at low frequencies in this hall is certainly low compared to that for the middle registers; it would be improved by stiffening the wooden wall panels. The Royal Festival Hall has similar difficulties and is not essentially different acoustically. The Kleinhans Hall in Buffalo is very much like the Alberta Jubilee Auditoriums but with richer bass. The plastic orchestra enclosure seems to reduce the loudness of the low-frequency notes. The enclosure could be improved by making it heavier, say, by adding a mastic vibration-damping material to it. The hall is excellent for speech."

TECHNICAL DETAILS*

Concerts

$V = 759,000$ ft^3	$T_{500-1000}$(Occup.) $= 1.42$ sec	$S_T = 23,000$ ft^2
$N_A = 2731$ seats	$S_A = 21,000$ ft^2	$S_A/N_A = 7.7$ ft^2
$t_I = 31; 8$ msec	$S_O = 2000$ ft^2	$V/S_T = 33.0$ ft

Opera

$V = 723,000$ ft^3	$T_{500-1000}$(Occup.) $= 1.35$ sec	$S_P = 2625$ ft^2
$N_A = 2731$ seats	$S_A = 21,000$ ft^2	$S_T = 24,575$ ft^2
$N_T = 2731$	S_O(Pit) $= 950$ ft^2	$S_A/N_T = 7.7$ ft^2
$t_I = 31; 8$ msec	S_{OF}(Pit) $= 1250$ ft^2	$V/S_T = 29.4$ ft

* The terminology is explained in Appendix 3.

ARCHITECTURAL AND STRUCTURAL DETAILS

Uses: all-purpose; homes of Edmonton and Calgary Symphonies. *Ceiling:* 2 in. of gypsum plaster on metal lath supported from the main structure. *Side walls:* 2 x 4 ft. panels of French walnut plywood, ¼ in. thick, glued to 1½ x 1½ in. frames and mounted 1½ in. from wall on ¾-in. wood furring and ¾-in. wedges; half of the plywood panels have glass fiber batts fastened against the backs of them. *Rear walls:* carpet over plywood with a small amount of diffusion obtained with 145 outward projecting panels. *Floors:* plastic tile on concrete. *Stage enclosure:* four-sided demountable, made of ¹⁄₁₆-in. plastic reinforced with glass fibers riveted to a light aluminum framework. *Stage height:* 42 in. above floor level at first row of seats. *Stage floor:* varnished pine boards; under orchestra, hollow wooden risers. *Carpets:* latex-sealed carpet with underpad in aisles. *Seating:* top of seat-bottoms, front of backrest, and arms are upholstered in foam rubber covered with a densely woven rep. The underseat is solid.

References: T. D. Northwood and E. J. Stevens, *Journal of the Acoustical Society of America,* **30,** 507–516 (1958). W. E. Rossman, M. F. Fayers, and A. B. Steinbrecher, Mimeographed Circular No. 25, *Research Council of Alberta,* 87th Avenue and 114th Street, Edmonton, Alberta (1958). Some details from M. F. Fayers, Architectural Branch of the Department of Public Works of Alberta. Details verified by the author during a visit. *Architect:* Architectural Branch of the Provincial Department of Public Works of Alberta, Ronald Clarke, chief architect, Arnold B. Steinbrecher, project architect, and G. A. Jellinek, senior architect.

Irwin Hoffman had just raised his hand to start the Saturday morning rehearsal of the Vancouver Symphony Orchestra as I entered the hall by a door under the balcony. The violins and the cellos of the 75-piece orchestra sounded clearly as I moved forward and dropped into a red plush seat. My eyes were drawn to the ceiling, which ripples like foamy waves, and to the large organ grilles on either side of the stage.

The architecture of the Queen Elizabeth Theatre has been well received, and has inspired the press to such comments as "breathtakingly fine," "original," and "satisfying," though a few dissidents have characterized it as "busy." The arms of the balcony zigzag downward toward the stage, and they too, like the ceiling, fail to fade into the background. But the 2800 seats are well disposed and the whole has a brilliance and unity that promises gay entertainment.

Since the hall was designed to serve a variety of purposes, with only a small percentage of its use assigned to music, it is not at its best for concerts, particularly for music of the late Classical and Romantic styles. This was anticipated in the following excerpt from a story released to the press prior to the opening by the acoustical consultants.

The Queen Elizabeth Theatre is a general purpose hall in which it is intended that musical events, opera, ballet, drama, and other speech activities will be held. We [Bolt Beranek and Newman Inc.] were informed when the design was initiated that the hall would not always be filled to capacity and that drama must be clearly understandable even with partial hall occupancy. Accordingly, the acoustics of the Queen Elizabeth Theatre were not designed to be optimum for concert music, especially late Classical and Romantic concert music.

Howard Taubman, who attended the dedication concert, wrote in the New York *Times* of July 17, 1959:

The tone, though well balanced, tended to be dry and thin. It was a bit richer upstairs. On the whole, mellowness and warmth were absent. They may appear later on [when the shell is completed]. For the moment one must feel that multi-purpose acoustics are not the ideal solution for strictly musical purposes.

215

VANCOUVER, QUEEN ELIZABETH THEATRE

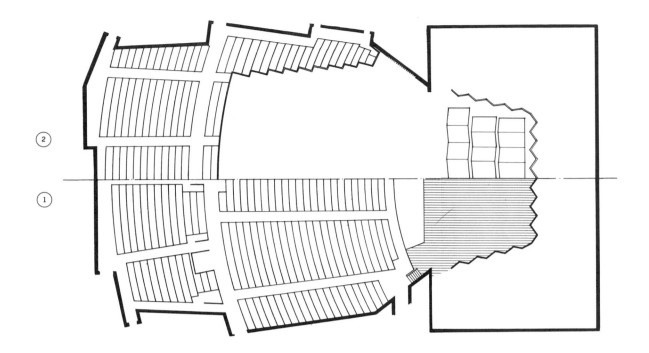

SEATING CAPACITY 2800

① 1818
② 982

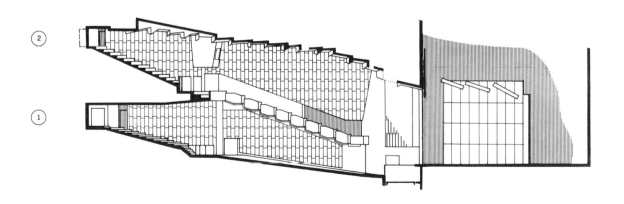

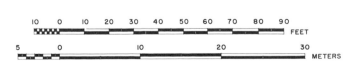

10 0 10 20 30 40 50 60 70 80 90
FEET

5 0 10 20 30
METERS

Even though this theater was designed as a multi-purpose auditorium, most of the touring conductors and artists who have performed in the theater have been satisfied with the results.

Herbert von Karajan, who started his musical career as a pianist and tends to favor dry halls, stated to me in an interview in 1959, "Certainly the Queen Elizabeth Theatre is the best solution for a hall that must serve a variety of purposes. The normal theater hall, if good for opera, is always less good as a concert hall, but Vancouver is excellent for concerts. On stage, when I directed, the impression was of a great volume of sound. A real advantage is the very big stage. Even if the hall is more quiet acoustically than one planned for concerts alone, to me as a conductor it has beautiful reverberance. I also like the ease with which the woodwinds come out from the full orchestra."

Sir Thomas Beecham said, "Your hall is not the best in the world, but it is very much better than most."

Isaac Stern wrote, "Generally speaking, there was almost a clinical accuracy. It was the shortness of the reverberation time that I felt was the hall's chief weakness."

Bruno Walter said, "Acoustically, this hall is very good. It has a nice sound. The music of the orchestra is very well blended. To me, this hall is absolutely satisfactory and sounds beautiful."

Many Vancouver musicians feel that Vancouver needs a concert hall as well as a multi-purpose auditorium. In particular, Irwin Hoffman speaks of his experiences with the Queen Elizabeth Theatre as a concert hall. "The sound is very clear and not at all unpleasant. Piano is excellent. The first problem is with the climaxes. One cannot get deep feeling from the Romantics, probably owing to the relatively short reverberation time. On the podium I hear almost no sound from the hall. Second, the ensemble is not nearly good enough, probably because of the height of the ceiling of the stage enclosure which, as you know, did not follow the design recommended by the acoustical consultants. Third, the basses and the lower strings on the cellos are not strong in tutti passages, giving the strings a somewhat brittle sound."

There is no argument with Mr. Hoffman about the reverberation time for orchestra—it is better suited to Baroque and early Classical than to

Romantic music. Changes in the stage enclosure would improve both the ensemble and the bass. Recommendations have been made, and if they are adopted they should, on the whole, eradicate these defects. For opera the Queen Elizabeth Theatre is nearly ideal.

Selections from reviews of various performances in the hall follow: Eric McLean, Montreal *Star*, July 18, 1959:

> I found the sound most attractive, warmly resonant and yet clear. More that that, one has the sensation of being close to the source and almost surrounded by sound—an odd experience, since the sound in most halls is uni-directional. . . . The quality of the acoustics admits the presentation of smaller theatrical productions besides the most extravagant operas.

Graham George, *The Canadian Music Journal*, Winter 1960 issue:

> The writer [moved] from one part of the hall to another without being able to change the quality or even perceptibly the quantity of the sound. . . . So high a degree of uniformity is a very remarkable achievement.

John Kraglund, *Globe and Mail*, Toronto, July 18, 1959:

> The Queen Elizabeth Theatre proved itself an excellent opera house tonight [during] the first of six performances of Gluck's *Orpheus and Eurydice*.

Stanley Bligh, Vancouver *Sun*, July 20, 1959:

> [The production of Gluck's *Orpheus and Eurydice*] tested the acoustic qualities of the new theatre which proved well-nigh perfect.

TECHNICAL DETAILS*

Concerts

$V = 592{,}000 \text{ ft}^3$	$T_{500-1000}(\text{Occup.}) = 1.5 \text{ sec}$	$S_T = 21{,}300 \text{ ft}^2$
$N_A = 2800$ seats	$S_A = 19{,}300 \text{ ft}^2$	$S_A/N_A = 6.9 \text{ ft}^2$
$t_I = 24; 6 \text{ msec}$	$S_O = 2000 \text{ ft}^2$	$V/S_T = 27.8 \text{ ft}$

Opera

$V = 525{,}500 \text{ ft}^3$	$T_{500-1000}(\text{Occup.}) = 1.35 \text{ sec}$	$S_P = 2215 \text{ ft}^2$
$N_A = 2800$ seats	$S_A = 19{,}300 \text{ ft}^2$	$S_T = 22{,}100 \text{ ft}^2$
$N_T = 2800$	$S_O(\text{Pit}) = 585 \text{ ft}^2$	$S_A/N_T = 6.9 \text{ ft}^2$
$t_I = 24; 6 \text{ msec}$	$S_{OF}(\text{Pit}) = 785 \text{ ft}^2$	$V/S_T = 23.8 \text{ ft}$

* The terminology is explained in Appendix 3.

ARCHITECTURAL AND STRUCTURAL DETAILS

Uses: general purpose 75%, orchestra 15%, opera 5%, recital 5%. *Ceiling:* ⅞-in. gypsum vermiculite plaster, shaped to provide uniform distribution of sound and reflections of sound back to the stage. *Side walls:* two-thirds are ½ to ¾-in. wood; one-third is a laminate of plywood and gypsum board, ¾ in. to 1½ in. thick. *Rear wall:* ½-in. gypsum board over glass fibers. *Floors:* concrete. *Stage enclosure:* side walls are ½-in. plywood; ceiling panels are ¾-in. plywood. *Stage height:* 41 in. above the level of the floor at the first row of seats. *Orchestra pit:* wooden floor, hard side walls. *Seating:* front of the backrest and top of the seat-bottom are upholstered; underseat is perforated. *Carpet:* on all aisles over underpad.

References: Russell Johnson, "Acoustical Design of the Queen Elizabeth Theatre," to be submitted to *Journal of the Acoustical Society of America.* Drawings from the files of Bolt Beranek and Newman Inc. Photographs and some details from I. H. Dobbin, manager of the theater. Details verified during a visit by author. *Architect:* Lebensold, Desbarats, Affleck, Michaud and Sise.

The Radiohuset is used primarily for broadcasts. The stage and the great organ dominate the room, and the audience area is small compared to a conventional concert hall. The very high ceiling and the short main floor add to the disproportion. Studio 1 has had a satisfactory history and continues to serve Denmark's radio audiences as one of their principal sources of concert music.

The reverberation time in Studio 1 is a little low by present-day standards, although there have been few complaints about lack of liveness. Before 1958 the musicians and the audience on the main floor murmured of a lack of intimacy and definition. The musicians felt they did not hear each other well and that the ensemble was not good. In 1959 flat glass panels were hung over the stage. The musicians now hear each other better and the audience on the main floor receives a more intimate sound.

One conductor said, "There is good blend in the audience area, but some musicians on the stage do not hear other sections of the orchestra. The suspended panels have not completely corrected the acoustics of this studio."

The other conductors and critics interviewed remember this hall as it was before the glass panels were installed, and no recent assessments were available. Most of the musicians who play there regularly say they are pleased with the change.

In the spring of 1960 after the glass panels were installed, I heard an orchestra rehearsal in Studio 1. The sound in the empty hall was quite loud—louder than I had expected. My chief complaint was the lack of orchestral balance. The percussion and brass overpowered the strings, probably because of the fairly low panels over the percussion and the hard surrounding wall areas. In looking back at some old photographs of the hall, I note that in 1946 twelve sound-absorbing panels, each about 6 feet wide and 5 feet high, stood around the rear of the stage just in front of the walls behind the orchestra. Those panels must have been provided to improve the orchestral balance. One wonders why they were not in use the day I was there, since they probably would have improved the orchestral balance considerably.

COPENHAGEN, RADIOHUSET, STUDIO 1

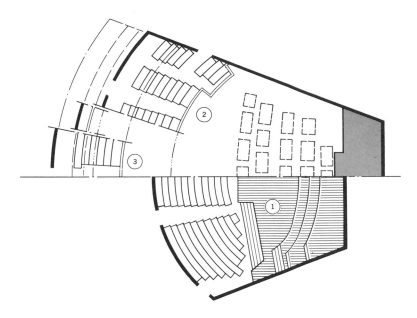

SEATING CAPACITY 1093

(1)   380
(2)   375
(3)   338

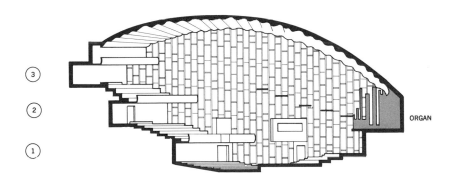

ORGAN

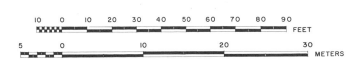

10   0   10   20   30   40   50   60   70   80   90
FEET

5   0   10   20   30
METERS

TECHNICAL DETAILS FOR CONCERTS[*]

$V = 420{,}000 \text{ ft}^3$ $T_{500-1000}(\text{Occup.}) = 1.5 \text{ sec}$ $S_T = 11{,}000 \text{ ft}^2$

$N_A = 1093 \text{ seats}$ $S_A = 8700 \text{ ft}^2$ $S_A/N_A = 8.0 \text{ ft}^2$

$t_I = 29; 27 \text{ msec}$ $S_O = 2300 \text{ ft}^2$ $V/S_T = 38.2 \text{ ft}$

[*] The terminology is explained in Appendix 3.

ARCHITECTURAL AND STRUCTURAL DETAILS

Uses: orchestra with some organ. *Ceiling:* wood in contact with plastered reinforced concrete; the concrete is 3 in. thick. *Side walls:* wood panels, ⅝ in. thick; half of the panels have air space behind; the other half are directly on concrete. *Rear wall:* same as the side walls on the floor and first-balcony levels; on second-balcony level, the rear wall is covered with ⅝-in. wood panels with air space behind. *Stage floor:* the lower part consists of wood directly on concrete; the rear part of wood on risers with a large air space beneath. *Stage height:* 26 in. above the floor at the first row of seats. *Floors:* wood parquet on concrete. *Added absorbing material:* to remove possible acoustic resonance between the floor and ceiling, about 250 helmholtz resonators are installed in the ceiling, half of which are tuned to about 63 cps and the others to about 93 cps. *Seating:* the tops and bottoms of the seats and the fronts of the backrests are upholstered in leather.

References: Arkitecten, published by the Academy of Architecture, Copenhagen, 1946. Private communication from V. L. Jordan, Copenhagen. Details confirmed by author during visits. *Architect:* Vilhelm Lauritzen.

In keeping with the spirit of the Tivoli entertainment park in Copenhagen, this new concert hall with 1789 seats is gay and intimate. Fan-shaped, with a small balcony that extends down the sides, this little theater seems particularly suited to drama and musical comedy. It is the home of the Tivoli Concert Hall Orchestra.

For orchestral concerts the reverberation time is short. But because it is narrow, the Tivoli Koncertsal overcomes some of the difficulties of the Kleinhans Hall in Buffalo, the Alberta Jubilee Halls in Canada, and the Royal Festival Hall in London, which also have reverberation times of 1.5 seconds or less. Music played in the Tivoli Concert Hall is intimate and warm.

Four of the music critics interviewed had heard concerts at Tivoli. One said, "This is a good little hall, quite homogeneous acoustically. I had the impression of its being a very bright, yet respectably warm, hall." No one of the other three music critics was quite as enthusiastic about the sound. The short reverberation time may well underlie their apathy.

Two conductors spoke favorably, but briefly, about the acoustics. Eugene Ormandy commented, "Very good sound. Of course, music always sounds good in small halls."

And Tauno Hannikainen said, "It is quite different from other halls, but the sound is good."

TECHNICAL DETAILS FOR CONCERTS[*]

$V = 450,000 \text{ ft}^3$ $T_{500-1000}(\text{Occup.}) = 1.3 \text{ sec}$ $S_T = 14,340 \text{ ft}^2$

$N_A = 1789 \text{ seats}$ $S_A = 12,230 \text{ ft}^2$ $S_A/N_A = 6.8 \text{ ft}^2$

$t_I = 16; 14 \text{ msec}$ $S_O = 2100 \text{ ft}^2$ $V/S_T = 31.0 \text{ ft}$

[*] The terminology is explained in Appendix 3.

ARCHITECTURAL AND STRUCTURAL DETAILS

Uses: orchestra, occasionally soloists, general entertainment. *Ceiling:* gypsum with a surface covering of fiberboard. *Side walls:* ⅝-in. wooden panels with air space behind; the side wall panels are mounted in sections parallel to the main axis of the hall. *Rear walls:* main floor is inclined

COPENHAGEN, TIVOLI KONCERTSAL

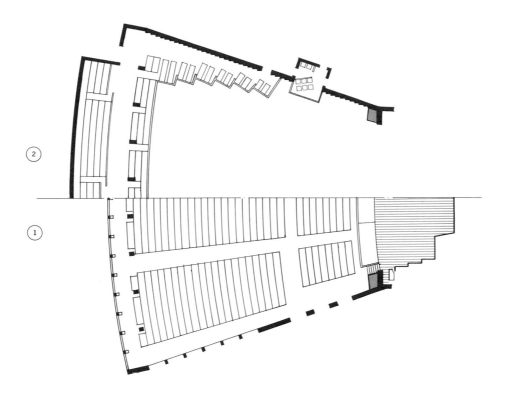

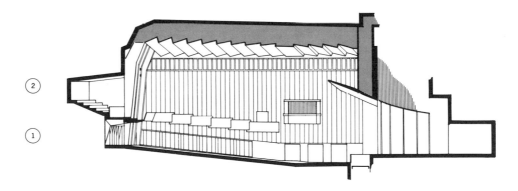

SEATING CAPACITY 1789

1   1316

2   467 + 6 in Royal box

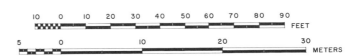

glass; upper level is wooden panels and plaster on concrete. *Floors:* tile on concrete and tile on wood on risers. *Stage enclosure:* ⅝-in. wooden panels; ceiling is wooden panels, turned vertical when stage is used for theatricals. *Stage floor:* wood on risers. *Stage height:* 38 in. above the floor level at the first row of seats. *Seating:* upholstered on both sides of backrest and top of seat-bottom. Underseat is perforated.

References: Private communication and photographs from V. L. Jordan, Copenhagen. Some details verified by author during a visit. *Architect:* Fritz Schlegel and Hans Hansen.

Helsinki's Kulttuuritalo is visually exciting both inside and out. Because the shape of its ceiling provides the essential short initial-time-delay gaps, this hall sounds much better than its low reverberation time and the wide fan shape of its plan would suggest.

A small orchestra of the Helsinki Broadcasting Company was rehearsing during my visit to the Kulttuuritalo. I had an opportunity to talk with Tauno Hannikainen, Director of the Helsinki City Symphony Orchestra, during the rehearsal. In his opinion this is the best concert hall in Helsinki; the musicians hear each other well and there is good contact with the audience. According to Hannikainen, a piano sounds better here than anywhere else in Finland; the upper registers are strong and clear, and the acoustics do not change appreciably when an audience is added.

In my opinion, this hall, at least as I heard it without an audience, is very good: the definition is excellent, and the music has adequate bass. The distribution of the sound through the hall is uniform. With an audience the hall may be somewhat dead.

David Oistrakh, the violinist, said, "It is wonderfully easy and pleasant to play in this hall, which has excellent acoustics. The sound is initiated and grows easily, freely and naturally. The color and dynamics of the performance are fully preserved."

TECHNICAL DETAILS FOR CONCERTS*

$V = 354,000$ ft^3 $T_{500-1000}$(Occup.) $= 1.05$ sec $S_T = 11,970$ ft^2

$N_A = 1500$ seats $S_A = 10,180$ ft^2 $S_A/N_A = 6.8$ ft^2

$t_I = 26; 17$ msec $S_O = 1790$ ft^2 $V/S_T = 29.6$ ft

* The terminology is explained in Appendix 3.

ARCHITECTURAL AND STRUCTURAL DETAILS

Uses: concerts, meetings, and conventions. *Ceiling:* 1 to 1¾-in. concrete with plaster. *Side walls:* partly concrete with wood strips in front to achieve sound diffusion; partly ⅞-in. wooden panels with about 6-in. air space behind. *Rear wall:* partly ⅞-in. wooden reflectors; partly concrete.

HELSINKI, KULTTUURITALO

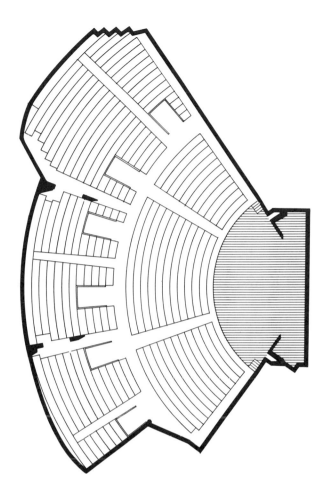

SEATING CAPACITY 1500

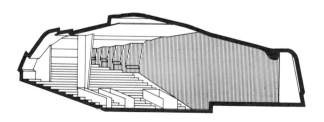

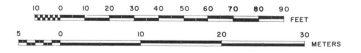

Floors: on the main floor, ⅞-in. flooring over 2-in. air space; in stadium, concrete with linoleum. *Stage floor:* 1¾-in. wood over about 30-in. air space. *Stage height:* 34½ in. above the floor level at the first row of seats. *Stage enclosure:* 1-in. wood, plastered, slightly slanted, and with cylindrical diffusers; ceiling 1-in. wood, plastered. *Seating:* top of seat-bottom and front of backrest are upholstered; underseat is perforated plywood.

References: Drawings from Alvar Aalto. Details from Paavo Arni, Finnish Broadcasting Company, Helsinki. Photographs by Kuvatyö Oy. Details verified by author during visit. *Architect:* Alvar Aalto.

On a cold, sunny winter day, we drove from Helsinki to Turku to visit the northernmost concert hall of this study. Except for the large glass windows in the facade, the hall suggests a fortress—a huge sculptured rock on the outside and many heavy columns in the main lower lobbies. Even the interior of the hall—monolithic white plaster—gives the feeling of being carved from frozen milk.

We found Peter Lacovich rehearsing the 50-piece Turku Symphony Orchestra and took the opportunity to listen in all parts of the hall. Acoustically, it does not achieve its full potentialities. It is amenable to improvement, but some experimentation would be required to know how to effect an improvement economically. Four things were obvious. First, the brass was so dominant that the strings could hardly be heard during loud passages. Second, there was some harshness in the upper registers of the strings. Third, the sound was not warm—it seemed to lack bass. And fourth, there was a small echo from the rear wall. Admittedly, some of these difficulties arose from the orchestra, which would profit from a larger string section, especially more violins and double basses.

After the rehearsal I met with the local music critics, and we talked of the paucity of stringed instruments and of means for reducing the echo. To remove the harshness, however, is more complex and needs further study. It may be that the harshness is largely a matter of orchestral balance, but it is also related to the corrugated side walls which could be modified to remove some of the acoustical "glare." The echo could be reduced by some changes in the design of the rear wall, for example, the addition of some sound-absorbing materials on the focusing area at the rear.

The conductors who have listened in this hall agree that it is not performing at its best, but none of them gave it a detailed rating. Peter Lacovich felt, along with the other conductors, that on the podium the orchestra sounds in good balance. Leonard Bernstein said that it is above the median of the halls of the world in which he has conducted.

TURKU, KONSERTTISALI

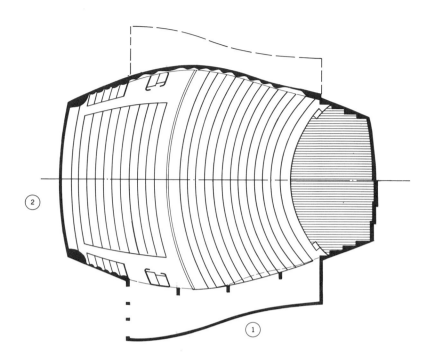

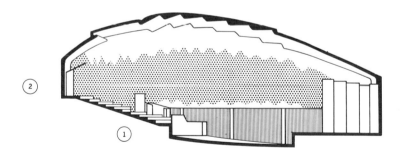

SEATING CAPACITY 1002

(1) 631

(2) 371

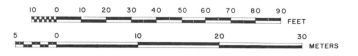

| 10 | 0 | 10 | 20 | 30 | 40 | 50 | 60 | 70 | 80 | 90 |
FEET

| 5 | 0 | 10 | 20 | 30 |
METERS

TECHNICAL DETAILS FOR CONCERTS*

$V = 340,000 \text{ ft}^3$ $T_{500-1000}(\text{Occup.}) = 1.6 \text{ sec}$ $S_T = 9750 \text{ ft}^2$

$N_A = 1002 \text{ seats}$ $S_A = 8000 \text{ ft}^2$ $S_A/N_A = 8.0 \text{ ft}^2$

$t_I = 37; 24 \text{ msec}$ $S_O = 1750 \text{ ft}^2$ $V/S_T = 35.0 \text{ ft}$

* The terminology is explained in Appendix 3.

ARCHITECTURAL AND STRUCTURAL DETAILS

Uses: general music. *Ceiling:* ½-in. wood with ⅝-in. plaster; the ceiling is vaulted. In the entrance corridors, the ceilings are sound-absorbent to reduce floor-ceiling resonances. *Sides walls:* 57% of the side walls are constructed as follows: ⅝-in. plaster on ½-in. wood, all perforated with holes 1 in. in diameter and spaced 4 in. apart. This layer is spaced 12 to 18 in. away from the concrete outer walls of the auditorium. One inch behind the perforated layer is a 1-in. layer of rockwool. Two inches behind the perforated layer is a layer of ½-in. wood. Finally, there is a 1-in. layer of rockwool against the concrete wall. The remainder of the side walls are ½-in. wood with ⅝-in. plaster on the surface; the side walls of the entrance corridors are wooden panels with air space behind. *Rear wall:* the front of the balcony and part of the rear wall are heavily absorbent. *Floors:* linoleum on concrete. *Stage enclosure:* wooden panels with air space behind. *Stage height:* 35 in. above the floor level at the first row of seats. *Seating:* top side of seats and front of backrests are upholstered; underseat perforated.

References: Plans and details from Paavo Arni, Finnish Broadcasting Company. Details confirmed by author during visit. Photographs courtesy of Nestor Lehtinen, manager of the Turku Concert Hall. *Architect:* R. V. Luukkonen.

This famous opera house, which opened in 1875, was designed by the architect Charles Garnier. Garnier pursued diligently the elusive factors of good acoustics, but in his book, *The Grand Opera in Paris*, he confesses that he finally trusted to luck, "like the acrobat who closes his eyes and clings to the ropes of an ascending balloon." *"Eh bien!"* he concludes, *"Je suis arrivé!"*

The Paris Opéra has very good acoustics—not the finest but very good. Garnier said, "The credit is not mine. I merely wear the marks of honor." He continues, "It is not my fault that acoustics and I can never come to an understanding. I gave myself great pains to master this bizarre science, but after fifteen years of labor, I found myself hardly in advance of where I stood on the first day. . . . I had read diligently in my books, and conferred industriously with philosophers—nowhere did I find a positive rule of action to guide me; on the contrary, nothing but contradictory statements. For long months, I studied, questioned everything, but after this travail, finally I made this discovery. A room to have good acoustics must be either long or broad, high or low, of wood or stone, round or square, and so forth." Garnier added, "Chance seems as dominant in the theatrical world as it is in the dream world in which a child enters Wonderland!"

The baroque interior of the Théatre National de l'Opéra combines tan-gold plaster "carvings" and gold trim with burgundy-red plush upholstery and box linings. The allegorical paintings on the ceiling, beneath which hangs a grand chandelier, place this theater in an age of elegance far removed from the frugal reconstruction of La Scala or the almost chaste interior of the Vienna Staatsoper. On the main floor, there are only 21 closely spaced rows, the last 8 of which are elevated above those in front. The architectural effect of this raised area is to foreshorten the main floor and give the hall an intimate appearance.

The acoustics of the Théatre de l'Opéra are no mystery today. Even better opera houses could be designed. But in order for a house to surpass the Paris Opéra, its audience area would have to be small. In the Paris house, the audience area is 12,000 square feet, which would seat 1700 people by New York's more luxurious seating standards. The cubic volume of the

PARIS, THÉATRE NATIONAL DE L'OPÉRA

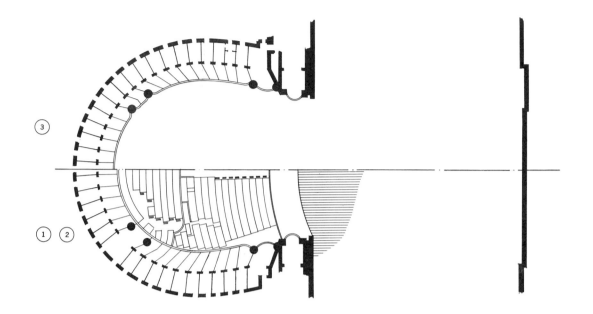

SEATING CAPACITY 2131

(1)	787
(2)	£40
(3)	242
(4)	268
(5)	588 + standees

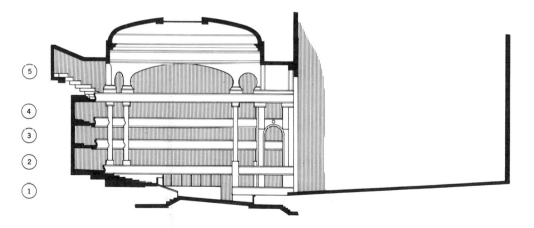

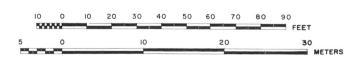

Paris Opéra is half that of the Metropolitan Opera House. Eighty-six of its 2131 seats fold down into the aisles during performances.

Most of the conductors who were interviewed reported that from the pit the music sounds excellent. The portion of the domed ceiling that faces the pit reflects the sound of the orchestra back to the conductor, and to him the crescendos sound wonderful. The singers also can hear their own voices reflected back, clear and loud. Herbert von Karajan said: "The acoustics of the Paris Opera House are marvelous. The ceiling brings back a beautiful tone to the conductor and the crescendos are beautiful."

The music critics rated the Opéra "very good," but not as good as Vienna or Milan. Not all the audience hears the music equally well. Because of the domed ceiling, the sound is unevenly distributed. The orchestra pit must be shallow in order to preserve the violin tone, which otherwise would not be heard in the rear of the parquet because of the unfavorable shape of the ceiling. It is said by the regular opera-goers that the orchestra has a tendency to dominate the singers. The best seats are in the front rows of the upper two rings, opposite the stage.

TECHNICAL DETAILS FOR OPERA[*]

$V = 352,000 \text{ ft}^3$ $T_{500-1000}(\text{Occup.}) = 1.1 \text{ sec}$[†] $S_P = 2538 \text{ ft}^2$
$N_A = 2131 \text{ seats}$ $S_A = 12,120 \text{ ft}^2$ $S_T = 15,500 \text{ ft}^2$
$N_T = 2231$ $S_O(\text{Pit}) = 840 \text{ ft}^2$ $S_A/N_T = 5.4 \text{ ft}^2$
$t_I = 17; 15 \text{ msec}$ $V/S_T = 22.7 \text{ ft}$

[*] The terminology is explained in Appendix 3.
[†] Estimated.

ARCHITECTURAL AND STRUCTURAL DETAILS

Uses: opera and ballet. *Ceiling:* dome is ³⁄₃₂-in. steel; above the top level (amphitheater) the ceiling is plaster; ceilings of the boxes are stretched damask cloth 1 in. away from the plaster. *Walls:* all visible surfaces (faces of the rings, columns, capitals, and so forth) are of plaster; the dividers between boxes are ½-in. wood covered with damask; inside and top of the balcony railing are covered with plush; rear of boxes are separated from cloak room by velour curtains; walls at the rear of the amphitheater are of plaster. The front of the rail dividing the main floor is of wood; rear is lined with carpet. *Floors:* wood throughout house. *Orchestra pit:* floor is of wood over air space; side walls are of solid wood. *Carpets:* main floor and all boxes fully carpeted; no carpet in amphitheater. *Note:* cyclorama on stage is of aluminum with canvas facing. *Seating:* Main floor: fully upholstered on all surfaces except for wood trim. Boxes: upholstered chairs. Amphitheater: seat-bottoms fully upholstered, backrests are of open wood.

References: Drawings and seating plan courtesy A. M. Julien, administrator général de La Réunion des Théatres Lyriques Nationaux. Photographs courtesy of Théatre National de l'Opéra. Roy McMullen, "New Deal at the Paris Opera," *High Fidelity Magazine,* January 1961. Details obtained by author during visits. *Architect:* Charles Garnier.

The Festspielhaus in Bayreuth is probably the world's most unusual opera house. Its design is unique; it was conceived by the composer Richard Wagner to satisfy his own image of how an opera house should look and sound; and it responds well only to the music of its master and best to *Der Ring des Nibelungen* and *Parsifal*. If ever a composer built his own world of music, this is it—a house for his music only, and his music at its best only in that house!

When Wagner was about 25 years old, he conducted in the town of Riga in a theater characterized as "old and paltry," but which he liked. There were three points, he said, that he remembered especially about this "barn": the steep rise of the seats in the form of an amphitheater, the sunken orchestra, and the handling of the lights. These three features are conspicuous in the Bayreuth Festspielhaus. For many years Wagner dreamed of his own opera house. When he began to plan it in 1863, he wrote in a letter: "Here [in one of Germany's smaller towns] a provisional theater would be erected, as simple as possible, perhaps entirely of wood, with only the interior designed for artistic purposes. I had discussed with a gifted and experienced architect plans which envisaged an auditorium in the shape of an amphitheater and also the great advantage of the sunken orchestra."

In 1876, Wagner's dream of a building for his operas solidified into reality. *Der Ring des Nibelungen* was performed at the dedication. Hans Richter conducted. Not only does the sunken pit (shown in the drawings) project under the stage, but the conductor and the strings are under a solid wooden cover. Their music radiates outward from a slot over the middle of the orchestra which extends from one end of the pit to the other. The whole orchestra is out of sight and the men can play, unseen, in their shirtsleeves!

The appearance of the hall is no less interesting than the story behind it. The seating area of the audience is fan-shaped, but the side walls of the theater are parallel. To fill in the progressively wider space between the walls and the seats toward the front of the hall, a series of seven piers is employed, each one penetrating deeper into the hall than the one behind

BAYREUTH, FESTSPIELHAUS

it, and each capped by a column that extends to capitals just beneath the ceiling. Although the ceiling is flat (I have checked it by walking in the attic space above it), one has the impression that it rises from the back toward the front, like a great awning stretched over a Greek amphitheater.

The average height of the ceiling above the sloping floor of the Festspielhaus is great, with the result that the reverberation time is long— longer than that of any other opera house described in this book. It is 1.6 seconds at middle frequencies when the theater is fully occupied, which is especially favorable to Romantic Wagnerian music.

The sunken-pit design is the center of endless controversy. One purpose of the sunken pit is to give greater balance between the singers and the orchestra. But this was not the only feature Wagner had in mind. He desired the unusual and dramatic effect of a "mystical abyss." He expected to create acoustically a mysterious sound, emanating from an invisible orchestra, with a modified, somewhat uncanny timbre. One can easily conclude that the overriding purpose of the Bayreuth pit was to emphasize the drama, rather than to preserve the vocal-orchestral balance.

One conductor who has directed many performances there does not like it. He feels that, although the sound is wonderful inside the pit, the string tone is completely lost on the outside and poor musical quality results. The balance between the singers and the orchestra, he feels, could be achieved by the conductor just as well.

Bruno Walter, when questioned, reminisced, "The last time that I attended a festival in Bayreuth I listened in the audience to a performance of *Der Fliegende Holländer* directed by another conductor. I was disappointed in the power of the orchestra. Also I found that the violin tone was not good from the audience."

There is no question that the closed pit with an overhang above the violins greatly reduces the sound of the violins to the audience. However, part of the appeal of the Festspielhaus results from this peculiar kind of blending of the sound of the Festspiel orchestra, which numbers over 100 members.

It is instructive to attend *Das Rheingold* with Joseph Wechsberg, who

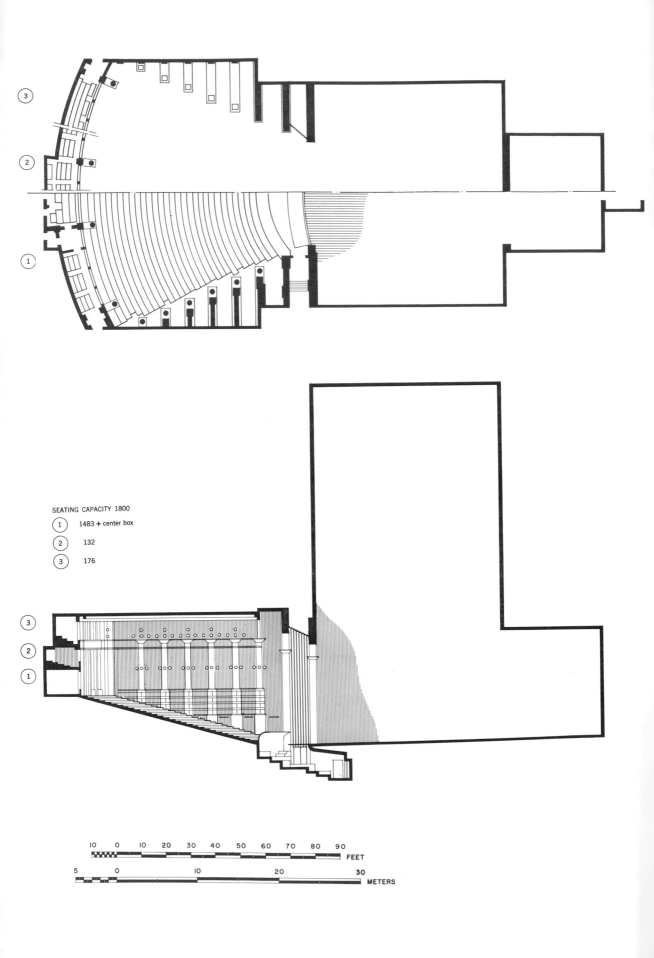

SEATING CAPACITY 1800

(1)   1483 + center box

(2)   132

(3)   176

10 0 10 20 30 40 50 60 70 80 90
FEET

5 0 10 20 30
METERS

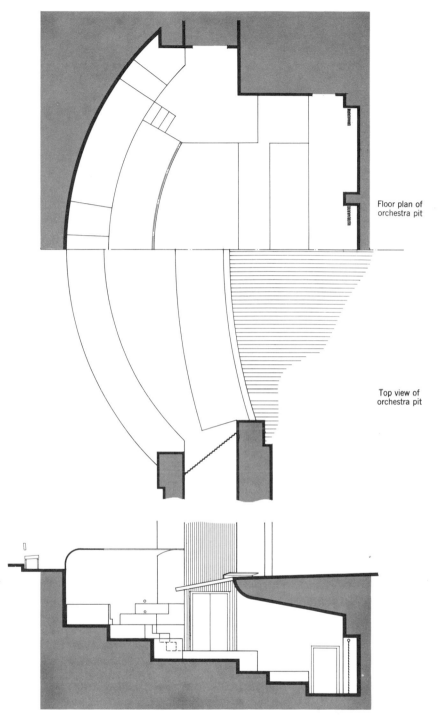

Floor plan of
orchestra pit

Top view of
orchestra pit

Cross section

described his experience in the August 18, 1956, issue of *The New Yorker* magazine:

Then there was silence, and out of the darkness came a sustained E flat—so low that I couldn't distinguish exactly when the silence ended and sound began. Nor could I be sure where the sound came from; it might have come from the sides of the auditorium, or the rear, or the ceiling. It was just there. Slowly the orchestra began to play melodic passages, barely audible at first and gradually increasing in volume until the auditorium was filled with music—the music of the waters of the Rhine. When the curtain parted, the whole stage seemed filled with water—blue-green waves, ebbing and flowing in precise synchronization with the music. The Rhine Maidens appeared from behind a rock, pretty, slim and wearing golden one-piece bathing suits, the music rose, and fell back to the pianissimo; and Woglinde started her "Weia! Waga!" It took me a moment to realize that there were no props and no stage set; the whole scene—rock and all—were created by means of projected film and light. The music, the singing, the waters, and the lights blended perfectly. Although the brass dominated, it did not sound brassy, as it often does in the large orchestra Wagner calls for. By accident or design, the strings, particularly the first violins, were somewhat subdued but that was a very minor flaw—if, indeed, it was a flaw. I was under a spell. . . .

Of listening in the pit, Mr. Wechsberg wrote:

Keilberth pushed his hair back and raised his baton. His downbeat was followed by a crashing fortissimo that made me jump. The brassy clamor was amplified a hundred times by the walls of the pit, and it seemed inconceivable that this horrible racket should emerge in the auditorium as pure tonal beauty. I hastily left the pit.

Wagner's grandson, Wieland Wagner, who with his brother Wolfgang manages the festival today, said: "We have plenty of reforms on our agenda. Last year—cautiously, to be sure—I took up a taboo question, acoustics. I suggested that if the violinists changed places with the viola players, we would get a brighter, stronger, more modern sound. Well, naturally, all the conductors condemned my idea. Sacrilege, they said. So I promised to wait a while, but ultimately we will make the change."

Irving Kolodin, critic for the *Saturday Review*, said during an interview in 1960: "This opera house is wonderful. It yields optimum results for Wagner, particularly for *Parsifal* which sounds better there than anywhere else. The orchestra accommodation is right. I like the Festspielhaus very much."

Most conductors love to perform in the Bayreuth pit. Every note can be heard at the podium. The orchestra can "let out the throttle" and not drown out the singers. They feel that, because the blending of the sound takes place in the pit, it merges in the form intended by the composer.

Dimitri Mitropoulos suggested that the sound in the Festspielhaus would be better if the cover over the violins was either removed or was partly open, perhaps perforated so as to be acoustically open. Herbert von Karajan told me that he tried this experiment in the Bayreuth Festspielhaus more than fifteen years ago. He removed the cover, but he found that, with the rest of the orchestra buried beneath the stage, the result was not satisfactory and the cover was replaced. W. Gabler of the Technical University, Berlin, says that a perforated hood tried recently gave good results, but when objections were raised by one of the conductors, the old hood was re-installed.

In present-day productions, almost no teaser curtains are used and there is a minimum of hanging scenery. Also, a heavy, sound-reflecting cyclorama canvas ordinarily surrounds the acting area. As a result, the stagehouse reverberation is long; the singers' voices project well into the house when the full, undraped height of the proscenium is employed. The stage is lower than the audience, and thus the forestage is important as a sound reflector.

For the highly articulated voice and orchestra of most Italian operas, the Bayreuth house has two unfortunate features. First, the reverberation time is somewhat high, and second, the string tone is muffled by the cover over the pit. Italian opera is more successful in an opera house of the type of Milan's La Scala or Vienna's Staatsoper.

The Bayreuth Festspielhaus contains no other unusual features. The interior finish is generally of plaster, either on brick or on wood lath. The ceiling combines wood and plaster. The horizontal ceiling contributes short-time-delay reflections at most seats. The projecting wings on the sides of the hall give a desirable mixing of the sound in the house. The Prinzregenten-theater in Munich is superficially similar in shape but does not have projecting wings—its side walls are located along the edge of the seats—

and the sound there is less satisfactory. The Festspielhaus is small—it seats only 1800 persons—and thus its size alone favors its acoustical quality.

TECHNICAL DETAILS FOR OPERA*

$V = 364{,}000 \text{ ft}^3$	$T_{500-1000}(\text{Occup.}) = 1.55 \text{ sec}$	$S_P = 1638 \text{ ft}^2$
$N_A = 1800 \text{ seats}$	$S_A = 8500 \text{ ft}^2$	$S_T = 10{,}509 \text{ ft}^2$
$N_T = 1800$	$S_O(\text{Pit}) = 371 \text{ ft}^2$	$S_A/N_T = 4.7 \text{ ft}^2$
$t_I = 14; 4 \text{ msec}$	$S_{OF}(\text{Pit}) = 1485 \text{ ft}^2$	$V/S_T = 34.6 \text{ ft}$

* The terminology is explained in Appendix 3.

ARCHITECTURAL AND STRUCTURAL DETAILS

Uses: Wagner opera. *Ceiling:* ½-in. plaster on reeds on ½-in. wood, with wooden carvings used as decorations. *Rear and side walls:* plaster on brick or on wood lath; the round columns and part of their capitals are of thick wood; the wing nearest the stage is closed off with corrugated asbestos sheet. *Floors:* wood. *Pit:* floor and ceiling of wood; rear wall under stage is of concrete, covered with unlined heavy velour curtains that can be pulled on a 4-cm rod. *Seating:* seats are wood with woven cane bottoms.

References: Drawings from Edwin O. Sachs, *Modern Opera Houses and Theatres,* Vol. I., London, B. T. Batsford, 1896–1897. Recent modifications of hall were verified during author's visit. Seating count from a box-office plan and other details, courtesy of Frau Suchanek, Secretary. Photographs by Lauterwasser, Uberlingen/Bodensee. Pit drawings were developed from measurements by the author during a visit. *Architect:* Otto Brückwald.

Berlin
BENJAMIN FRANKLIN
KONGRESSHALLE

About ten years after the end of World War II, the United States Government built the Benjamin Franklin Congress Hall near the Brandenburg Gate and presented it as a symbol of free speech to the City of West Berlin. At the simple and impressive dedication ceremony in October 1957, all 1220 of its seats were filled by official visitors. A string ensemble played before the speeches began. The American architect Hugh Stubbins praised German workmanship and gave the key of the building to the new owners. Speeches followed, by Ralph Walker, Chairman of the Benjamin Franklin Foundation, and Franz Amrehn, Acting Mayor of West Berlin. Clare Boothe Luce, then United States Ambassador to Italy, spoke, saying that the Hall should stand as a symbol of freedom in the city of West Berlin, which itself is a symbol of freedom. All could be heard clearly; only the faintest babble from the headphones of the simultaneous translation system served as a mild distraction.

The hall is modern in appearance. The ceiling has a double curvature, downward at the ends and upward at the sides, thus avoiding the "dome" acoustics of many contemporary halls. Sound-reflecting surfaces behind vertical slats and a canopy over the podium guide the sound uniformly to all parts of the auditorium.

Professor Lothar Cremer of the University of Berlin wrote to me after the opening:

I listened to three modern opera sketches conducted by Hermann Scherchen. Although the room was certainly not built for musical performances, these special musical dramas sounded excellent. The voices were reinforced by the wooden backwalls of the stage and, moreover, by the well-formed ceiling and perhaps also by the unseen reflectors behind the wood lattice. The orchestra never masked the singers' voices as is sometimes found in opera houses. Prof. Hermann Scherchen, the conductor, was so enthusiastic about the room that I asked him to write to you. Also, a string quartet recital was given in the hall. I, personally, did not hear it but my colleague, Prof. H. Stuckenschmidt, who is a well-known music critic in Berlin, said that it sounded very fine. The Franklin Hall is regarded as a full success.

Hermann Scherchen wrote in his letter:

It is with great pleasure that I am presently performing three operas— Stravinsky's *Mavra*, Blacher's *Abstrakte Opera No. 1*, and Hindemith's

BERLIN, BENJAMIN FRANKLIN KONGRESSHALLE

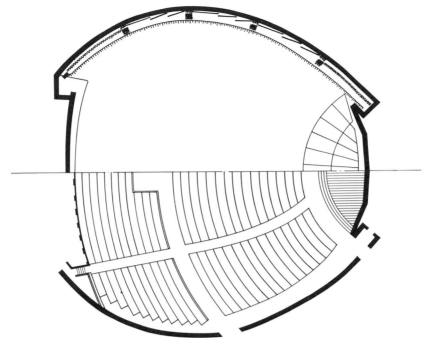

SEATING CAPACITY 1220

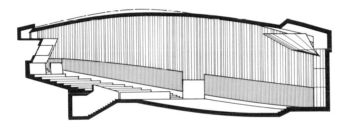

Longitudinal section

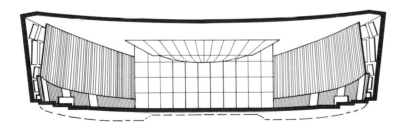

Cross section

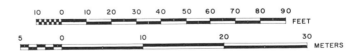

Hin und Züruck, in the new Congress Hall in Berlin, and that I am able, from a practical standpoint, to evaluate the acoustics which you have designed for the hall.

Many technical people had said that since the hall was primarily constructed for speaking purposes, it could not be good for music, having too little reverberation. My first impression of the Hall was an immediate surprise—its acoustics possess a transparency for sound, which makes everything acoustically comfortable and sensitive, *with* the necessary reverberation.

I have seated my orchestra so that all the brass and winds do not blow directly into the public, but parallel to both the public and the wooden stage panels. As a result of this seating arrangement, in the Stravinsky and the Blacher, where there are 4 trumpets and 4 trombones, the sound remains excellent in quality and delicate in timbre. Above all, because the auditorium was planned for large-scale speech clarity, from the theatrical viewpoint, when the singers are forward on the stage, the acoustical results are better than in most opera houses.

H. Alwyn Inness-Brown wrote in *Chapter One* (February 1958):

That evening [September 19, 1957] a concert was given by Eileen Farrell, dramatic soprano, accompanied by George Trovillo. Her glorious voice clearly demonstrated the perfect acoustics of the auditorium.

There is little to add to these comments. The hall is particularly suited to music of the Baroque style, which demands an articulation comparable to that of speech—and to Italian opera. It is not the best hall for music of the Romantic period, as indeed it was not designed to be. But its rich warm bass gives it a quality quite unlike many other contemporary halls whose sound is brittle because of a deficiency in bass.

TECHNICAL DETAILS FOR CONCERT OPERA[*]

$V = 457{,}500 \text{ ft}^3$	$T_{500-1000}(\text{Occup.}) = 1.2 \text{ sec}$	$S_T = 11{,}300 \text{ ft}^2$
$N_A = 1220 \text{ seats}$	$S_A = 10{,}300 \text{ ft}^2$	$S_A/N_A = 8.4 \text{ ft}^2$
$t_I = 25; 19 \text{ msec}$	$S_O = 1000 \text{ ft}^2$	$V/S_T = 40.5 \text{ ft}$

[*] The terminology is explained in Appendix 3.

ARCHITECTURAL AND STRUCTURAL DETAILS

Uses: meetings, lectures, and recitals. *Ceiling:* plaster on wire lath. *Side walls:* vertical strips of wood, about 50% open area, behind which are

½-in. asbestos-board panels in flat sections. About half the side-wall area is in panels, the other half is 2-in. glass fiberboard cemented to the outside wall. *Rear wall:* lower section behind seats, vertical strips of wood, about 50% open area, behind which is a 2-in. layer of glass wool over a 3-in. air space. *Floors:* carpet over concrete, covers entire floor in front half and aisles only in rear half. *Stage height:* 24 in. above the level of the floor at the first row of seats. *Canopy:* partly plywood with cloth-covered open portion to permit penetration by sound from the loudspeakers. *Seating:* all seats fully upholstered; undersides of seat-bottom solid.

References: Records of Bolt Beranek and Newman Inc. Photographs courtesy architect. All data verified during visit by author. *Architect:* Hugh Stubbins. *Associated architect:* Werner Duettmann and Franz Mocken.

The remarkable period of post-war recovery in Germany has witnessed a restoration of the German people's musical traditions. Concert halls, opera houses, and chamber-music salons have risen everywhere. Berlin is no exception. A new opera house was opened in 1961 and a new Philharmonic Hall is now under construction.

The Hochschule für Musik (College for Music) found the necessary funds, though their budget was limited, to complete the 1340-seat Konzertsaal. The architect broke with tradition and designed a modern hall with which West Berliners were none too happy at first. But their attitude has relaxed with time. H. H. Stuckenschmidt wrote in *Musical America*, August 1960: "Despite the hostility shown towards the acoustically modern concert hall of the Berlin Hochschule by the conservatives, it has become the center of Berlin's musical life."

The hall has had both a favorable reception and intense adverse criticism. It is excellent for chamber music, piano, and soloists. Like the Kresge Auditorium, it has been criticized mainly when a large symphony orchestra has played in it.

During a symphony concert I attended in this hall, I sat in the center of the balcony. There I was aware of an obvious lack of orchestral balance. The shape of the ceiling tends to direct the sounds of the rear half of the orchestra into the balcony, with the result that the brass and percussion come through much louder than the violins. The increase in sound level of the brasses is of the order of 6 decibels, which means that their loudness is about 80 per cent greater than what would be transmitted by the average stage. Throughout the hall there is a deficiency in bass, due partly to the directional ceiling, but also to the large areas of thin plywood, which shorten the reverberation time at the lower frequencies.

A German music critic wrote to me recently that he considers this hall only "fair," acoustically, and that "the sound is hard and glassy."

In November 1955, *The New Yorker* magazine commented on the first year's experience with the Berlin Konzertsaal. It spoke of echoes, dead spots, and unwelcome noises. It concluded by saying that changes had been made

BERLIN, MUSIKHOCHSCHULE KONZERTSAAL

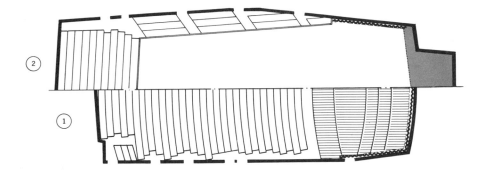

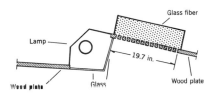

Glass fiber

Lamp

19.7 in.

Wood plate

Glass

Wood plate

Detail "A"

SEATING CAPACITY 1340

1   860

2   480

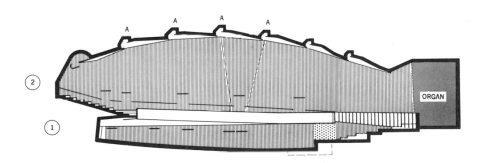

A   A   A   A

ORGAN

2

1

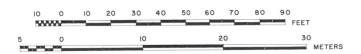

10   0   10   20   30   40   50   60   70   80   90
                                                    FEET

5   0   10   20   30
                                            METERS

which were helpful, but that the acoustics are still far from satisfactory.

This criticism was exaggerated. One can hear sound, loud sound, everywhere. The echoes are not too troublesome. Some changes were made in the first year: sound-reflecting surfaces were placed behind the balcony railing; some sound-absorbing material was taken out of the walls. However, the weakness of the bass still makes the high-frequency tones seem strange and the sound generally brittle.

One should not be surprised to find that improvements can be made in a hall after is is completed. There is hardly another field of endeavor in which the designer has so little opportunity to check his visualization against concrete reality before a huge expenditure is made. A bridge, a skyscraper, an automobile—each one can be tested in prototype. Even an airplane can be test flown before it is put into large-scale production. If our desire for a safe solution makes it impossible for our architects and acoustic experts to experiment in the only way they can—by combining their experience and imaginations with the use of new ideas and new materials—then we can only copy the old halls, using outdated and frequently inadequate ways, and progress and change will not take place.

TECHNICAL DETAILS FOR CONCERTS[*]

$V = 340{,}000 \text{ ft}^3$	$T_{500-1000}(\text{Occup.}) = 1.65 \text{ sec}$	$S_T = 9830 \text{ ft}^2$
$N_A = 1340$ seats	$S_A = 8000 \text{ ft}^2$	$S_A/N_A = 6.0 \text{ ft}^2$
$t_I = 18; 4$ msec	$S_O = 1830 \text{ ft}^2$	$V/S_T = 34.6 \text{ ft}$

[*] The terminology is explained in Appendix 3.

ARCHITECTURAL AND STRUCTURAL DETAILS

Uses: 30% orchestra, 60% chamber music and soloists, 10% other. *Ceiling:* wooden reflectors varying in thickness from ¼ to ¾ in. *Side walls:* upper parts are of plaster on brick; below the balcony, ¼-in. plywood panels with slits; behind and covering the slits, ⅜-in. plywood sheets are attached directly; the panels can be removed, if desired, to open the slits and increase the absorbing area. *Rear walls:* above the balcony, ¾-in. plaster on metal lath; below the balcony, about 200 sq ft of highly perforated panels behind which is a deep layer of glass fiber blanket. *Floors:* linoleum on concrete.

Stage floor: 1¾-in. wooden planks over large air space. *Stage enclosure:* around the stage there are polycylindrical diffusers made of ¾-in. gypsum plaster, covered with acoustically transparent, perforated metal sheets; the width of a cylindrical projection is about 3 ft, and the depth of a projection at the center is about 1 ft; on each side of the forward stage just under the balcony ends there are 20 to 30 sq ft of absorbing material to prevent cross-stage flutter echoes; four rows of ceiling light covers are perforated, as is shown in Detail A of the drawing; over the entire length of the perforated strip are wooden boxes; only 25% of their length is filled with glass fiber material. *Stage height:* 37 in. above the floor at the first row of seats. *Seating:* the top of the seat-bottom and the front of the backrest are fully upholstered in tight-weave cloth; the underseat is about 25% perforated with holes about 2½ in. apart.

References: Details from W. Gabler, Technical University of Berlin, and Erich Streubel, director of the Konzertsaal. Some details verified by author during a visit. *Architect:* Paul Baumgarten.

Berlin
SENDER FREIES BERLIN
GROSSER SENDESAAL

The Large Studio of Radio Free Berlin, completed in 1959, is very interesting because of its careful acoustical planning and its long reverberation time. It is used extensively for the recording of orchestral music, and the results receive very favorable reviews.

The studio is included in this study for several reasons. First, through the medium of hanging ceiling panels, short-time-delay reflections are provided on the main floor. Second, the reverberation time as calculated by the modern concept of audience absorption (discussed in Appendix 1) agrees closely with the measured reverberation time. Third, the high ceiling of the hall, necessary for a long reverberation time, is rendered invisible by an acoustically transparent lower ceiling (shown as a row of dots on the drawings). The shape of the room, the materials used, and the over-all acoustical design incorporate many of the important elements of good concert-hall design.

Two trained listeners, of whom one is a music critic, have expressed their reactions after hearing music here. One found a deficiency of high-frequency sound in the hall, which he attributed to the lower, open ceiling. He feels that only the mid and lower frequencies return from the ceiling. The other thought the acoustics "good," but no better than that, and described the sound as "somewhat blunt." I have not heard music in this hall and cannot verify their comments.

The hall is used regularly for the subscription concerts of the Radio Symphony of Berlin and by visiting orchestras.

TECHNICAL DETAILS FOR CONCERTS[*]

$V = 455{,}700$ ft^3 $T_{500-1000}$(Occup.) $= 1.95$ sec $S_T = 10{,}600$ ft^2
$N_A = 1120$ seats $S_A = 8600$ ft^2 $S_A/N_A = 7.7$ ft^2
$t_I = 21; 13$ msec $S_O = 2000$ ft^2 $V/S_T = 43.0$ ft

[*] The terminology is explained in Appendix 3.

BERLIN, SENDER FREIES BERLIN, GROSSER SENDESAAL

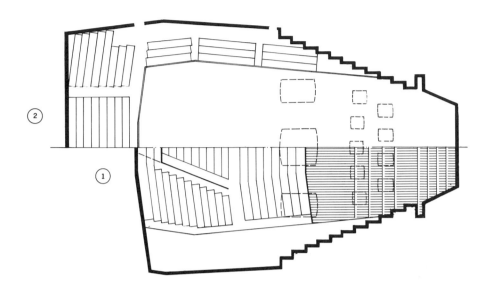

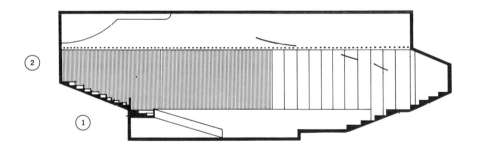

SEATING CAPACITY 1120

① 573
② 547

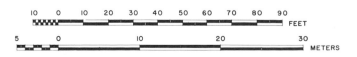

ARCHITECTURAL AND STRUCTURAL DETAILS

Uses: broadcasting studio for music both with and without audience. *Ceiling:* lower ceiling, grid of wooden rods; upper, acoustically effective ceiling, thick plaster. *Side and rear walls:* ¾-in. to 1¼-in. plywood at various distances from the rear wall. *Floor:* concrete floating floor, covered with cork-linoleum or wood parquet. *Stage floor:* concrete steps, covered with wood parquet. *Stage height:* 30 in. *Seats:* top of seat-bottoms and backrests are upholstered; one-third of the seats have highly perforated bottoms, one-third are partially perforated, and one-third are not perforated. *Note:* a movable, acoustically transparent curtain can close off the space for chorus from the stage when desired.

References: L. Cremer, Technical University of Berlin, supplied details and drawings. Some details and photographs supplied by the technical director of Sender Freies Berlin. *Architect-Engineers:* Sonder-Vermögens und Bauverwaltung.

The Beethovenhalle project in Bonn is one of the most impressive of the cultural centers that have been built in Germany since World War II. Separated from the Rhine by a narrow mall on one side, and backed by ample parking space at the rear, the hall is well situated. Viewed from an airplane, its striped, molded roof suggests a lively whale at play. Its lobbies are typical of contemporary architecture in Germany, spacious, a little aseptic but relieved by colorful murals. The Beethovenhalle was completed in 1959.

The architecture of the interior takes the visitor by surprise. The main floor, which contains 1030 seats, is flat, and the hall may be used for banquets, dances, or exhibitions. An asymmetrical balcony seats 377 listeners. On entering, one's eyes are immediately carried to the ceiling, which looks like a many-tufted yellow bedspread, held by an upward pull of gravity against a domed ceiling. From the ceiling down, the interior of the hall suggests the classic struggle between architecture and acoustics: the architect wants a majestic domed ceiling, and the acoustician, faced with the acoustics usual with domes, must find a means of scattering the sound. The busy side walls also show the studied influence of acoustical considerations.

The 1760 acoustical elements on the ceiling are designed not only to scatter the sound impinging on them but also to absorb sound in the region of 125 cycles per second. The need for this added low-frequency sound absorption is debatable. As Chapter 10 emphasizes, musicians and music critics express a preference for a rich, strong bass—such as results from a room finished in heavy plaster. The Beethoven Hall is not as deficient in bass as are halls that are lined with thin wood, but the bass does seem less than optimum (see the table of reverberation times in Appendix 2).

In a letter to me, Erwin Meyer of the University of Göttingen wrote: "The Beethoven Hall has been used for two years now. Inquiries were made among authorized people concerning its acoustical success. Not a single negative opinion was given; the acoustical reputation of Beethoven Hall is excellent."

BONN, BEETHOVENHALLE

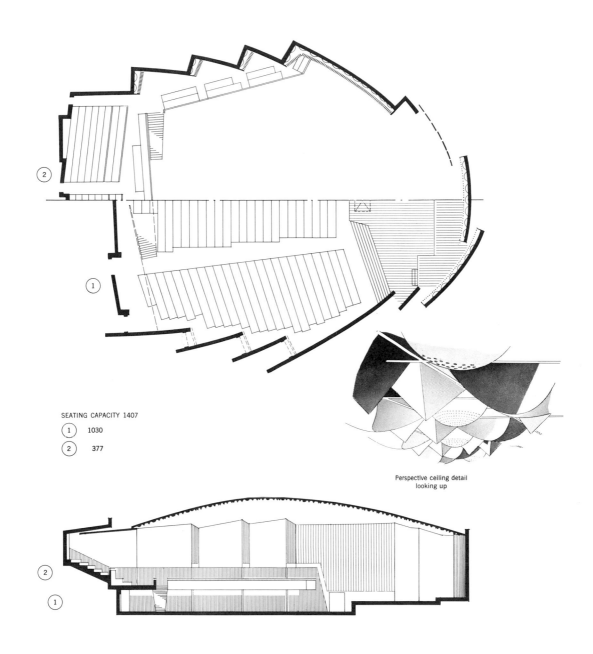

SEATING CAPACITY 1407

(1) 1030
(2) 377

Perspective ceiling detail
looking up

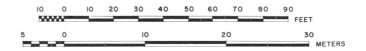

10 0 10 20 30 40 50 60 70 80 90
                                              FEET

5 0 10 20 30
                                              METERS

On the other hand, a music critic from a neighboring city wrote me that he considered the acoustics of this hall to be "good" but not "excellent."

TECHNICAL DETAILS FOR CONCERTS*

$V = 555,340 \text{ ft}^3$ $T_{500-1000}(\text{Occup.}) = 1.7 \text{ sec}$ $S_T = 14,200 \text{ ft}^2$

$N_A = 1407 \text{ seats}$ $S_A = 12,000 \text{ ft}^2$ $S_A/N_A = 8.5 \text{ ft}^2$

$t_I = 27; 14 \text{ msec}$ $S_O = 2200 \text{ ft}^2$ $V/S_T = 39.1 \text{ ft}$

* The terminology is explained in Appendix 3.

ARCHITECTURAL AND STRUCTURAL DETAILS

Uses: mainly concerts, but also meetings and social events. *Ceiling:* beneath the concrete roof of the hall is hung a rhombic (egg-crate) grid of 1-in. reinforced-gypsum sheets. Inside each rhombic unit, a "sound-scatterer" is placed, of one of three shapes, made from a gypsum-vermiculite mixture, $\frac{5}{16}$ in. thick; each of these 1760 scatterers, with an average height of 1 ft (the total area covered being 12,000 ft^2) is either a double pyramid, a spherical segment, or a cylindrical segment obliquely cut on both sides with the curvature facing downward; for the purpose of absorbing low-frequency sound around 125 cycles per second, each spherical segment has on its lower part 250 holes $\frac{1}{4}$ in. in diameter, spaced about $1\frac{3}{16}$ in. apart; inside the perforated spherical segments is a 1-in. layer of rock wool; the ratio of spherical segments to double pyramids to cylindrical segments is 6:5:1. *Side walls:* the large area of wall on either side of the hall and the four small areas of wall facing the stage on either side of the hall above the balcony are built as follows: an acoustically transparent grid of vertical slats covers some vertically oriented cylindrical diffusers, each with a chord of 3 ft and a depth of 1 ft separated from each other by 1 to 2 ft. Some damped resonators tuned to 250 cps are located between each pair of the cylinders; the four sections of wall above the balcony on either side of the hall that face the audience are $\frac{3}{4}$-in. wooden panels over air spaces that vary between $\frac{3}{8}$ in. and $3\frac{1}{2}$ in. deep; behind half the panels there are 2-in. glass fiber blankets; the lower walls are of plaster. *Floor:* oak parquet. *Stage floor:* wood over air space. *Stage height:* 43.5 in. *Seats:* the tops of the seat-bottoms and the fronts of the seat backs are upholstered.

References: Deutsche Bauzeitung, **65,** 59–75 (February 1960). E. Meyer and H. Kuttruff, in a letter to the editor of *Acustica,* **9,** 465–468 (1959). Other information courtesy E. Meyer and the architect. *Architect:* Siegfried Wolske.

The "New" Gewandhaus is the only hall described in this study that is not standing today. To the musical world, the loss by bombing of the Neues Gewandhaus was an unfortunate concomitant of World War II. Ever since its completion in 1886, it had stood as a model of a concert hall with fine acoustics, loved by both musicians and music lovers.

Before discussing this celebrated hall of 1560 seats, let us recall its predecessor—the "old" Gewandhaus in Leipzig, built in 1780 and razed in 1894, after the new hall had become established. The old Gewandhaus became famous for its excellent acoustics during the period of Mendelssohn's successful directorship (1835 to 1847). It had a volume of only 75,000 cubic feet and at first it accommodated an audience of only about 400 people. In 1842, the addition of long side-balconies increased the capacity to about 570. Think of the difference between listening to Bach in Leipzig in 1800 in a hall that seated 400 persons and listening to the same work at Tanglewood in Lenox, Massachusetts, in 1962 in a structure that seats 6000 persons! The ceiling of the old Gewandhaus was flat. Small in size, it was built like a modern broadcasting studio, with relatively low reverberation time and walls of thin wood. In a very small hall, especially one in which the music played is primarily of the Baroque period, there may be thin wooden walls and a somewhat short reverberation time and still the hall may rank as acoustically excellent. By contrast, the successful large concert halls of today, which must serve music of other periods as well, have walls and ceilings that are predominantly of plaster or *thick* wood, and a ceiling that is high. The results are a long reverberation time and a rich bass.

For many years before the construction of the new hall, Leipzig was identified with great music, and the cordial interest of the community may account for the ready acceptance of the Neues Gewandhaus when it opened in 1886. The fame of the new hall may well have been enhanced when it was chosen as one of two models used in 1895 for the design of the successful Symphony Hall in Boston.

The Neues Gewandhaus was architecturally beautiful, about twice as long as it was wide, with rounded corners. A clerestory of fourteen vaulted

LEIPZIG, NEUES GEWANDHAUS

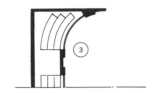

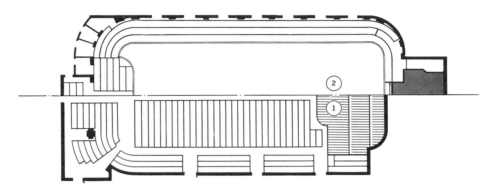

SEATING CAPACITY 1560

1. 966
2. 482
3. 112

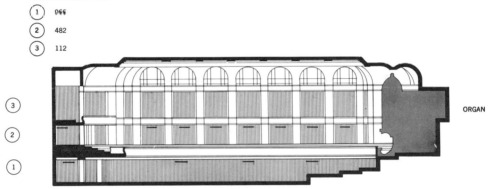

ORGAN

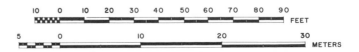

windows cut through the sides of the ceiling. Especially prominent were fourteen large panels on the two side walls. Ten of these panels held magnificent murals, oil on canvas. Three enormous candle-laden chandeliers hung from the 50-foot ceiling.

The reverberation time in the Neues Gewandhaus was longer than that of the Philadelphia Academy of Music and shorter than that of Symphony Hall in Boston. Its narrow width gave it a vitally short initial-time-delay gap.

Bagenal and Wood in their *Planning for Good Acoustics,* written in the early 1920's, say of the Neues Gewandhaus:

> The tone is "full" and "bright" and at the same time musical notes are distinct; the instruments have "power" and preserve their distinctive character; the *pianissimo* playing of 'cellos and double basses is something unrealized in England; accompanying is easy; treble and bass parts are at equal strength; there are no bad seats in the hall. The only criticism is that the brasses are slightly too loud.

Bruno Walter, who knew the hall well, told me, "The Gewandhaus was a fine concert hall. But it was not as good as the Musikvereinssaal in Vienna. The sound was not as live or as noble." German music critics remember it as "very good" to "excellent."

Today, if it were standing, the Neues Gewandhaus would probably rank higher than the Vienna Grosser Musikvereinssaal for music of Bach and the early Classical period, and less satisfactory than the Vienna hall for music of the Romantic and late Classical styles.

TECHNICAL DETAILS FOR CONCERTS[*]

$V = 375,000$ ft^3	$T_{500-1000}$(Occup.) $= 1.55$ sec	$S_T = 11,000$ ft^2
$N_A = 1560$ seats	$S_A = 9750$ ft^2	$S_A/N_A = 6.3$ ft^2
$t_I = 8; 6$ msec	$S_O = 1250$ ft^2	$V/S_T = 34.0$ ft

[*] The terminology is explained in Appendix 3.

ARCHITECTURAL AND STRUCTURAL DETAILS

Uses: symphony orchestra, chamber music, organ and general purpose. *Ceiling:* lime plaster on wood lath. *Side and rear walls:* wooden paneling, including doors, about ¾ in. thick, that extended up to a height of about 9 ft above the floor at the rear of the balcony. Upper part of the hall was plaster on wood lath. Ten large canvas oil paintings, each with an area of about 130 sq ft, hung on these upper walls. The walls under the balcony, except for the doors, were of plaster on brick. *Stage floor:* wooden boards over air space. *Stage height:* 48 in. above the level of the floor at the first row of seats. *Floors:* wood parquet floor over wood joists; measurements showed that sound was conducted easily along this wooden floor and that it had a well-defined resonance frequency (without seats) at 100 cps. *Added absorptive material:* in 1930 there were about 800 sq ft of thick plush draperies: later these were removed. *Seating:* the seat-bottoms were upholstered with plush material; the front of the backrests was upholstered with leather over hair.

References: Erwin Meyer, Göttingen University, Germany. Walter Kuhl, Institut für Rundfunktechnik GmbH, Hamburg. H. Bagenal and A. Wood, *Planning for Good Acoustics*, E. P. Dutton and Co., Inc., New York, 1931. Photographs courtesy of *Musical America*. *Architects:* Paul Gropius and H. Schmieden.

Each distinguished hall has a unique appearance and personality. The flat floor, small area, large tapestries hanging high on the walls over a colonnade below give the Herkulessaal the appearance of a lecture room although it was designed specifically as a concert and festival hall. However, the long reverberation time, due to the high ceiling, renders the hall less than excellent for lectures, and the quality of the overhead reverberation, which is usually so pleasant in a concert hall, is marred to some extent by the hanging tapestries.

In 1953 the Herkulessaal was constructed with the same proportions and dimensions as the old throne room of the Royal Palace, which was destroyed during World War II. A feature of the construction was twenty flat, transparent, plastic panels hung above the orchestra and the front section of the audience. These panels, which were about $3/16$ of an inch thick, were designed to increase the strength of the violin tone in the rear of the audience and to improve contact among the musicians. Professor L. Cremer in *Die Schalltechnik*, Vol. 13 (1953), reported that there was some difficulty in arranging the panels so as to produce the desired quality of sound simultaneously on stage and in the audience. Various arrangements and heights were tried. In their final placement (1961), the first violins profited from the panels, but their tone did not quite equal the beauty of the woodwinds and violas. There were some complaints by the musicians of the balance among the sections of the orchestra.

As part of the construction, the architect requested that thirteen large tapestries, each about 300 square feet in area, be hung on the upper side walls. These tapestries reduced the reverberation time so much that, within the first year after the hall was completed, it was decided that three of them should be removed. The remainder were distributed at greater intervals along the walls and were made less absorbent by the addition of a plastic backing.

In 1958 some experiments were performed, without audience, by the radio broadcasting engineers on the position of the plastic reflectors. The

MUNICH, HERKULESSAAL

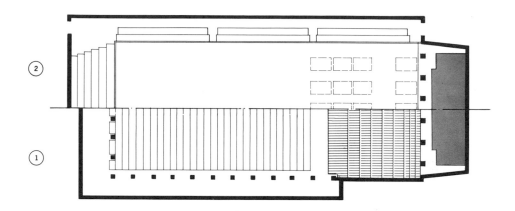

SEATING CAPACITY 1287

① 853

② 434

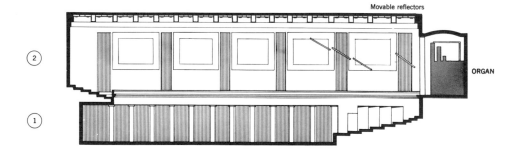

Movable reflectors

ORGAN

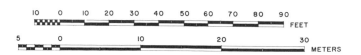

```
10    0    10   20   30   40   50   60   70   80   90
                                                      FEET
5     0         10              20            30
                                                      METERS
```

only clear-cut result they obtained relative to radio broadcasts was that the microphone pickup was best when the panels were all hung horizontally 35 feet above the center level of the stage. But in this location the sound at the rear of the hall was changed because the reflectors no longer directed sound there. The reactions of the critics quoted in the next paragraph are therefore not surprising.

Of two American music critics asked to comment on the Herkulessaal, one found the acoustics "average." The other said, "Near the rear of the seating area the sound was distant. The reverberation did not seem connected with the music from the orchestra. In the front half of the hall, the sound was better, but not as good as that in some other halls."

In late 1961, a 75-stop pipe organ was installed and the reflecting panels were removed. At this writing they have not been replaced. Because the Herkulessaal is narrow, the panels are not needed to shorten the initial-time-delay gap. However, with a flat main floor they would help to increase the strength of the higher harmonics of the orchestra in the rear seats. A German music critic now comments on "poor balance between strings and brass" everywhere in the hall.

The reverberation time at frequencies near 250 cycles per second is shorter than it should be relative to the frequencies just above and just below, owing to the selective sound absorption in the ceiling caused by the thin wood construction. Since the installation of the organ, I have heard a string quartet perform in the Herkulessaal, and in the rear part of the main floor there is lack of strength in the middle register of the cello. This deficiency is due to the selective sound absorption in the ceiling at 250 cycles per second. In the front rows of the hall, the cello has its normal warm sound. The violin sound is excellent in the first two-thirds of the hall, but without the reflecting panels it lacks brilliance in the rear.

This hall might take its place among the best in the world if the ceiling did not selectively absorb the music, that is to say, if it was made of plaster rather than of thin wood, and if more of the tapestries were removed.

As a supplementary note, a center aisle may be created by the removal of some chairs. The photograph shows the arrangement usual for concerts.

TECHNICAL DETAILS FOR CONCERTS[*]

$V = 480{,}000 \text{ ft}^3$ $T_{500-1000}(\text{Occup.}) = 1.85 \text{ sec}$ $S_T = 9060 \text{ ft}^2$

$N_A = 1287 \text{ seats}$ $S_A = 7250 \text{ ft}^2$ $S_A/N_A = 5.6 \text{ ft}^2$

$t_I = 24; 8 \text{ msec}$ $S_O = 1810 \text{ ft}^2$ $V/S_T = 53.0 \text{ ft}$

[*] The terminology is explained in Appendix 3.

ARCHITECTURAL AND STRUCTURAL DETAILS

Uses: 60% orchestra; 10% chamber music; 5% chorus; 10% soloists; 15% other. *Ceiling:* 3/16-in. to 3/8-in. plywood, backed by rock wool over 4- to 20-in. air space; laboratory tests indicate that the ceiling has the following absorption coefficients: 100 cps, 0.25; 200 cps, 0.33; 400 cps, 0.22; 800 cps, 0.12; and 1600 cps and above, about 0.035. *Side walls:* plaster on solid brick masonry, except that 4000 sq ft consist of 1/4-in. sheets of gypsum board separated by 2 in. from the solid wall behind. *Rear wall:* plastered brick; great doors are metal and plywood. *Stage floor:* 2-in. wooden planks over air space. *Stage height:* 40 in. above floor level at front row of seats. *Carpets:* none. *Added absorptive material:* 10 tapestries having a total area of about 3000 sq ft are hung on the upper walls for architectural reasons. *Seating:* upholstered on both sides of backrest and on top of seat-bottom; the under-seat is solid.

References: L. Cremer, *Die Schalltechnik,* **13,** 1–10 (1953); L. Cremer, *Gravesaner Blätter,* Nos. 2/3, pp. 10–33 (January 1956); E. Meyer and R. Thiele, *Acustica,* **6,** 425–444 (1956); letters from L. Cremer, H. Mueller, and W. Kuhl. Recent information from F. Gumppenberg, president of Staatliche Schlösser, Gärten und Seen. Details verified by author during visit. *Architect:* Rudolf Esterer.

Situated on one of Stuttgart's busiest streets, the Liederhalle contains three halls which seat 2000, 750, and 350 persons. Of these, the middle hall is the most spectacular from the outside, and the large hall is the most interesting from the inside. On descending from the street car, one's eyes are drawn to the five-sided exterior of the middle hall, covered with large multicolored mosaics. Inside the three-hall complex, there is a flight of stairs down to the foyer. At the entrance at the rear of the large hall, one is struck by its unusual shape—like a grand piano—a shape chosen for architectural and not acoustical reasons. The striking balcony rises like a grand staircase from the left side of the main floor, and with graceful line soars over the main floor seats and sweeps around the rear of the hall to the wall on the right-hand side. A large, convex concrete wall, on which there is a mosaic of painted wooden pieces and gold threads, connects the left side of the stage to the rising portion of the balcony. The right-hand wall of the hall, which is finished in teak, is irregular with projecting boxes and control booths for radio and television broadcasting. All the other walls are of teak.

The main floor is flat, and unusual groupings break the monotony of regular seating. The ceiling is interestingly contoured to provide sound diffusion and to give desirable short-time-delay sound reflections to the back of the hall. Reflecting panels, hanging over the orchestra, direct the sound of the strings to the audience at the rear of the main floor. Without these panels, the string sound would be lost in the sea of intervening heads between the listeners and the stage.

Reports from visiting conductors about the acoustics have been largely favorable. Eugene Ormandy was much pleased with the hall. He felt that on stage, particularly, the sound was excellent. When he spoke with me in 1959 he called this the best of the modern halls. Lengthening the reverberation time, he felt, would improve the hall. He also suggested that the stage seemed to him somewhat wide for acoustical excellence. Charles Munch said that the sound on stage was marvelous.

Herbert von Karajan, who has listened throughout the hall, said: "This hall is very good for rehearsing, but there is a great difference when it is

STUTTGART, LIEDERHALLE, GROSSER SAAL

full. With an audience, the music tends to lose its 'soul.' On the podium, one can hear everything, even the smallest error in the performance. The acoustics are best in the balcony directly opposite the stage."

Generalmusikdirektor Ferdinand Leitner wrote in the *Stuttgarter Nachrichten* (1956):

> I am happy to be able to say nothing but good about it. . . . There is not one acoustically weak place in the hall. . . . The acoustics are excellent. I would not have considered such acoustics possible in a concrete hall. [Actually, only one wall of the hall is concrete.]

Reverberation measurements (reported in Appendix 2) were obtained by L. Cremer and H. A. Mueller when a chorus of 200, an orchestra of 120 persons on the stage, and a full audience were in the hall. The results agree closely with the theoretical predictions of Appendix 1. The hall is slightly more reverberant than the Royal Festival Hall but less reverberant than the Boston and Vienna halls.

Antonio Mingotti, who is a music critic, considers this hall "very good" but not as good as the Concertgebouw of Amsterdam, the Neues Gewandhaus that stood in Leipzig, or the Grosser Musikvereinssaal of Vienna.

For my part, I find the hall very interesting. The sound in the balcony is good. On the main floor, it is less pleasing. This is due partly to the flat floor and partly to the great width of the hall. There is a deficiency of bass, which is due to the large areas of low-frequency sound-absorbing materials in the ceiling and on the walls. In the rear half of the hall, but not too far under the balcony, the desirable short-time-delay reflections give an intimate, brilliant sound. In my opinion, this hall ranks as very good but falls below the quality of Symphony Hall in Boston and the Grosser Musikvereinssaal in Vienna.

TECHNICAL DETAILS FOR CONCERTS*

V = 565,000 ft^3	$T_{500-1000}$(Occup.) = 1.62 sec†	S_T = 16,500 ft^2†
N_A = 2000 seats	S_A = 14,000 ft^2	S_A/N_A = 7.0 ft^2
t_I = 29; 12 msec	S_O = 1900 ft^2	V/S_T = 34.2 ft

* The terminology is explained in Appendix 3.

† With chorus area fully occupied.

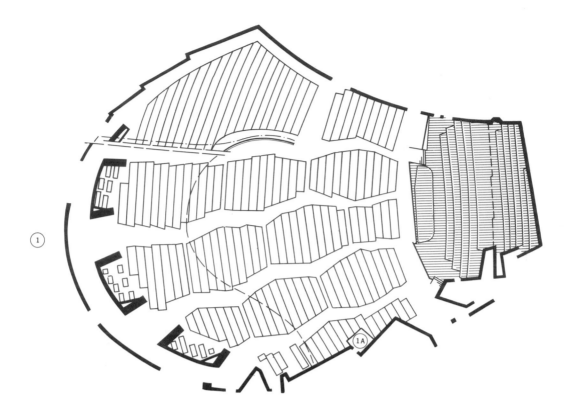

SEATING CAPACITY 2000

① 1175

①A 25

② 800

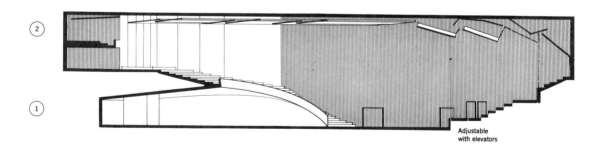

Adjustable
with elevators

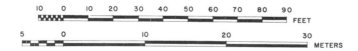

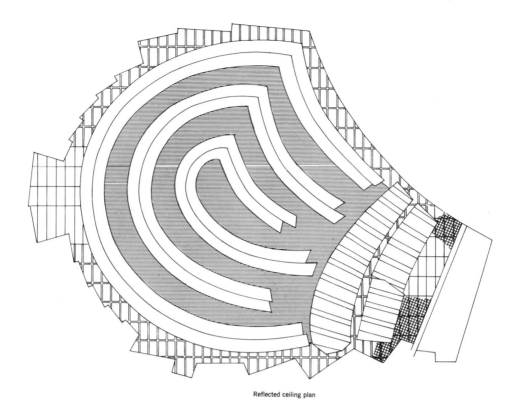

Reflected ceiling plan

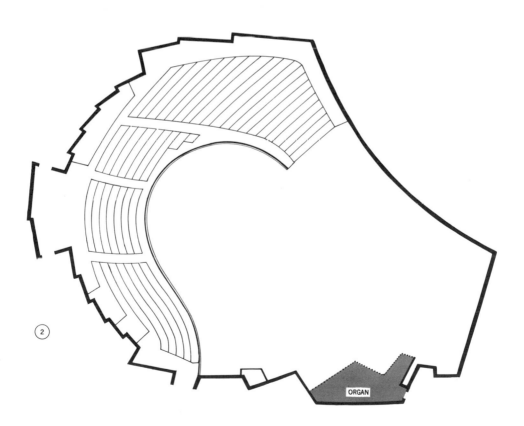

ORGAN

②

ARCHITECTURAL AND STRUCTURAL DETAILS

Uses: 45% orchestra, 10% organ, 10% chorus, 13% chamber and soloists, 22% miscellaneous. *Ceiling:* gypsum plaster on metal lath except for a strip about 10 ft. wide near the walls that is one-third of ⅝-in. fiberboard with air space behind and two-thirds of slotted fiberboard backed by a ⅜-in. layer of glass fiberboard. Deep irregular coves are molded into the ceiling; over the stage, reflectors made of ¾-in. plywood have been added. *Walls:* the large convex wall is concrete; all other walls are plywood panels, designed to absorb the lower frequencies; these panels vary from ⅜ in. to ⅞ in. thick and are over an air space 1 to 5 in. deep; the panels are backed by absorbing materials in strips; half of a few panels, near the concrete wall, are slotted and have ⅜-in. glass fiberboard behind; a few others are thin plywood; the slotted panels and the thin panels are backed with a fiberboard egg-crate structure; these variations yield walls that absorb sound over a wide range of low frequencies. *Stage enclosure:* largely ⅞-in. plywood; splayed ⅞-in. plywood reflectors are hung over the orchestra and the front two rows of seating; a soloist is expected to use the right-hand side of the stage where the rearmost reflectors can be lowered; the chorus seating can be closed off visually from the orchestra platform by an acoustically transparent, movable wall; the organ is located behind closable "jalousies" on the right-hand side of the stage. *Floors:* wood parquet; no carpet. *Stage floor:* 2-in. boards on elevators. *Stage height:* 49 in. above level of floor at first row of seats. *Seating:* the top of the seat and the front and rear of the backrest are fully upholstered in cord fabric; between the cord fabric and stuffing is a thin non-porous foil; the underseats are solid; the armrests are upholstered in leather.

References: L. Cremer, L. Keidel, and H. Mueller, *Acustica,* **6,** 466–474 (1956). Details from L. Cremer and H. Mueller, and from a booklet, "Konzerthaus Stuttgarter Liederhalle," Dr. Pollert Verlag, Stuttgart (1956). Details verified by author during visits. *Architect:* A. Abel and R. Gutbrod.

On a crisp winter afternoon we passed under Bristol's medieval gate, crossed the street and puffed ourselves up the hill to the Colston Halls. An afternoon social function was just adjourning from the smaller hall and the steep steps inside the building were jammed with ladies. Begging their leave, we threaded our way by and opened a door to the corridor of the main hall. The music of the Bournemouth Symphony Orchestra greeted us. Henry Krips of Australia had just started rehearsing the evening's concert, and the hall was ours to roam and study quietly.

This was not the first Colston Hall. The original was destroyed in 1898 and immediately rebuilt. It was reconstructed in 1936, only to burn in 1945. The present hall was dedicated on July 9, 1951.

The shape of the hall is rectangular, a plan partly dictated by its being reconstructed within the old walls. It deviates from its Leipzig model by having a large balcony with a deep overhang underneath, necessitated by the usual demands for large seating capacity. The high ceiling and narrow width declare that the architect and his acoustical consultant wanted to provide a fairly long reverberation time, together with satisfactory acoustical intimacy. A dominant architectural feature is the large suspended canopy over the concert platform which directs the sound uniformly over the hall and enables the performers to hear their own instruments and other sections of the orchestra.

Other architectural features that arose from acoustical considerations are the sawtooth shape of the balcony faces and of the panels on the upper side walls. The clearly visible, elaborate grid of closed holes in the ceiling was provided as a kind of insurance for later adjustments of the acoustics, but it has not been needed. The over-all design has been successful.

The British, in all their halls that I have visited, seat part of the audience behind the orchestra in a rather large area provided for the chorus when choral music is performed. Another recurring British feature is the steeply raked steps on the rear half of the orchestra platform. An interesting innovation in the large Colston Hall is a wall six feet high, separating the

BRISTOL, COLSTON HALL

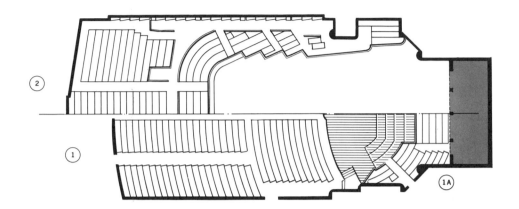

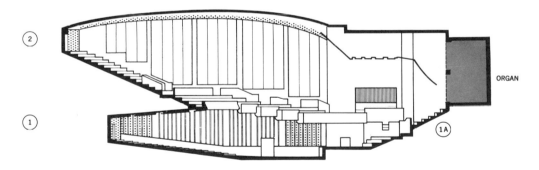

SEATING CAPACITY 2180

- (1) 1054
- (1A) 182
- (2) 944

ORGAN

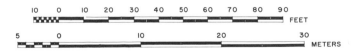

orchestra from the audience behind it. This wall tends to overemphasize the horns, brass, and percussion.

It is generally held among criticial listeners that Colston Hall is the best of the modern British halls. Its small size—it seats 2180—and narrow width are in its favor. For the purpose of evaluating its acoustics, a group of selected listeners attended a concert in the late fall of 1951 and moved about to various parts of the hall. The majority preferred the balcony because there the orchestral balance and the brilliance of the strings were judged best. These attributes are undoubtedly enhanced by the front portion of the canopy. The hall was judged to have satisfactory liveness and a warm orchestral tone. As one would expect, the listeners remarked that the wall behind the orchestra acts as an amplifier which occasionally causes the timpani to override the rest of the orchestra and the French horns to sound too loud. The cello sound was judged particularly good throughout the hall.

Sir Malcolm Sargent said, "The acoustics of Colston Hall are good. It is not large and has a wide open platform, which makes the sound full and resonant and very clear." Sir Adrian Boult's comments were essentially the same.

Sir John Barbirolli wrote to me, "I subscribe wholeheartedly to the remarks of Sir Malcolm Sargent. It is an excellent hall in every way."

T. Somerville and C. L. S. Gilford of the B.B.C. [in the *Gravesaner Blätter*, No. 9, 1957] commented favorably on the hall and said that the tonal quality is fuller than in either the Royal Festival Hall in London or the Free Trade Hall in Manchester. They added that definition is good but not, perhaps, exceptional. With the hall empty, they wrote, there is a tendency for the timpani and brass to be prominent, but this is less noticeable with a full audience.

My own opinion after attending a concert there is that the hall is very good, almost excellent. It has clarity, brilliance, warmth, and adequate liveness for Classical music. It is superior in warmth and liveness to Philharmonic Hall in Liverpool and the Royal Festival Hall in London. On the other hand, the materials used in finishing the hall are more austere and the seats are less comfortable than in either of those halls. For late Classical and Romantic music, St. Andrew's Hall in Glasgow is superior to Colston

Hall. The night I attended a concert, the horns and trumpets were not seated against the dividing wall, and the timpani player showed admirable restraint. Hence, the orchestral balance was excellent, both in the balcony and on the main floor. The only criticism I have is that on several occasions noises outside the hall were disturbing.

TECHNICAL DETAILS FOR CONCERTS[*]

$V = 475,000$ ft^3 $T_{500-1000}$(Occup.) $= 1.7$ sec $S_T = 13,460$ ft^2

$N_A = 2180$ seats $S_A = 12,310$ ft^2 $S_A/N_A = 5.6$ ft^2

$t_I = 14; 6$ msec $S_O = 1150$ ft^2 $V/S_T = 35.3$ ft

[*] The terminology is explained in Appendix 3.

ARCHITECTURAL AND STRUCTURAL DETAILS

Uses: principally concerts. *Ceiling:* ¾-in. hard plaster on metal lath backed with 1½-in. vermiculite plaster; the junction of the ceiling with the side walls is formed with unplastered, curved, sound-absorbent wood-wool slabs (1400 sq ft). *Side walls:* portions of the upper parts of the side walls are paneled with ½-in. painted wooden chipboard with 5-in. air space behind; the rest of the upper side wall is of plaster on metal lath; a small portion of the walls (260 sq ft) below the balcony is of slotted wooden panels with absorbent material behind; the rest is curved ½-in. wood with 4-in. air space behind; except at the very low frequencies (below 50 cps) the paneling on the side walls, acoustically, is hardly different from plaster on metal lath. *Rear walls:* ¹³⁄₁₆-in. perforated acoustic tiles on 1½-in. wooden battens on brick walls. *Floors:* rubber and cork tile on concrete in rear third of main floor; wood on battens on concrete in front of main floor; concrete in balcony. *Stage enclosure:* overhead reflector is of plaster on metal lath; walls are plywood panels on furring on brickwork, large organ grille at the rear covered with curtains. *Stage floor:* 1¼-in. hardwood boards over deep air space; choir (audience) area behind is wood on concrete; the percussion alcove is wood on concrete. *Stage height:* 43 in. above floor level at first row of seats. *Carpets:* none. *Added absorptive material:* curtains in doorways. Side wall panels as noted above. *Seating:* the top of the seat-bottom and the front of the backrest are upholstered in tightly woven cloth; the underseat is solid; the choir seats are partly upholstered in leather.

References: Drawings and details from P. H. Parkin and E. Stacy of Building Research Station, Watford, England, and T. Somerville of British Broadcasting Corporation Research Laboratories. Photographs by Desmond Tripp, Bristol, England, published with permission of the Entertainments Committee of the City and County of Bristol. Other information from T. Somerville and C. L. S. Gilford, *Gravesaner Blätter,* **3,** No. 9 (1957); and P. H. Parkin, W. E. Scholes, and A. G. Derbyshire, *Acustica,* **2,** 97–100 (1952). Details confirmed by author during visits. *Architect:* J. Nelson Meredith.

In 1896, Mr. Andrew Usher "gifted" a sum of one hundred thousand pounds to the City of Edinburgh for a "City Hall." Mr. Usher stated that "his desire and intention was that it should become and remain a centre of attraction to musical artists and performers, and to the citizens of Edinburgh and others who might desire to hear good music, instrumental and vocal; and that the opportunities afforded by the Hall and its adjuncts might promote and extend the cultivation of, and taste for, music, not only in Edinburgh, but throughout the country." His gift took form eighteen years later when, in 1914, the Usher Hall of 2760 seats was dedicated.

Would that every hall fulfilled its purpose as well. Usher Hall has helped to maintain the Edinburgh International Festival as an important musical event in spite of intense European competition. Most of the world's important orchestras and conductors appear here at one time or another.

The stage commands one's attention on first entry. Double columns painted ivory and trimmed in gold form the sides of the proscenium opening. The orchestra is seated as in a theater pit—extending far on either side of the conductor and shallow in depth. Behind the orchestra, on steeply raked platforms, are seats for 333 listeners. Above these seats the great organ cabinet rises to the ceiling in rich polished wood fronted by gold pipes. The hall itself seems small and the orchestra seems close to the listeners. Aside from the stage, only the two graceful lines of the balcony make an architectural impression.

To me, the music in Usher Hall is muffled. There is insufficient force, even when the conductor calls for double forte. The orchestra sounds as though it were playing in a separate room from the audience and not penetrating well the boundary between. This hall illustrates the opposite of the word "transparency" often used by musicians. There seems to be an acoustically murky curtain across the proscenium that refuses to let the full power of the orchestra come through.

Sir John Barbirolli wrote, "A very handsome hall, but with very patchy acoustics. By this I mean that it sounds vastly different even at seats

EDINBURGH, USHER HALL

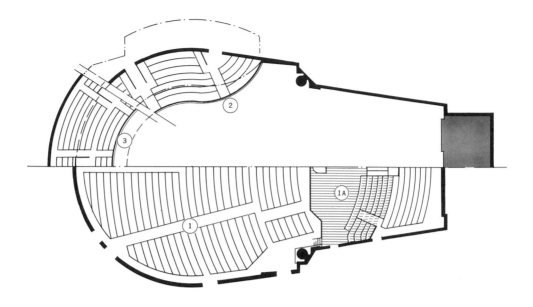

SEATING CAPACITY 2760

①	1186
①A	333
②	428
③	813

③

②

①

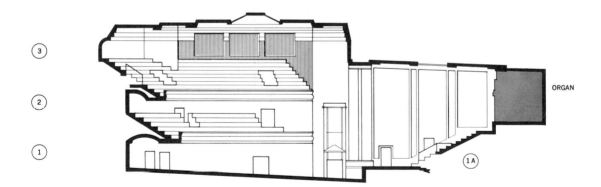

ORGAN

①A

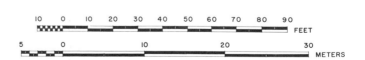

```
10   0   10  20  30  40  50  60  70  80  90
                                            FEET

5    0           10          20          30
                                            METERS
```

comparatively short distances apart. I also agree that the music in Usher Hall is muffled. . . . The upper balcony is the best place from which to listen."

Alexander Gibson, who has conducted in Usher Hall since 1955, observes, "A large body of strings is required in this hall to make the result worthwhile. An orchestra of 70 players sounds very thin and at the rear of the main floor the cut-off is marked. In any part of the hall, richness in sound can only be achieved by at least 56 to 60 strings. The reverberation is pleasant but not too marked. The acoustics require the quality and quantity of the many great orchestras that play in it at the time of the Edinburgh Festival to make it good." Sir Adrian Boult and Sir Malcolm Sargent were not as specific, but they indicated that it is not a hall in which musicians enjoy performing, and they too called the sound "patchy." Three of England's leading music critics rated it as acceptable but not outstanding.

Returning to my own observations, the upper balcony unquestionably has the best acoustics. There the music, though subdued in level, is clear and conveys the intent of the musicians. The uncomfortableness of the hard seats is more than compensated by the improved tone quality.

In the center of the first balcony, where in most halls the sound is best, the acoustics are least good. The music lacks clarity and brilliance. The different orchestral sections do not blend well; they maintain a "stereo" separation. The pizzicato playing of the first violins sounds blunted. There are insufficient short-time-delay reflections to give brilliance or clarity to the string tone. The reverberation of the hall is not apparent. The sound has little after-ring and is weak.

A British music critic agrees with this evaluation, saying, "I have sat only in the first balcony. There the sound is drab, heavy and lack-lustre, without either the clarity of the Royal Festival Hall or the richness of the Grosser Musikvereinssaal."

On the main floor, in back of about the fifth row, the sound is much better. The string tone comes through clearly, and the blend of orchestral tone is better. The balance of the strings, woodwinds, brass, and percussion is good. The loudness is much better than in the first tier, but the hall still sounds "dead." Because the orchestra is spread so wide for its depth, cross echoes can be heard when a section at either end plays alone.

T. Somerville and C. L. S. Gilford of the B.B.C. [*Gravesaner Blätter* (No. 9, 1957)] wrote:

The tonal quality is, by comparison, a little harsh although the hall is quite good. . . . The extensive hard surfaces near the sides of the orchestra sometimes cause accentuation of instruments which happen to be placed in the vicinity. There is . . . some observed variation in acoustics between different positions in the auditorium.

In 1949, Parkin et al. [*Acustica*, Vol. 2, p. 97 (1952)] sent a questionnaire on concert-hall acoustics to a number of music critics, professors of music, and composers in Great Britain, of whom 75 responded. Of 21 who had some knowledge of Usher Hall and its acoustics, 65 per cent ranked the hall in the highest category, "good" on a scale of "good," "fair," and "bad." Sixteen respondents, who knew six or more of the ten halls being compared, ranked Usher Hall below St. Andrew's Hall in Glasgow and Philharmonic Hall in Liverpool. The Royal Festival Hall, Colston Hall and Free Trade Hall had not yet been built.

Three of the American and European conductors whom I interviewed know this hall well. Their comments follow: "The sound in this hall is very good. However, on stage, the room gives the feeling that the sound has no volume. The audience behind the orchestra and the distant rear wall of the stage contribute to this feeling." "The sound is good, but the rear wall of the stage is too far back and I don't like the public on the stage." "I have conducted there during several festivals. This is a very fine hall, although not as good as the Boston Symphony Hall or the Grosser Musikvereinssaal in Vienna."

Three American music critics rank Usher Hall well below the Boston and Vienna Halls and below Carnegie Hall in New York.

In summary, Usher Hall has satisfactory acoustics on the main floor and in the upper balcony. It is not as good in the first balcony. The reverberation is somewhat short and music played in the hall lacks loudness. Acoustically, it ranks below St. Andrew's in Glasgow and the Colston Hall in Bristol.

TECHNICAL DETAILS FOR CONCERTS*

$V = 565,000 \text{ ft}^3$ $T_{500-1000}(\text{Occup.}) = 1.65 \text{ sec}$ $S_T = 16,500 \text{ ft}^2$

$N_A = 2760 \text{ seats}$ $S_A = 15,300 \text{ ft}^2$ $S_A/N_A = 5.5 \text{ ft}^2$

$t_I = 33; 11 \text{ msec}$ $S_O = 1200 \text{ ft}^2$ $V/S_T = 34.2 \text{ ft}$

* The terminology is explained in Appendix 3.

ARCHITECTURAL AND STRUCTURAL DETAILS

Uses: musical performances of all types. *Ceiling:* plaster on wooden lath with thick plaster ornamentation. *Walls:* plaster on wooden lath on wooden battens with air space behind. *Floors and carpets:* in the front half of the main floor and in the first balcony about 60% of the wooden floor is covered by carpet under the feet and in the aisles; in the rear half of the main floor, there are wooden boards under the seats, cork in the rear cross aisle; carpet on the other aisles; in the second balcony, there are wooden boards under the seats and cork in the aisles. Behind the orchestra there is carpet in the aisles and wooden boards under the seats. *Stage floor:* planks over large air space with wooden boxes for risers. *Stage enclosure:* plaster on wooden lath; organ case forms rear wall. *Stage height:* 53 in. above floor level at first row of seats. *Seating:* in the front half of the main floor and the first balcony, both top and bottom of the seat-bottoms are upholstered; two-thirds of both sides of the backrests are upholstered and also the armrests. In the rear half of the main floor the upholstery is thinner. Thin, plain plywood seats are used in the upper balcony; heavy, plain wooden seats are used behind the orchestra.

References: Drawings from T. Somerville and C. L. S. Gilford, *Gravesaner Blätter*, **3**, No. 9 (1957). Details from T. Somerville of B.B.C. Research Laboratories. Brochure from Edinburgh Corporation. Photographs from F. C. Inglis and Son, Edinburgh. Results of questionnaires and some details from P. H. Parkin, W. E. Scholes, and A. G. Derbyshire, *Acustica*, **2**, 97–100 (1952). Details were confirmed by the author during visits. *Architect:* Stockdale Harrison and Sons, and H. H. Thomson.

St. Andrew's Hall is cast in the same general mold as the concert halls of Leipzig, Vienna, Boston, Basel, and Amsterdam. Opened in 1877, it is rectangular in shape, with a low, shallow balcony extending around the hall, and beautiful, ornate coffers in the ceiling; it is in the style of an eighteenth-century palace ballroom. Daylight illuminates the ceiling from windows high up on the walls between the pilasters. At night, the ceiling is lighted by fluorescent tubes along the sills of the windows. The seating of the hall has been replaced recently so that it now holds 2434 persons for small performing groups and 2133 for a large orchestra. As is common in Great Britain, there are seats for 189 members of the audience to sit behind the orchestra. St. Andrew's Hall is little known in America. Only the British conductors whom I interviewed had an intimate knowledge of it.

I have listened to the Scottish National Orchestra perform in St. Andrew's Hall. Concert music there is excellent. The acoustics are as uniform as they are in any hall in which I have attended concerts. The tone of the strings comes through beautifully. The music has brilliance and liveness, although it is somewhat deficient in warmth. All instruments come forth with just the right loudness. The blend of the different sections of the orchestra is excellent. The hall is completely quiet—the faintest sound of the strings can be heard clearly.

Because of its general excellence, it can be compared with Symphony Hall in Boston and Vienna's Grosser Musikvereinssaal. It has the same growth of sound in the climaxes and the same beautiful, clear sound. The presence of some audience behind the orchestra subdues the brass and percussion and produces ideal string-brass-percussion balance. Since there is no second balcony, there is less shielding of seats, and the hall has more uniform acoustics than Symphony Hall in Boston. Its reverberation time is a little shorter than that in the Musikvereinssaal, and for Baroque, Classical, and Modern music this is an advantage, without harming appreciably the sound of Romantic music. With part of the audience behind, on the two sides, and above the orchestra, the distance between the conductor and the listeners averages less than in Boston.

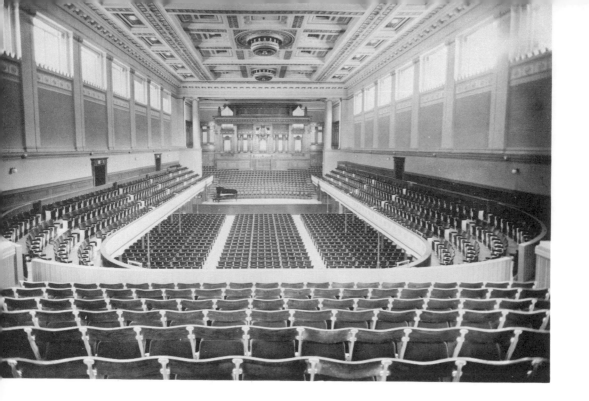

GLASGOW, ST. ANDREW'S HALL

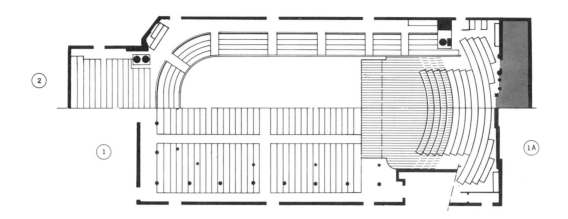

SEATING CAPACITY	Large orchestra 2133	Small performing groups 2434
1	1060	1168
1A	189	382
2	884	884

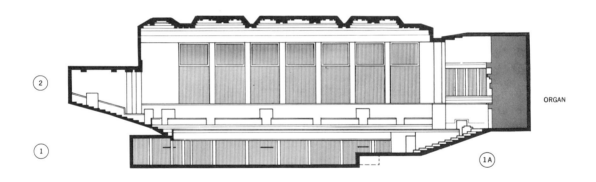

ORGAN

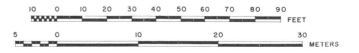

T. Somerville and C. L. S. Gilford of the B.B.C. speak of St. Andrew's Hall's "excellent acoustics" in the *Gravesaner Blätter*, No. 9, 1957. They describe its long reverberation time and the uniform diffusion of sound throughout the room. Another characteristic of this hall, they say, is that, although the reverberation time is long, it is possible to hear all the individual voices, even in loud passages. They believe that audience behind the orchestra is beneficial because it serves to keep the powerful instruments of the orchestra under control. They mention that performers find it an extremely easy hall to play in, because they can obtain smooth tone without exertion and can hear each other without difficulty.

Alexander Gibson, who by 1961 had conducted the Scottish National Orchestra in this hall more than 70 times wrote to me, "I have no hesitation in agreeing with the late Sir Thomas Beecham that this is one of the finest concert halls in Europe and is probably the finest in the British Isles. The hall is resonant enough to make a smaller body of strings sound large, without the lack of definition one associates with over-resonance. Solo string players find the acoustics most sympathetic and the contrast to them with Edinburgh is most marked." Sir John Barbirolli said, "Having been in this hall regularly for five years or more as conductor of the then Scottish Orchestra, I can only echo what my colleague, Alexander Gibson, says."

Sir Adrian Boult observed, "One gets beauty of tone and freshness of quality in St. Andrew's Hall, Glasgow. There is no hall [in the British Isles] comparable to the Leipzig Gewandhaus and Symphony Hall, Boston, though I think the St. Andrew's Hall comes nearest to them."

Frank Howes, music critic for the *London Times*, wrote to me that music sounds good in St. Andrew's Hall and it is well liked.

There is no question that this hall is very fine and could easily be one of the great halls of the world. One feature adversely affects its acoustics, in my opinion, and that is the use of ⅜-inch plywood, with an air space behind it, over the walls beneath the balcony. This large amount of thin wood helps to reduce the reverberation time at low frequencies to less than the values at mid-frequencies. The loss of bass is particularly noticeable at the rear of the main floor. The reverberation at low frequencies should be appreciably longer than that at mid-frequencies. If the bass-absorbing thin plywood were removed and replaced by painted plaster, then St. Andrew's Hall would very likely take its place high among the other halls of its kind in Boston, Vienna, Basel, and Amsterdam.

When these suggestions were made to John Dunsmore, general manager of Public Halls in Glasgow, he replied, "Painted plaster has not been on these walls within living memory, and there is no doubt that in an all-purpose hall, such as St. Andrew's Hall, the present paneling is much superior despite the slight loss in acoustical values."

TECHNICAL DETAILS FOR CONCERTS*

$V = 569,000 \text{ ft}^3$	$T_{500-1000}(\text{Occup.}) = 1.9 \text{ sec}$	$S_T = 14,900 \text{ ft}^2$
$N_A = 2133 \text{ seats}$	$S_A = 13,500 \text{ ft}^2$	$S_A/N_A = 6.3 \text{ ft}^2$
$t_I = 20; 8 \text{ msec}$	$S_O = 1400 \text{ ft}^2$	$V/S_T = 38.2 \text{ ft}$

* The terminology is explained in Appendix 3.

ARCHITECTURAL AND STRUCTURAL DETAILS

Uses: orchestra and general purpose. *Ceiling:* plaster on wood lath, coffered in thick plaster. *Side and rear walls:* Balcony: plaster on wood lath except for a 45-in. wood-paneled dado; Main floor under balcony: paneled in ⅜-in. plywood on battens; balcony fronts are of heavy wood. *Floors:* oak strips on joists over a basement. *Carpets:* none. *Stage enclosure:* none. *Stage floor:* wooden planks over deep air space. *Stage height:* 56 in. above floor level at front row of seats. *Seating:* front of backrests, armrests and top of seat-bottoms are upholstered in velour; seat-bottoms and rear of backrests are of solid wood.

References: Drawings from P. H. Parkin and W. E. Scholes of British Building Research Station. Details from T. Somerville of B. B. C. Research Laboratories and P. H. Parkin, W. E. Scholes, and A. G. Derbyshire of Building Research Station. Photographs courtesy of John Dunsmore, manager of the hall. Details confirmed by author during visits. *Architect:* John Cunningham. *Interior design:* James Sellers.

Philharmonic Hall, pleasant, warm, and comfortable, was clearly not built in a period of post-war austerity. Completed in 1939, it barely preceded the Battle of Britain. It is similar in architecture to the Kleinhans Music Hall in Buffalo and differs only in that it has boxes and there are no seats under the balcony. Its side walls are continuous with the ceiling, and together they form a shell inside the basic construction, consisting of a series of transverse sections, each about 15 feet wide. These sections, of plaster decorated with classical figures in bas relief, extend down to the floor of the balcony and to the wooden panels over the boxes on the main floor. They form a series, arranged in echelon, with the front edge of each section rolled back to leave a recess for lighting. The light, which is reflected from each section, indirectly illuminates the hall with a warm, ivory glow.

The seats are luxurious, and every square foot of the floors is carpeted. There is adequate space for legs, each seat being allotted 6.7 square feet of floor area (including aisle space). An audience of 184 is seated on a permanent stadium, semi-circular in shape, partially surrounding the orchestra. The exposed ends of this stadium and the wall behind it are finished in warm mahogany, as is the semi-circular ring of boxes.

Gerald McDonald, General Manager of the Royal Liverpool Philharmonic Society, says, "From the point of view of artists performing in the hall, the fact that there are only 754 seats enclosed by a ring of most attractive boxes, with a further audience of 885 in the balcony, is an unusual and stimulating feature."

I sat with Mr. McDonald in his office to talk about the auditorium. Philharmonic Hall is almost the only hall in England that is managed directly by an orchestra. "Its relatively low reverberation time and beautiful, well-defined tone," says Mr. McDonald, "make it uniquely favorable for Baroque and Classical music starting with Bach, for Modern music, and for any music that is cerebral in nature or requires refinement of definition. The hall does not have a cathedral sound and, hence, for many kinds of liturgical music, it does not provide the best environment for organ." I fully

LIVERPOOL, PHILHARMONIC HALL

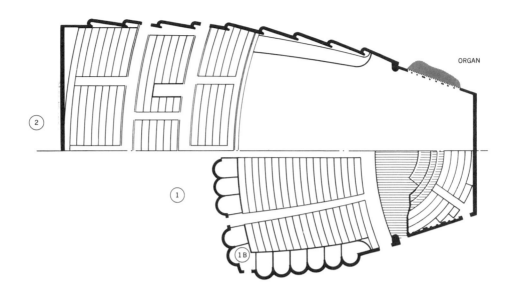

ORGAN

SEATING CAPACITY 1955

1   754

1A   184 plus 150 removable

2   885

1B   132

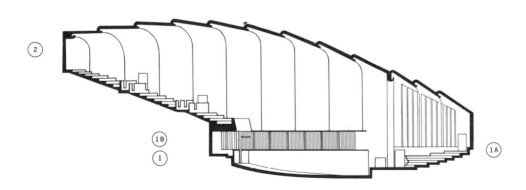

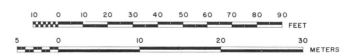

| 10 | 0 | 10 | 20 | 30 | 40 | 50 | 60 | 70 | 80 | 90 | FEET |

| 5 | 0 | 10 | 20 | 30 | METERS |

agree with the observations of this discerning musician-turned-manager.

In the questionnaire sent by Parkin et al. [*Acustica*, Vol. 2, p. 97 (1952)] to music critics, professors of music, and composers in Great Britain, 25 of those who responded were acquainted with the Liverpool Philharmonic Hall and some 16 knew six or more of the ten halls in the group under study. Of these 25 respondents, 90 per cent rated the hall "good" on a scale of "good," "fair," and "bad." Of the 14 who knew Liverpool, St. Andrew's, and Covent Garden, 10 gave top rating to Liverpool, although they liked St. Andrew's about as well. No other hall in Great Britain was said to be better. (Colston Hall, Free Trade Hall, and Royal Festival Hall, which were not completed until 1951, were not represented in the comparison.)

Colin Mason of the Manchester *Guardian* writes, "The Liverpool Philharmonic Hall is certainly excellent and very agreeable to be in."

Frank Howes of the London *Times* writes, "Philharmonic Hall is not very resonant, compared with St. Andrew's in Glasgow, but from sitting on the floor and in the gallery, it is my recollection that it is a good general purpose hall, not too "dry" nor so austere as the Festival Hall."

Sir Adrian Boult adds, "The quality of the sound is rather on the dry side, but pleasant."

Sir Malcolm Sargent says, "This hall is excellent, though it could be a little more resonant. Clarity is its strongest point. The sound from the boxes is very lopsided. One loses the tone from instruments on whichever side one is sitting, but the center of the hall and the gallery are very good."

Peter Heyworth of *The Observer* says, "I think that this is the best English concert hall, although I have not heard choral music in it. To my mind, it strikes a happy balance between clarity and roundness of tone."

T. Somerville (*B.B.C. Quarterly*, April 1949) writes, "Listening tests showed that the definition was good and that all instruments of the orchestra could be heard clearly. The lack of reinforcement of the music and the deadness of the hall, however, result in a hard tone in loud passages, which robs crescendo passages of their brilliance. . . . The reverberation time is low and only a few discrete reflections reach the audience after the original sound, and the strings are on the deadest part of the stage." Somerville observed a low-frequency "boom" in the hall. He writes, "There is little doubt that the method of construction employed in this hall is responsible for notes in the region of 110 cps [two octaves below middle A] being noticeably accentuated." He also stated, "There appeared to be a slight increase in liveness as the source of sound was moved towards the back of the stage, and this increase probably accounts for the prominence of the timpani and brass, which are normally placed there, and for the hardness of the strings, which lack reinforcement through being on the deader part of the stage."

Sir John Barbirolli says, "I would be inclined to rate the acoustics as 'fair' rather than 'good,' owing to its dryness of sound, though it is not unpleasant. It shares some of the properties of the Royal Festival Hall in its clarity and inclination to dryness, but I rate it higher in tone quality."

Of the four American and European conductors who knew this hall, three rated it as "good" to "excellent," and the fourth said, "The sound in this hall is too dry. There is not a nice warm resonance."

I listened to Arriaga's *Symphony in D*, Beethoven's *Concerto No. 5 for Piano*, and Stravinsky's ballet music *Petrouchka* while moving among three seats. The music is unquestionably clear, brilliant, and absolutely faithful. The piano sounds glorious; I have never heard better. The violin pizzacato is absolutely true, as is the sound of each instrument. The blend and ensemble are excellent. The hall has little apparent reverberation, which means that the growth of the crescendo, which characterizes the halls of Boston and Glasgow, is lacking. And this lack would certainly detract from symphonies of the Romantic period.

Only one fault is discernible: the basses and cellos are weak. Whether this is due to sound absorption by the organ grilles on either side of the stage enclosure, to the concentrated grouping of the basses, to the audience on the stage, to something involving the walls of the hall, or to a little of each, I am not prepared to say. However, the basses are stronger here than in the Royal Festival Hall. On the main floor, the brass-percussion-strings balance is good. In the rear of the balcony, the brass and percussion tend to be overly loud.

TECHNICAL DETAILS FOR CONCERTS*

$V = 479{,}000 \text{ ft}^3$	$T_{500-1000}(\text{Occup.}) = 1.5 \text{ sec}$	$S_T = 15{,}300 \text{ ft}^2$
$N_A = 1955 \text{ seats}$	$S_A = 13{,}900 \text{ ft}^2$	$S_A/N_A = 7.1 \text{ ft}^2$
$t_I = 25; 18 \text{ msec}$	$S_O = 1400 \text{ ft}^2$	$V/S_T = 31.3 \text{ ft}$

* The terminology is explained in Appendix 3.

ARCHITECTURAL AND STRUCTURAL DETAILS

Uses: half for symphonic music and half for speech. *Ceiling and side walls:* plaster on metal lath, divided above the boxes by lighting coves into 15-ft sections; there are about 4350 sq ft of wood paneling on the lower side walls; the boxes are of wood. *Rear upper walls:* rock wool batts covered with draperies. *Floors:* concrete. *Carpet:* all floors. *Stage enclosure:* the side walls are occupied by organ grilles; the back wall is paneled in wood. *Stage floor:* boards on joists over air space. *Height of stage:* 36 in. above floor level at front row of seats. *Seating:* both sides of backrest and seat are upholstered in tightly woven cloth.

References: Drawings from T. Somerville and C. L. S. Gilford, *Gravesaner Blätter*, **3**, No. 9, 1957. Details and listening judgments from T. Somerville, B.B.C. Research Laboratories, and P. H. Parkin, W. E. Scholes, and A. G. Derbyshire, *Acustica*, **2**, 97–100 (1952). Other information from E. Stacy, Building Research Station. Photographs courtesy of City of Liverpool, Gerald McDonald, general manager of the Philharmonic Hall. Details confirmed by the author during visits. *Architect:* Herbert J. Rowse.

London
ROYAL ALBERT HALL

On Wednesday, March 29, 1871, Queen Victoria, in one of her rare public appearances after the death of the Prince Consort, appeared in the Royal Box of the newly completed Royal Albert Hall of Arts and Sciences, surrounded by members of the Royal Family, to participate in the official opening. The official record (see References, Clark, p. 58) relates: "Prince of Wales . . . began to read a welcoming address . . . speaking distinctly in a clear voice that could be heard in all parts of the building; in many parts it could be heard twice, a curious echo bringing a repetition of one sentence as the next was begun." Thus began 90 years of experiments in an attempt to transform into a concert hall a space that is much too large ever to be fully successful for this purpose.

The Royal Albert Hall holds 5080 persons seated plus about 1000 standees. It is nearly elliptical in shape, about 230 feet long and 200 feet wide, with a volume of about 3,000,000 cubic feet, twice as great as any other hall represented in this study. Its uses are many—pageants, lectures, exhibitions, balls, organ recitals, choral presentations, symphony concerts, solo recitals, even athletic events. It fulfills London's need for a hall with a large seating capacity. After the 1941 destruction by bombing of the Queen's Hall, which had 2200 seats, the Royal Albert Hall became the principal concert hall of London. It remained so until 1951 when the Royal Festival Hall was opened.

The principal acoustical problems of the Royal Albert Hall arise from its size. They are: (1) the decrease in loudness of the direct sound emanating from the performers as it travels such large distances in the hall (consider the difficulty of an instrument or voice trying to fill nearly ten times more cubic volume of air than there is in any of the typical European concert halls); and (2) the audible return of very-long-delayed reflections from distant surfaces in the hall back toward the front of the hall, which are identified as "echoes."

From the beginning it was recognized that, of all the problems plaguing the Royal Albert Hall, the "echo was perhaps the most potentially damaging," and that "the presentation of great choral works was undoubtedly the

LONDON, ROYAL ALBERT HALL

type of event best suited to the hall's size, to its acoustics and, not least, to the emotional possibilities of the closed ring of seats." One of the building's most famous features is the great pipe organ, installed in 1871, and rebuilt sixty years later over a nine-year period that culminated in a second official presentation in 1934.

In 1873, a Royal Albert Hall Choral Society was formed. Its initial series of concerts was so successful that the hall began to be accepted as a place where "one could hold musical entertainments. . . . Music was one of the main reasons for the Hall's existence."

From its beginning until 1949 a large velarium of cloth weighing 1¼ tons was draped beneath the ceiling. This velarium was raised and lowered from time to time in an effort to better the acoustics. At one point, Sir Joseph Barnby, conductor of the Choral Society, wrote, "The lowering of the velarium and the fixing of the new hangings have proved to be much more effectual than I could have supposed possible."

Richard Wagner, who directed a Wagner festival in 1877, was in such despair at the acoustics that he required Hans Richter to take over the bulk of the conducting duties. Several concert singers have had spectacular successes in the Royal Albert Hall. The first was Adelina Patti. The official record says, "Even the great spaces of the hall could not affect the extraordinary carrying power of Patti's voice, the most striking example of this being in the inevitable 'Home Sweet Home.' . . . It seemed as if, in some queer way, the Hall acted as a challenge. . . . She did more than merely succeed." The second was Clara Butt. "Only the voice of Clara Butt, it was often claimed, could acoustically fill the building, and in later years an American writer asked whether the Hall had been built in intelligent anticipation of Clara Butt or whether nature, abhorring a vacuum, had created Clara Butt for the Hall. *Land of Hope and Glory* and the *National Anthem* were her set-piece performances." She said, "If I die soon, I shall have 'She died of singing *God Save the King*' put on the tombstone."

By 1914, the record shows, "Even the most ardent devotee admitted that the acoustics were still an embarrassment under certain conditions. Yet for some musical events the building was ideal. The steadily growing tradition—adding a certain lustre even to the sound, veiling the echo, disguising

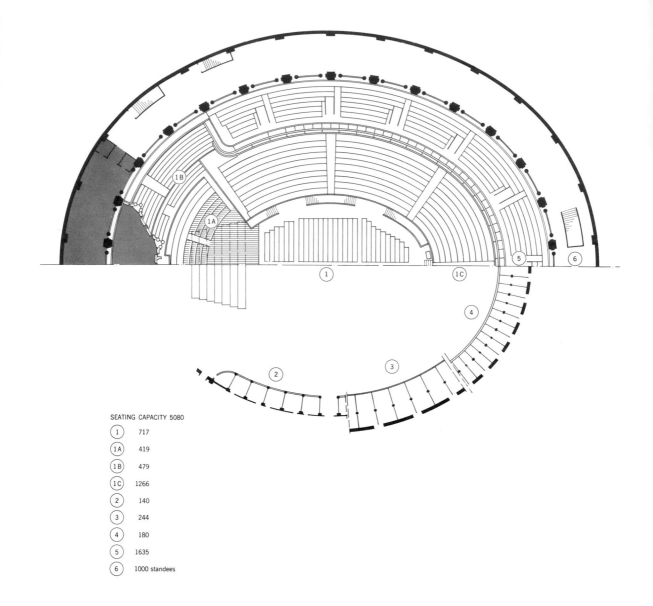

SEATING CAPACITY 5080

(1)	717
(1A)	419
(1B)	479
(1C)	1266
(2)	140
(3)	244
(4)	180
(5)	1635
(6)	1000 standees

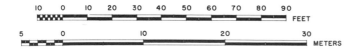

10 0 10 20 30 40 50 60 70 80 90
FEET

5 0 10 20 30
METERS

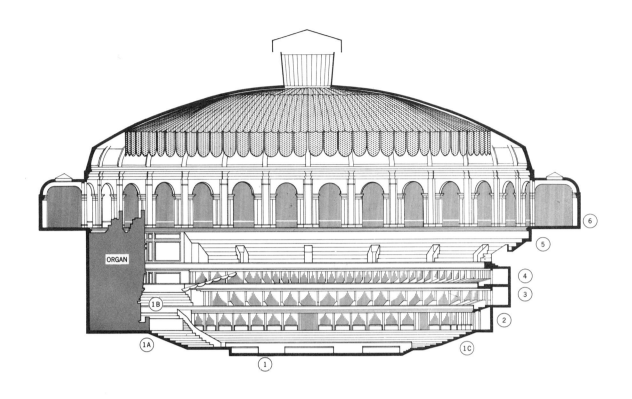

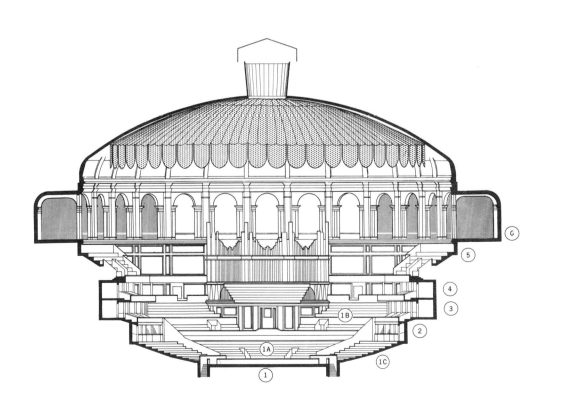

the dissonances—was at last beginning to transform public opinion. Between 1900 and 1914 there grew up a musical respectability that even the Hall's most spiteful critic could not entirely discount."

In 1934, we read, "The echo persisted and there was even some suggestion that it had grown worse. The public may have grown more critical . . . in some seats practically nothing can be heard; in others every note is heard twice, so that many people have the satisfaction of hearing two concerts without extra charge. . . ."

On Empire Day in 1938 a choir of 2000 and one of the largest audiences the Hall had known joined to sing *Jerusalem*. "Whenever the demand was for a hall in which music was intended to arouse the emotions more than normally, the Hall of Arts and Sciences was chosen almost automatically."

In 1941 Keith Douglas, with the help of the Building Research Station undertook thorough remedial measures in order to ensure the success of the Promenade Concerts which had been transferred from the bombed Queen's Hall. The platform was partly enclosed by screens 20 feet high, a canopy reflector was slung over the orchestra, various areas of curved wall in the hall had draperies added, and the velarium was lowered. A real improvement resulted, and the "Proms," conducted by Sir Henry Wood and Basil Cameron, were continued through the war.

In 1949 the 12,000 square-foot cloth velarium and the glass dome were replaced by a 2-ton, fluted, perforated, aluminum inner dome, on top of which is a layer of rock wool. This new dome is designed to absorb sound that would otherwise reflect from the dome. This change is said to have vastly reduced the echo. In 1950 *The Times* wrote, "We laugh at the Albert Hall, we shrug our shoulders in despair at its acoustics, but we have an affection for it, and we will even grudgingly admit that its Victorian size and accoutrements have a certain swagger and solidity which we envy." Moreover, "to see it when full, when an audience rises to its feet to sing carols or a National Anthem is an inspiring sight."

In closing, the official record of the hall states, "Yet it is as a concert hall capable of holding nearly 7000 people that its full stature has come to be appreciated. Its virtues, both acoustic and financial, were illustrated by the report of the Government Committee set up in October, 1954 to investigate the need for, and economic prospects of, a new building on the Queen's Hall site. Acoustically, it underlined what many experts have been stating privately for many years—that while the Royal Albert Hall's acoustics were deficient in some respects, those of even the ultra-modern Royal Festival Hall were by no means perfect; for while these were admitted to be very fine, 'it appears', said the Committee's report, 'to be commonly agreed that neither its (Royal Festival Hall's) platform nor its acoustics are altogether well suited for the performance of choral music.' "

The European and American conductors who are familiar with the Royal Albert Hall are unanimously unhappy about it. They characterize it as "one of the world's worst halls"; "two of everything for the price of one"; "terrible, too big"; "too large and too long a reverberation time"; and "a very bad hall."

Sir Adrian Boult, who is particularly fond of the Royal Albert Hall, said, "This hall has a beautiful quality of sound; in fact it comes nearer than any other hall in the country, except St. Andrew's Hall in Glasgow, to our ideal, which is Symphony Hall in Boston. The Albert Hall is marred by a definite echo towards the back of the ground floor. On the ground floor, and the first two tiers of boxes also, the sound varies considerably as you move towards the sides, in fact it is only in the highest parts of the hall that you get a real perfection of sound. The Promenade Gallery at the very top, which is set back over the corridors of the floors below, and so almost outside the hall in a sense, gives one a most lovely distant picture of the music in hand, but it is, of course, very distant as it comes through a series of arches. The reverberation in the Royal Albert Hall is too long for general clarity, but, as I say, the quality makes up for this."

Sir Malcolm Sargent says: "This building has a sadly noticeable echo. Many people love it from associations of ideas. Religious music, with large choirs, sounds magnificent owing to the cathedral-like quality. It is not ideal for orchestral music although quiet string music sounds beautiful. The building, of course, is very large, and this necessarily gives to all music a sense of distance to which one has to become accustomed."

Alexander Gibson writes: "The affection I have for this old hall does not blind me to the fact that its size requires the largest of forces for any measure of success. I recently conducted a concert with one of our major symphony orchestras and the combined Brass Band of the Guards. This is the only time I have felt that the sound has been adequate to fill the huge arena. With a full sized symphony orchestra the general effect is, to the listener, slightly more pleasant than the Royal Festival Hall."

Colin Mason of the Manchester *Guardian* writes: "The Albert Hall, of course, has its famous echo, which at worst really does give you everything double, though there are patches where it doesn't disturb. I've never been able to reach any conclusion about the best place, but the worst seems to be directly opposite the platform."

Desmond Shawe-Taylor of the *Sunday Times* comments: "The acoustic difficulties—not to say—horrors!—of this Hall are too famous to need repetition. Despite all the unsightly means taken to kill the echo, a good deal of it remains, and the results can be—from certain parts of the hall—agonizing, especially in piano concertos, where one often hears two of each note. Singers like the hall, and I have always liked listening to singers there; good ones have no difficulty in making even a small-scale voice tell in the large space."

Finally, we hear from Frank Howes of *The Times:* "This Hall is probably the worst in the world, owing to its oval shape with two foci. The famous echo has been to some extent subdued by modern devices. The only possible places for hearing music in it are the top gallery and the stalls at the sides fairly near the front. What one would expect to be the best seats, i.e., immediately opposite the platform, are the worst."

Early in 1961 I attended a concert by the London Philharmonic Orchestra in the Royal Albert Hall. The screens around the orchestra were not used. The canopy was mounted as shown in the drawings. The first part of the program, which included Schubert's *Unfinished Symphony* and Grieg's *Piano Concerto in A minor,* was disappointing. I listened from three different locations: a box on one side of the hall just above the oval of stadium seats; a seat directly opposite the stage in the second row of the balcony; and a seat on the main floor. I have never heard an orchestra or a piano sound as weak. The direct sound was audible and the audience was very attentive, but the individual instruments and the piano sounded much too faint except in the fortissimo passages.

But then the orchestra played Tchaikovsky's *Overture 1812*. The hall demonstrated its well-told ability to stir the emotions of its patrons. The great organ sounded out at the climax and the "cannon" boomed forth (an especially durable bass drum was struck often with all the drummer's might; sometimes, I am told, yachting cannons are fired instead). The chimes clanged loudly through their part and, finally, in combination with the military fanfare theme, the *Russian Imperial Anthem* thundered forth. The echo enhanced the gunfire, the chimes, and the fanfare. The general reverberation swelled with the increased vigor of the composition. Above all, the great organ sounded like the voice of Jupiter. The audience was left breathless and tingling. It is for these moments of ecstasy that the Albert Hall continues to exist.

TECHNICAL DETAILS FOR CONCERTS[*]

$V = 3,060,000$ ft^3	$T_{500-1000}$(Occup.) $= 2.5$ sec	$S_T = 40,000$ ft^2
$N_A = 5080$ seats †	$S_A = 37,800$ ft^2	$S_A/N_A = 6.2$ ft^2
$t_I = 65(35); 70$ msec	$S_O = 2200$ ft^2	$V/S_T = 76.5$ ft

[*] The terminology is explained in Appendix 3.

† Plus 1000 standees for which there are some chairs available.

ARCHITECTURAL AND STRUCTURAL DETAILS

Uses: general purpose. *Ceiling:* roof over balcony is of plaster directly on the structure; the original cloth valance is replaced by perforated aluminum flutes, about 5 ft wide at the maximum and convex in cross section; behind the aluminum are several inches of mineral wool. *Walls:* generally plastered, but the back of the boxes are of thin wood. *Floors:* arena floor is 1-in. wood on wooden joists over large air space; balcony is of concrete; boxes are of wood. *Stage enclosure:* wooden canopy over orchestra. *Stage floor:* thick wood over air space. *Stage height:* 40 in. above floor level at first row of seats. *Carpets:* Often used on arena floor. *Added absorptive material:* several inches of rock wool are located on the upper side of the fluted perforated aluminum ceiling; canvas "banners" about 10 to 12 ft long are hung in front of the cove to control echoes. *Seating:* arena and main floor surrounding, tops of seats and fronts of backrests are sponge rubber pads with cloth covering—all other surfaces are of wood; boxes, loose occasional chairs upholstered the same as for arena; balcony, theater-type tip-up chairs with springs covered by horsehair and cotton waste and upholstered in cloth—front of backrests are sponge rubber covered with cloth—rest of chair is solid wood; gallery, 300 wooden chairs for use in the standing areas.

References: Ronald W. Clark, *The Royal Albert Hall,* Hamish Hamilton, London, 1958. Christopher R. Hopper, Manager and Secretary, supplied many details including the book by Clark and photographs. Drawings and other details furnished by D. L. Robinson, and W. A. Allen, Building Research Station. Most details confirmed by author during visit. *Designers:* Capt. Francis Fowke (who died during design in 1865) and Lt. Col. H. Y. D. Scott (who succeeded Fowke and continued as Director of Works under the supervision of a "Committee on Advice").

The Royal Festival Hall with 3000 seats is one of the most interesting buildings dedicated to music in Europe. London, hardly famous for its cloudless skies or twinkling stars, has concentrated all the sparkling glamour of a Mediterranean night into the interior of this one edifice. After locating the entrance—which is not easy for a newcomer in the dark—one enters a large foyer and proceeds through a fascinating mosaic of stairways, carpets, lighting, and interior vistas. The two-level restaurant, filled before the concert, looks inviting and one plans to visit it later. (But, alas, when I was there the kitchen closed early and after the concert there were only some pallid cold plates available.) Through the broad windows of the outer walls beyond the restaurant are views upriver to the spires of Westminster and downriver to the dome of St. Paul's.

The approach up the stairs and through foyers is so cleverly made and so beautiful that it promises an evening of excitement. The designers have achieved beauty through proportion and color and admirably contrived lighting.

Every effort was made to give this hall as fine acoustics as its size would permit. All the available publications on architectural acoustics were studied. The talents of the Building Research Station, with its staff of scientists, and England's most experienced consultant on architectural acoustics were employed to work with the architect. Help and critical comments were obtained from America, Denmark, and Germany. The British musical world was enlisted to aid in the evaluation of existing British halls.

From 1900 until 1948, when the design was undertaken, only a few large halls had been built anywhere in the world and only one of them, the Salle Pleyel in Paris, was in an important musical center. But the Salle Pleyel had been a notorious disappointment. Consequently, except for the lessons the Salle Pleyel taught, most of the experiments of the first half of the twentieth century had to be run in the Royal Festival Hall. And much was unknown.

The reactions of the British music critics to the hall, since its dedication in 1951, have been lively and contradictory. Their criticisms range over the

LONDON, ROYAL FESTIVAL HALL

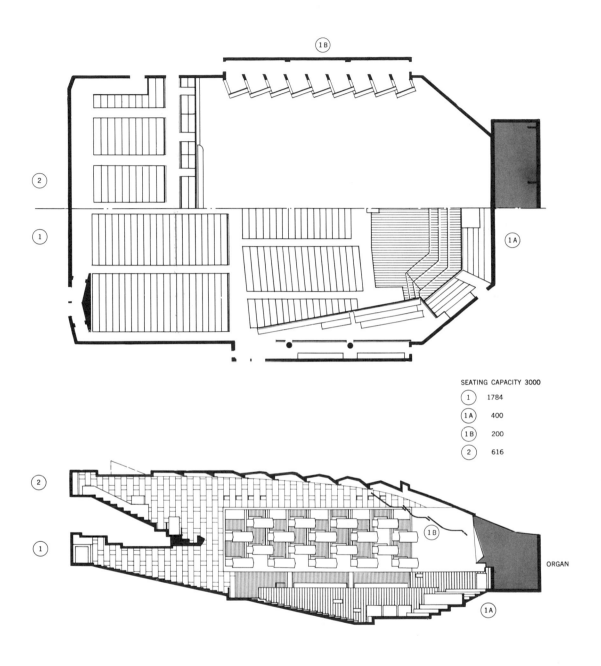

SEATING CAPACITY 3000

1	1784	
1A	400	
1B	200	
2	616	

ORGAN

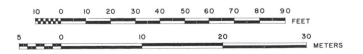

10 0 10 20 30 40 50 60 70 80 90
FEET

5 0 10 20 30
METERS

whole spectrum. But first let us review the analysis published by the Building Research Station experts who have borne the brunt of the pre- and post-completion argument.

Parkin, Allen, Purkis, and Scholes [*Acustica,* Vol. 3, pp. 1–21 (1953)] state:

> The Royal Festival Hall is a good hall acoustically with no serious faults; the rectangular plan is still favored . . . the canopy and the raking of the seats have produced excellent definition and uniform conditions. The only criticisms which have been at all serious are those concerning lack of fullness. The authors hold to their original view that this lack would be overcome by a longer R. T. [reverberation time]; . . . an increase in volume per seat would be the most important method for lengthening the R. T. . . . any increase in the R. T. at mid-frequencies should be supplemented by a corresponding increase in low frequencies. It might be that a greater increase at low frequencies, or even an increase only at low frequencies, would be the most effective way of increasing the fullness. . . . The canopy in the Royal Festival Hall has, for the sake of the organ, been made higher than the authors would have wished, and although this does not appear to have hindered the definition, it has probably detracted from the blend. Apart from a slight weakness at the back of the Terrace Stalls, the uniformity of the acoustics is good.

Frank Howes of the London *Times* wrote to me in 1961, "The Royal Festival Hall is too dry. It is hard work for singers, though if their technique is good, they will not sound any worse than they are even if they are not flattered. More detailed criticism is that bass frequencies are extinguished too easily. . . . But its clarity has transformed London orchestral playing by exposing faults of ensemble and intonation. . . . Chamber music is audible and clear, though the hall is too big for it.

T. Somerville and C. L. S. Gilford of the B.B.C. [*Gravesaner Blätter,* Vol. 3, No. 9 (1957)] say:

> The Royal Festival Hall is very good for the hearing of speech because of its deadness and the absence of prominent echoes. It is also good for chamber music and for the Mozart-size orchestra. As the size of the orchestra increases a true ensemble becomes more difficult to obtain, and for a full-size symphony orchestra, conditions, in the authors' opinion, are not entirely satisfactory.

Somerville and Gilford go on to describe the divergent reactions of the press to such qualities as fullness and resonance, liveness, blend and balance. In this connection, they quote from an article in the *New Statesman and Nation,* with which they are in agreement [D. Shawe-Taylor, October 27, 1951]:

Two kinds of music seem to suffer the most; the elusive atmospheric piece, and the sumptuous late Romantic scores of Wagner, Strauss and Rachmaninoff. . . . It is doubtless one and the same fault which prevents these categories of music from having their proper effect. Probably the reverberation period of the hall is still just too short; possibly the steep slope of the orchestra and auditorium encourages the brass and percussion to drown the strings in the valley between. Whatever the cause it is quite astonishing how differently music of a fully saturated texture can sound in a suitable auditorium such as the Concertgebouw in Amsterdam. By the way, I must protest at the assumption that those of us who are not quite satisfied . . . are displaying a taste vitiated by long experience with the Albert Hall. . . . I can think of no famous auditorium with the peculiar dryness of tone which is to be felt at every big climax in the Festival Hall.

Shawe-Taylor, who is music critic for *The Sunday Times,* wrote to me in 1961, "The hall strikes me as excellent at rehearsals—i.e., when empty; but the fuller it is, the more lifeless the quality of the sound. It is quite free from echo, and the music sounds very clear."

Sir Malcolm Sargent says, "Here the acoustics are first-class with regard to clarity, in fact frighteningly so. The fault is that the hall is lacking in resonance. . . . One never gets the feeling of a tremendous sound of a resonant chording. The part writing is always too clear when chordal climaxes are desired."

Sir Adrian Boult tells me, "The Royal Festival Hall has amazing clarity and textural exactness. I would say that the designers tried so hard to project the sound outward that though a pianissimo string quartet will comfortably reach the back row of the top gallery, the extremes of fortissimo take on a rather hard quality and any forcing of tone by voices or brass instruments can become most unpleasant."

Twelve of the conductors from outside the British Isles whom I interviewed are acquainted with this hall. Some have conducted there more than a dozen times. Herbert von Karajan gives the most favorable report: "This is the best of the modern halls. The tonal quality is especially notable. The reflections from the floor of the stage are strong and give the conductor an electrifying feeling. From the standpoint of the orchestra, on stage and at the podium, there is perfect blend on short forte chords." Two other conductors agree with von Karajan.

Stanislaw Skrowaczewski said, "The acoustical conditions seem very good from the conductor's podium. I could hear each instrument distinctly without losing good blend. I certainly liked the wonderful transparency."

Leopold Stokowski speaks for another group of three conductors: "In the Royal Festival Hall the double basses simply cannot be heard. Even when the basses are encouraged, they cannot be heard in the audience. There is over-absorption at all frequencies so that the reverberation time is too short. There is also lack of sound diffusion. In this hall, the sound is metallic and tinny. There is no warmth."

Five of the conductors felt that there is too much definition, that the sound is too precise even at the back of the hall. They agree that the sections of the orchestra sound as if they were isolated groups, there is no ensemble, no cohesion; the horns are too loud on one side of the hall and cannot be heard on the other side; the basses can be heard on only one side of the hall.

Hope Bagenal, who was the principal acoustical consultant to Festival Hall, wrote to me, "In respect of R.F.H. you ought to relate 'definition' and 'fullness of tone' to *tempo*. At slow speeds 'definition' is easy, but when you come to 12 or 15 notes a second, it is difficult. A great test of a hall is a piano concerto—the piano picks out an echo owing to its percussion. The R.F.H. permits good phrasing at high speeds; a piano concerto in the hall is most dramatic and communicates excitement and audience response. In the converse—'fullness of tone' is most desirable for choral music and true polyphonic music, but it will demand a slower tempo if phrasing is to be clean. The logic of the above leads clearly to the demand for two types of large concert halls in each city. Also, I doubt whether with a reverberation time of 2 seconds you could play a modern *prestissimo* as you can in the R.F.H."

Four American music critics who know the hall well agreed that the acoustics are sharp, but the hall has too little blend and almost no acoustical color. Everything is articulated and clear, but the bass is weak and there is no impact, no fullness of tone on the climaxes. Sir John Barbirolli writes, "I would subscribe completely to the comments of the four American music critics."

Robert C. Marsh of the Chicago *Sun-Times*, when interviewed said, "Conductors like Leopold Stokowski, who put great emphasis on the low frequencies, dislike Festival Hall. I feel that the hall is quite well balanced. If there is a valid criticism, it is that the propagation of the low frequencies is not quite as firm as many musicians desire. But many musicians love it, particularly those who play music requiring great clarity and definition for contrapuntal lines. Nothing in Festival Hall could possibly cause undesirable overhang or blurring."

Peter Heyworth of *The Observer*, London, says, "The sound is splendid when the place is empty—very fresh, lively and clear, although a bit deficient in bass and roundness. Deadness and dryness come in direct proportion to the size of the audience."

Colin Mason of the Manchester *Guardian* was surprised at the amount of negative criticism. "I wonder," he wrote, "whether the fact that it falls as much lower in the general estimation is not a criticism of the conductors and listeners who reported on it rather than of the hall itself. I have often heard its acoustics described as 'dry' and 'clinical' but surely this merely means that those who find it so prefer their music wrapped up in a flattering haze provided by what they would call a 'mellow' hall. Perhaps it is a point worth considering; is it not we who are at fault rather than the hall if we cannot bear 'truthful' acoustics which reveal every blemish?"

But I must have my say: Reverberation can make a positive contribution to music, and composers of every period seem to have taken this contribution into account. Thus, Baroque, early Classical, and some Modern music sound best in a relatively dry hall. But Romantic music needs the blend, the liveness, and the fullness of tone provided by a long reverberation time. Reverberation, like the broad brush stroke, does more than just cover the blemishes of the artist's technique. For contrapuntal music, I agree with Mr. Mason, this hall is most transparent—most honest in its acoustics and very successful.

I have attended and enjoyed many concerts in the Royal Festival Hall. It is free of extraneous noise and this makes it possible to hear the faintest sound—an unusual and pleasant experience when the orchestra is of the first rank. In checking back through notes that I have been making since 1951, I find the following summary of my feelings:

> The definition is excellent and the hall is very good for piano, chamber music, and modern music. Except for the seats along the edge of the hall on the same side as the bass viols, I hear too little bass. My feeling is that the lack of bass in the hall is the most serious problem.
>
> On the main floor, the hall reverberation is hardly noticeable—there is little liveness. In the upper gallery, the hall is more alive, the reverberation seems to come from the upper center of the hall.
>
> The woodwinds are particularly good everywhere. The strings are also good, but they would enjoy more hall liveness. When the French horns are at the rear and one side of the orchestra, the wall behind them amplifies their sound too much relative to the rest of the orchestra. Piano is marvelous.

I was pleasantly surprised when I sat in the second box from the rear in the second tier on the left side. The orchestral sounds that were reflected from the wall and the boxes on the opposite side of the hall gave to the music a pleasant liveness that I have not heard in other seats. If the entire hall sounded as it does here, there would be much less discussion of the "dry" acoustics.

The science of acoustics owes a great debt to those who planned this hall and published such thorough reports after its completion. The Royal Festival Hall is and will remain one of the world's most important concert halls. We have all benefited from its presence and from its lessons. Above all, it illustrates that one hall cannot be all things to all people.

TECHNICAL DETAILS FOR CONCERTS[*]

$V = 775,000 \text{ ft}^3$	$T_{500-1000}(\text{Occup.}) = 1.47 \text{ sec}$	$S_T = 23,090 \text{ ft}^2$
$N_A = 3000 \text{ seats}$	$S_A = 21,230 \text{ ft}^2$	$S_A/N_A = 7.1 \text{ ft}^2$
$t_I = 34; 14 \text{ msec}$	$S_O = 1860 \text{ ft}^2$	$V/S_T = 33.6 \text{ ft}$

[*] The terminology is explained in Appendix 3.

ARCHITECTURAL AND STRUCTURAL DETAILS

Uses: symphonic music, soloists, chamber music, ballet, and lectures. *Ceiling:* 2 to 3 in. of plaster, prefabricated with wood lath and rags for binding. *Side and rear walls:* ⅜-in. elm plywood with 3- and 4-in. air space behind, erected in two sizes, 30 x 72 in. and 18 x 30 in., with random bracing on the larger size; vertical, overlapping strips of wood (Copenhagen treatment) with air space behind, several inches deep over brick, is located below the side galleries; the doors, the rears of the side balconies, and the rear walls are covered with leather, backed by rock wool with several inches of air space behind; exposed wood wool, 2 in. thick, is used in 33% of the cornice regions. *Floors:* principally thin, hard, compressed cork on concrete. *Stage enclosure:* a canopy made of 2-in. formed sycamore wood is hung over the orchestra. *Stage floor:* except for the upper step, which is of wood on concrete, the stage is wooden boards over air space. *Stage height:* 30 in. above floor level at first row of seats. *Added absorptive material:* (see Walls above) wool cloth with candlewick embroidery is used in the backs of the quadruple tiers of boxes. *Seating:* the top of the seat-bottom and the front of the backrest are upholstered in very porous, ribbed, hard cloth; the armrests are upholstered in leather; the underseat is perforated, with rock wool inside.

References: P. H. Parkin, W. A. Allen, H. J. Purkis, and W. E. Scholes, *Acustica,* **3,** 1–21 (1953); E. Meyer and R. Thiele, *Acustica,* **6,** 425–444 (1956); T. Somerville and C. L. S. Gilford, *Gravesaner Blätter,* **3,** No. 9, 27–42 (1957). Private communications from V. Jordan, O. Brandt, P. H. Parkin, R. Thiele, and T. Somerville. Details verified by author during visits. Drawings courtesy of Hubert Bennett, architect to the London County Council. Photographs courtesy T. E. Bean, general manager of the Royal Festival Hall. *Architect to the London County Council during design and construction:* Robert Mathew. *Deputy architect:* J. L. Martin.

The Royal Opera House, Covent Garden, stands in the middle of a vegetable market. But do not be deceived by the lorries—it is a dignified theater, perhaps without the majesty of Milan's La Scala or the plush décor of the Théatre de l'Opéra in Paris, but by no means undistinguished. Rebuilt for the third time in 1858, it has since then seen its patrons forsake evening dress for the lounge suit. It has presented the world's finest singers and has boasted of some celebrated music directors—Frederich Gye, Augustus Harris, Sir Thomas Beecham, and Bruno Walter. Covent Garden has kept its position as a leading opera house and as a theater in which artists appreciate success. Today it is also the home of the Royal Ballet and it gives Londoners an almost year-round season of first-rate ballet and fine opera.

Sir John Barbirolli said to me, "This lovely old house has excellent acoustics. Perhaps the orchestral sound there is not as brilliant as in many of the great Italian opera houses in which I have conducted—La Scala, San Carlo in Naples, or La Fenice in Venice—but if due care is taken with the seating of the orchestra, some splendid results can be obtained."

Sir Malcolm Sargent said of Covent Garden, "Very good acoustics indeed. If anything, it is a little unflattering to the orchestral tone, the pit being perhaps a little unnecessarily deep, but this, of course, is an advantage to the smaller voices. It is not as brilliant in quality as La Scala or the Teatro Colón in Buenos Aires, but it is very good indeed, particularly in the boxes and upper parts of the house."

Frank Howes of *The Times*, London, wrote to me: "Of conventional, theater shape, it is pretty good in all parts. I had a box on the second tier to which the voices from the stage and the sound of the orchestra rose in their right proportions, with some bias in favor of the singer—which is good for critical purposes. Downstairs the balance is rather different. The galleries are good, especially for voices."

Desmond Shawe-Taylor of *The Sunday Times*, London, remarked, "This theater has the normally good acoustics of the traditionally round-shaped opera interior. It has always been true that the best blend and clarity of tone is to be found in the large upper tier. In the lower tiers, all but the front

LONDON, ROYAL OPERA HOUSE

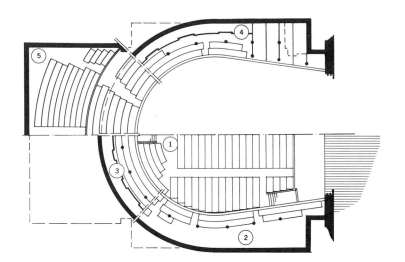

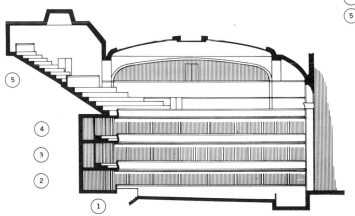

SEATING CAPACITY 2180

① 565
② 305 + 58 standees
③ 217
④ 221
⑤ 872

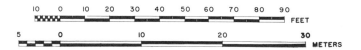

10	0	10	20	30	40	50	60	70	80	90	

FEET

5	0	10	20	30	

METERS

rows tend to have some tone cut off by the low balcony overhangs."

Alexander Gibson wrote me recently, "In the seasons 1957–1958 and 1958–1959 I conducted several performances there and found the acoustics from the orchestra pit very pleasant. This old building has, like so many other old theatres, extremely lively acoustics which can handle the largest volumes of sound without any bad effect on the clarity of the sound and yet at the same time can give a good account of a quiet pianissimo. My own observation sitting in the theatre is that the string tone sounds slightly thin and pinched although a full body of strings is used, but apart from this the balance is, in general, satisfactory."

In 1958, I attended several operas in this house. My immediate reaction was that there is a serious deficiency in the bass tones. On investigation I found thin plywood barriers behind the seats at all levels of the house, which accounts for the absorption of the bass. I also agree to some extent with John Christie who has been quoted in the *Journal of the Royal Institute of Architects* (January 1950) as saying, "At Covent Garden, if you sit on the main floor or in the lowest ring you simply do not hear the violins, and when you hear Wagner there, all you hear is the winds and the 'cellos."

The Royal Opera House, like so many opera houses, has its best acoustics in the upper tier of the balconies. There, the initial-time-delay gap is small and the music has clarity and brilliance without sacrificing liveness, although the level of the singers' voices changes noticeably as they move about, presumably because of the manner in which the domed ceiling reflects sound. A domed ceiling is not the best shape for distributing the sound among the seats of an opera house. A flat ceiling with some irregularities on its surface to provide diffusion of reflected sound is markedly better.

Taken all in all, I rate La Scala in Milan and the Staatsoper in Vienna as acoustically superior to the Royal Opera House. It is, perhaps, on a par with the Théatre de l'Opéra in Paris, or even slightly inferior to it, owing to the large amount of thin wood that forms its interior surfaces.

Peter Heyworth of *The Observer* wrote to me in 1962, "I agree . . . that this theatre is pretty good, though not outstanding, for sound. The orchestral sound is round rather than clear."

Regardless of the critics and the writers, Covent Garden will remain one of the world's most important centers for opera and ballet. England will continue to profit from Covent Garden's long heritage and interest in producing all that is internationally good in opera, whether Italian, French, Austrian, German, English, Slavic, or other. And what other opera company can better this boast?

TECHNICAL DETAILS FOR OPERA[*]

$V = 432{,}500$ ft^3	$T_{500-1000}$(Occup.) $= 1.1$ sec	$S_P = 1700$ ft^2
$N_A = 2180$ seats	$S_A = 14{,}630$ ft^2	$S_T = 17{,}000$ ft^2
$N_T = 2209$	S_O(Pit) $= 670$ ft^2	$S_A/N_T = 6.6$ ft^2
$t_I = 19; 13$	S_{OF}(Pit) $= 670$ ft^2	$V/S_T = 25.4$ ft

* The terminology is explained in Appendix 3.

ARCHITECTURAL AND STRUCTURAL DETAILS

Uses: opera and ballet. *Ceiling:* plaster on ⅜-in. resin-board; Soffits of tiers: plaster. *Walls:* Faces of all tiers: plaster on wood lath; Rear of main floor, and two tiers: thin plywood screens, wallpapered; Gallery: plywood on battens. *Floors:* wood, all levels. *Carpet:* carpet on underpad on main floor, boxes, and the two tiers; linoleum in front balcony; bare wood, rear gallery. *Seating:* Main floor, two tiers, and front balcony: seat, backrest, and armrests are upholstered, rear of backrest is cloth over wood; Upper gallery: continuous benches with moquette cloth over thin underpadding; Boxes: 4 upholstered chairs in each box. *Orchestra pit:* hardwood floor over 18-in. air space; walls brick and papered; no sound-absorbing materials. Rail: 2-in. solid teak.

References: Technical details courtesy Royal Opera House, T. Somerville, B.B.C. Research Laboratories, and W. A. Allen, Building Research Station. Photographs courtesy of British Travel Association. Details verified by author during visit. *Architect:* Edward Barry.

The Free Trade Hall in Manchester opened in 1951, the same year as the Royal Festival Hall. The architect had to build within the boundaries of the old walls, the façade being the only part of the building that remained after the bombings. The Free Trade Hall resembles no other modern hall. In keeping with the practice in many halls in the provinces, most of the main floor is flat in order that it may be used for dances, banquets, and other public functions. The stage and the wall behind it form a pleasant background for the orchestra. A most striking feature is the ceiling, with 35 octagonal indentations, each 3 feet deep. The inner sides of the coffers have seven or so steps, each of which is painted a different brilliant color—turquoise, red, yellow, green, pink. The large panels between the columns on the side wall are painted turquoise with a small brown panel at the top of each, in the center of which is a coat-of-arms. The rear wall of the stage is tan with sections in bold relief, painted brown. The dominant architectural feature at the front of the hall is the tremendous three-part acoustical canopy over the orchestra. The stage is steeply terraced so that each musician can be seen from the two balconies. Viewed from the stage, the hall appears to be predominantly balconies.

I attended a symphony concert by the Hallé Orchestra in the Free Trade Hall early in 1961. The music was louder than in any other hall in my experience. The lone bass horn in one composition sounded like eight. In double forte passages the trombones, trumpets, and percussion completely drowned out the strings, especially in the first balcony. The hall was overly brilliant, like a bright light in a white room. From a seat in the front of the first balcony, the piano was not too clear; the notes seemed to be jumbled together. From the balconies the reverberation sounded unreal, as though it were being amplified in some way at the sides and over the stage. The audience's applause sounded very loud.

From the main floor (tenth row, center), the piano sounds were more articulated. The violins sounded much clearer than in the balconies, and the peculiar reverberation was not as apparent. Instead I heard the actual reverberation time of 1.6 seconds (at mid-frequencies). The basses, cellos,

MANCHESTER, FREE TRADE HALL

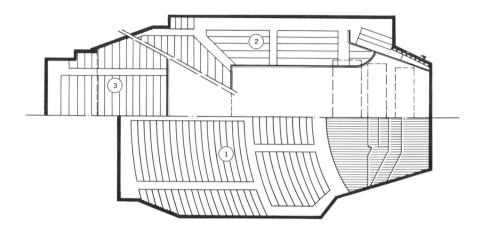

SEATING CAPACITY 2569

①	1231
②	872
③	466

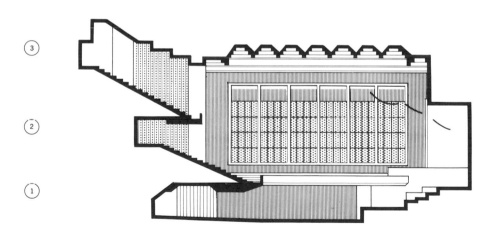

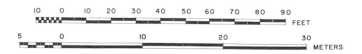

and woodwinds were also clearer on the main floor. I was not aware of any echo in the hall.

I believe that the stage should not be as steeply raked as it is. The bells of the trombones and trumpets are in the open and their sounds are very loud, especially straight ahead in the hall.

Questionnaires handed out during the pre-dedication test concert in 1951 revealed criticisms of balance, weakness of woodwinds in all positions, dominance of brass and percussion in the balcony, dominance of first violins on the front main floor; and also the tone quality was rather often called "thin," "hard," "steely," or "cold."

Sir John Barbirolli, who is conductor-in-chief of the Hallé Orchestra in Manchester wrote to me, after reading my observations: "I think that the Free Trade Hall is an excellent compromise, architecturally, between the old and the new. I don't know when you visited the Hall, but it has certainly matured greatly through the years and I personally find it—after the St. Andrew's Hall in Glasgow—one of the most satisfactory, acoustically, in England. Another admirable feature, which many of the great artists who visit the hall mention, is the intimacy they experience there, i.e., the contact with the audience is quite remarkable for a hall of its large seating capacity."

Sir Adrian Boult and Sir Malcolm Sargent find the hall comfortable to listen in and the sound satisfactory. Colin Mason, music critic of the Manchester *Guardian*, wrote to me, "The Free Trade Hall, Manchester, was not built exclusively as a concert hall, and is therefore not ideal for symphonic orchestra music. Very big sound seems squashed up in it and is uncomfortable to hear, but otherwise I have no complaint on the score of its acoustical properties."

TECHNICAL DETAILS FOR CONCERTS[*]

$V = 545,000 \text{ ft}^3$	$T_{500-1000}(\text{Occup.}) = 1.6 \text{ sec}$	$S_T = 16,740 \text{ ft}^2$
$N_A = 2569 \text{ seats}$	$S_A = 14,800 \text{ ft}^2$	$S_A/N_A = 5.8 \text{ ft}^2$
$t_I = 25; 7 \text{ msec}$	$S_O = 1940 \text{ ft}^2$	$V/S_T = 32.6 \text{ ft}$

[*] The terminology is explained in Appendix 3.

ARCHITECTURAL AND STRUCTURAL DETAILS

Uses: general purpose. *Ceiling:* 3-ft-deep coffering of plaster; a Heraklith wood-wool slab with underside plastered is laid over the holes at the top of each of the 35 coffers. *Side walls:* plaster on brick; side wall panels (5000 sq ft) of 2-in. rock wool over air space with hardboard cover, 5% perforated; also 1000 sq ft of exposed wood wool; wooden panels on wall beneath balcony. *Rear wall:* plaster on brick; acoustically absorbent tiles added to suppress echoes (1970 sq ft). *Stage enclosure:* rear stage wall is of plywood; side walls are of plywood on lower part and plaster on concrete on upper part. Reflector over stage is of solid wood. *Main floor:* wood over some air space. *Stage floor:* wooden boards on wooden framework with wooden risers. *Height of stage floor:* 60 in. above level of floor at front row of seats. *Seating:* balcony and main floor seats (1338) fully upholstered.

References: Drawings from T. Somerville and C. L. S. Gilford, *Gravesaner Blätter*, **3,** No. 9 (1957). Other information from H. Bagenal and T. Somerville. Photographs and some details courtesy P. Parkin, Building Research Station. Details verified by author during visit. *Architect:* Leonard C. Howitt.

The Jerusalem Congress Hall, containing 3142 seats, was designed initially for conventions. The shape of the hall, the balcony around the stage, and the inward sloping side walls were fixed with that purpose. Construction was started in 1950, then suspended for several years. On resumption, the purpose of the hall was changed to include musical performances. Such modifications as could be made to improve its acoustics for music were then recommended by the acoustical consultants, Bolt Beranek and Newman Inc., and were incorporated into the design. One result was an increase in the reverberation time to 1.75 seconds at mid-frequencies with full audience. The Binyanei Ha'Oomah has a ceiling higher than that of the Fredric Mann Auditorium in Tel Aviv. It is constructed of materials that preserve the warmth and liveness of the sound. Dedicated in 1960, it was used with temporary seats for concerts before that date.

The over-all architectural effect is one of simplicity and nobility. This is one contemporary hall that provides a handsome background for whatever event takes place on its stage. The rich wood interior is especially designed not to absorb the bass. When flooded with light, the white coffers overhead act to diffuse the light and provide uniform illumination to the seating areas.

The Binyanei Ha'Oomah has earned favorable comments from most of the conductors who have used it. Members of the Israeli Philharmonic Orchestra prefer it to the Fredric Mann Auditorium, primarily because of its longer reverberation time.

Izler Solomon and Stanislaw Skrowaczewski both thought the acoustics of the Binyanei Ha'Oomah better than those in the Mann Auditorium of Tel Aviv. In their opinion the acoustics of the Binyanei Ha'Oomah are "pretty good."

Charles Munch of the Boston Symphony Orchestra commented in 1959: "This hall is very good. There is better resonance in Jerusalem than in Tel Aviv. The orchestra can hear itself very well. I like to conduct here."

In November 1960, the architects, Rechter, Zarhy, and Rechter, wrote to the acoustical consultants: "The reaction of people here to the musical quality of the hall is quite favorable, and that goes for us as well."

JERUSALEM, BINYANEI HA'OOMAH

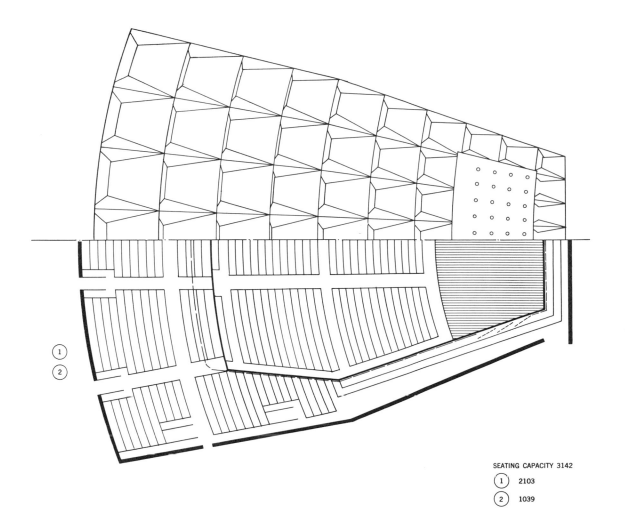

SEATING CAPACITY 3142

(1) 2103

(2) 1039

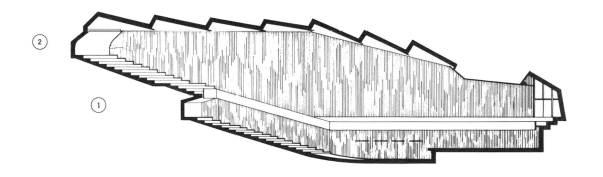

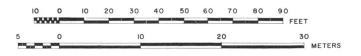

| 10 | 0 | 10 | 20 | 30 | 40 | 50 | 60 | 70 | 80 | 90 | FEET |

| 5 | 0 | 10 | 20 | 30 | METERS |

Again in April 1961 the architects wrote, "Orchestral concerts continue to be held regularly with the occasional participation of soloists. The spontaneous enthusiasm of the public in regard to the musical quality of the hall after the first concerts has been consolidated so that at present there is unanimous approval on this point. During the Zionist World Congress we tested the acoustics and the sound system from the point of view of intelligibility of speech with the hall both full and empty. Everybody agreed that speech intelligibility was satisfactory in all parts of the room."

Paul Paray of the Detroit Symphony Orchestra, after conducting two concerts there, said in 1960: "A conductor expects a hall to allow him to hear all instruments in correct balance. The new hall does this and, in addition, gives each instrument a beautiful resonance. I can only speak from the conductor's point of view; as to the sound on the podium, I am perfectly satisfied."

A typical review of a performance of the Netherlands Kamerorkest (1960) reads:

Seeing the small number of chairs on the huge stage of Binyanei Ha'Oomah, one wondered how their occupants would be able to fill the hall with a sufficient volume of sound. But doubts were dispelled as soon as the concert started. Beauty of tone and the complete union of the 20 musicians into a single body made this concert one of the finest heard for some time. The sensitive acoustics allowed one to enjoy every phase and every shade of dynamics employed in a highly polished presentation.

Moshe Segal of Israel Radio wrote in 1960: "My opinion is that, the acoustics of the hall being based on smooth side walls, there is not enough sound diffusion so that a slight directional effect can be detected. As for sound on the stage, all opinions are very positive. The orchestra is satisfied and we found the placing of our microphones surprisingly easy from an acoustical point of view. The general opinion is that it is a good hall for concerts, certainly an improvement on the Tel Aviv hall."

The Chairman of the Board of Binyanei Ha'Oomah Ltd., Mr. Grossman, wrote in November 1961, "Our hall is receiving high commendation for its marvelous acoustics from all and sundry, conductors of orchestras, musicians and singers."

Though not essential, one area for improvement suggests itself. The movable ceiling above the stage platform could be modified to emphasize the string sections at the expense of the instruments located against the upstage wall; then good orchestral balance would be easier for conductors to accomplish.

The hall's fan shape (required by the 3142 seats) means that the initial-time-delay gap is not ideally short. Though it is not as good for concert performances as smaller rectangular concert halls (for example, Symphony Hall in Boston and the Grosser Musikvereinssaal in Vienna), the Binyanei Ha'Oomah is superior for symphonic music to most of the larger multi-purpose halls built to date. In addition, its acoustics are satisfactory for lectures and conferences, many of which can be heard without an amplifying system.

TECHNICAL DETAILS FOR CONCERTS*

V = 873,000 ft^3 $T_{500-1000}$(Occup.) = 1.75 sec S_T = 25,800 ft^2
N_A = 3142 seats S_A = 23,000 ft^2 S_A/N_A = 7.3 ft^2
t_I = 26; 13 msec S_O = 2800 ft^2 V/S_T = 33.8 ft

* The terminology is explained in Appendix 3.

ARCHITECTURAL AND STRUCTURAL DETAILS

Uses: orchestra, general music, and meetings. *Ceiling:* prefabricated from 2-in. gypsum plasterboard. *Side walls:* ½-in. plywood affixed to 2-in. plaster. *Rear walls:* Upper: ½-in. plywood over air space; Lower: ½-in. plywood on masonry. *Floors:* asphalt tiles on concrete. *Stage enclosure:* Ceiling: ½-in. plywood, fabricated into a movable canopy; Back wall: ½-in. plywood on masonry. *Side walls:* large plywood wooden doors, adjustable into sawtooth splays. *Stage floor:* heavy wood over air space. *Stage height:* 44 in. above floor at first row of seats. *Seating:* tops of seat-bottoms and fronts of backrests upholstered; underseats perforated (³⁄₁₆-in. holes, 1 in. on center with glass fiber blanket inside).

References: L. L. Beranek and D. L. Klepper, "The Acoustics of the Binyanei Ha'Oomah Jerusalem Congress Hall," *Journal of the Acoustical*

Society of America, **33,** 1690–1698 (December 1961). Drawings and details from Bolt Beranek and Newman Inc. files. Photographs courtesy of architect and D. Klepper. Details verified by author during visits. *Architect:* Rechter, Zarhy, Rechter.

The Fredric R. Mann Auditorium in Tel Aviv is a pleasant contemporary concert hall. The unusual arrangement of the seating reduces the apparent size of the hall, even for the viewer in the balcony. The pattern and lighting of the ceiling and the warm interior of wood give this hall a handsome yet relaxed appearance.

The design of the Mann Auditorium was begun in 1951 after a building committee was chosen to advise the architects. The committee and the architects wanted a hall that resembled Kleinhans Music Hall in Buffalo rather than one of the older halls such as Symphony Hall in Boston. The late Serge Koussevitsky and the Israel Philharmonic Orchestra both spoke favorably of Kleinhans. Both the committee and the architect understood that Kleinhans Hall and Symphony Hall sound different, but there was no evidence at that time that either one would not be satisfactory.

It was agreed that the reverberation time in the Mann Auditorium should be about halfway between that of Symphony Hall (then thought to be 2.3 seconds when the hall was full) and that of Kleinhans Hall (then thought to be 1.5 seconds full).

The architects wanted a low ceiling. In the original discussions, a volume of 300 cubic feet per person was agreed upon, but the final plans called for a considerably lower ceiling. The final cubic volume per seat is greater than that of the Royal Festival Hall in London, for which a reverberation time of 1.75 seconds was reported in 1951.* Not until 1953 (*Acustica*, Vol. 3, p. 12) was the reverberation time in the Royal Festival Hall reported as 1.5 seconds at mid-frequencies with full occupancy. In the *Acustica* article of 1953, the unexpectedly lower reverberation time of the Royal Festival Hall was attributed, not to the small volume per person, but rather to large ceiling absorption. This analysis has proved to be incorrect. In a paper published in 1960 (reprinted in Appendix 1) I demonstrated

---

* H. Bagenal, "Music Taste and Concert Hall Design," *Proceedings of the Royal Musical Association*, Session LXXVIII, December 15, 1951: "The measured figures for hall full are: bass 1.6 seconds; middle 1.75 seconds; upper register 1.7 seconds (2,000 cycles)." This information also appeared in *Nature*, Vol. 168, p. 264 (August 18, 1951).

TEL AVIV, FREDRIC R. MANN AUDITORIUM

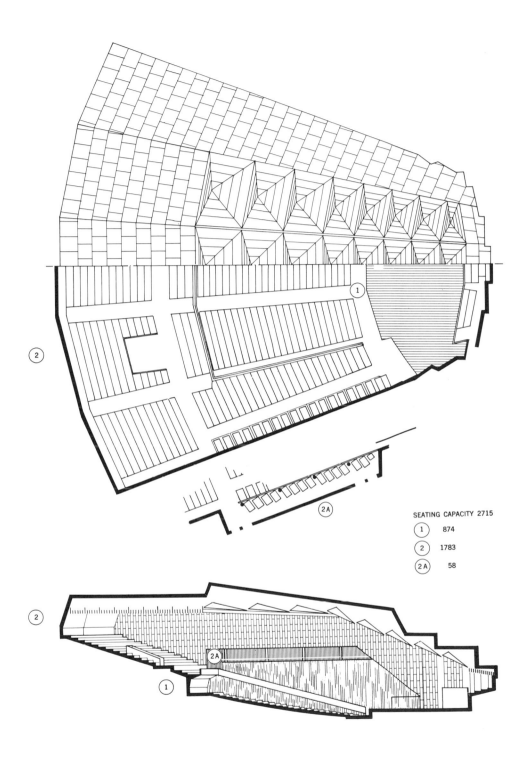

SEATING CAPACITY 2715

1 874

2 1783

2A 58

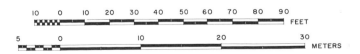

10 0 10 20 30 40 50 60 70 80 90
                                      FEET

5   0   10   20   30
                                        METERS

that a seated audience absorbs twice as much sound as was assumed by the Royal Festival Hall designers in 1953. Hence the only way that the difficulty of short reverberation time in either the Royal Festival Hall or the Fredric Mann Auditorium could be overcome would be by increasing the cubic volume and not by changes in the material of the ceiling.

The reverberation time with full occupancy in the Fredric R. Mann Auditorium is 1.55 seconds at mid-frequencies, which now turns out to be roughly halfway between the correct values for the reverberation times in Kleinhans Music Hall and Symphony Hall, namely, 1.3 seconds and 1.8 seconds at mid-frequencies, fully occupied.

Four visiting conductors have spoken well of the acoustics of the Fredric R. Mann Auditorium. Some conductors have objected to its relatively short reverberation time.

Charles Munch, conductor of the Boston Symphony Orchestra, said during an interview in August 1959, "I liked the sound on the Tel Aviv stage. The music sounded good. The piano concerto with Iturbi was terrific."

The late Dimitri Mitropoulos said in September 1951, "This hall is wonderful. I like everything about it except that the rear wall of the stage is too high." The Israel orchestra, on the other hand, would like to try a higher rear stage wall.

Antal Dorati, who conducted the London Symphony Orchestra there, said he found the Mann Auditorium "acoustically the most satisfying hall among those newly built by engineers."

Leonard Bernstein said in 1958, "The Mann Auditorium is excellent without audience but with audience the sound is a little too small. It has a beautiful clear tone."

On the other hand, the Mann Auditorium has received unfavorable criticism from the Israel Philharmonic Orchestra, its principal tenant, "Our main complaint is the lack of a certain sonority which we especially observe in the sound of our string body and which is particularly noticeable at the climaxes of the orchestra music."

An American conductor says, "There is not enough reverberation. The brass and percussion too easily overwhelm the strings." And according to another conductor, "This hall is very difficult for the soloists and conductors.

Standing next to the violin soloist, I barely heard him."

The Mann Auditorium, like many other contemporary auditoriums, reveals very clearly that, in order for a modern concert hall to be praised by musicians who are partial to the Boston and Vienna halls, it must have (a) an adequate reverberation time, (b) the necessary short initial-time-delay gaps, (c) a bass ratio of 1.2 or more (see Chapter 10), and (d) good blend and ensemble. In my opinion, a partly open false ceiling, of the kind installed at Tanglewood, would improve the acoustics in all respects. This ceiling would be hung below the existing plaster fire ceiling and would replace the asbestos and wood grated hung ceiling, thereby decreasing the bass and treble absorption.

TECHNICAL DETAILS FOR CONCERTS*

$V = 750{,}000 \text{ ft}^3$ $T_{500-1000}(\text{Occup.}) = 1.55 \text{ sec}$ $S_T = 20{,}800 \text{ ft}^2$ †

$N_A = 2715 \text{ seats}$ $S_A = 18{,}300 \text{ ft}^2$ $S_A/N_A = 6.7 \text{ ft}^2$

$t_I = 30; 7 \text{ msec}$ $S_O = 2100 \text{ ft}^2$ $V/S_T = 36.0 \text{ ft}$

* The terminology used is explained in Appendix 3.
† With chorus area.

ARCHITECTURAL AND STRUCTURAL DETAILS

Uses: orchestra, chamber music, soloists. *Ceiling:* solid upper ceiling, ¾-in. plaster; hung center portion (⅛ of area) is pyramid shaped to diffuse sound, made of 0.16-in. asbestos board; hung peripheral portion is 6-in.-deep wooden egg-crate sections, each 12 x 12 in. *Side and rear walls:* on the upper side walls are three types of panels, each 18 x 56 in. One-third of the panels are made of ¼-in. ash plywood, to the back of which a 2 x 2 x ¾ in. egg-crate structure is glued. One-third of the panels have the same egg-crate backing, but two layers of ¼-in. plywood. The remaining one-third of the panels are a sandwich of two ¼-in. plywood panels, with about ½ in. of softwood filling, making a solid panel of 1 in. The lower part of the side walls is styled after the familiar "Copenhagen" construction, of vertical slats about 2 in. wide. However, no air spaces are left between the slats and no absorbing material is mounted behind; the rear wall is made of ¼-in. plywood panels, each about 2 x 2 ft. *Floors:* vinyl tile on concrete. *Stage enclosure:* None. Elevated section of choir is behind the orchestra. *Stage floor:* wooden planks over large air space; wooden boxes for risers. *Stage height:* 30 in. above floor level at front row of seats. *Seating:* rear of backrest and armrest are of wood; front of backrest and top of seat are upholstered in Cairo cloth, backsprayed with vinyl; underseat is solid.

References: L. L. Beranek, "Acoustics of the F. R. Mann Concert Hall," *Journal of the Acoustical Society of America,* **31,** 882–892 (1959), and "Audience and Seat Absorption in Large Halls." *Journal of the Acoustical Society of America,* **32,** 661–670 (1960). Drawings and details from files of Bolt Beranek and Newman Inc. Photographs courtesy of the architects. Details verified by author during visits. *Architect:* Z. Rechter and D. Karmi. *Associate architect:* J. Rechter.

On August 3, 1778, La Scala opened its doors to a future of great music, glamor, and tradition unequaled elsewhere. Since that time, great opera composers, such as Verdi, Rossini, Puccini, Donizetti, and Bellini have been intimately identified with La Scala. Its lineage of famous conductors includes Franco Faccio, Arturo Toscanini, Cleofonte Campanini, Herbert von Karajan, and Carlo Maria Giulini. Singers such as Beniamino Gigli, Adelina Patti, Enrico Caruso, Renata Tebaldi, Maria Callas, and scores of others have achieved fame there.

The architect of La Scala was Giuseppi Piermarini. He designed and built the largest and best equipped theater of his day. The exterior of La Scala looked in 1778 very much as it does today. Until World War II there were only minor changes made inside the building—in 1830 it was refurnished, in 1883 it got electric lights. In 1943, however, La Scala was the victim of a bombing attack; the walls remained standing, but very little else was left intact.

As its present-day, white-haired superintendent, Antonio Ghiringhelli, said to me recently, "A theater must first have a 'soul,' a tradition. After that technical matters enter." The soul of La Scala persisted, and in May 1946, the famous opera house reopened, its appearance almost as before. The only change was the elimination of the small top gallery. Today it has 2289 seats, including 154 unnumbered seats from which the stage is not visible. With standees the number can be considerably augmented.

La Scala is a beautiful and engaging theater. It is a horseshoe in plan with large high balcony faces and a vaulted ceiling 6 feet higher at the center than at the sides. A feeling of intimacy is conveyed by its narrow main floor; nevertheless the hall has a regal air that derives from the great height of its ceiling. The theater is lighted by a huge central chandelier of 365 lights, and white glass globes in groups of five are placed at intervals along the bases of the balcony faces.

The acoustics are excellent for those lucky enough to sit either at the front of the boxes, on the main floor, or in the galleries. For those at the rear of the boxes, particularly in the side boxes, a radio broadcast would present

MILAN, TEATRO ALLA SCALA

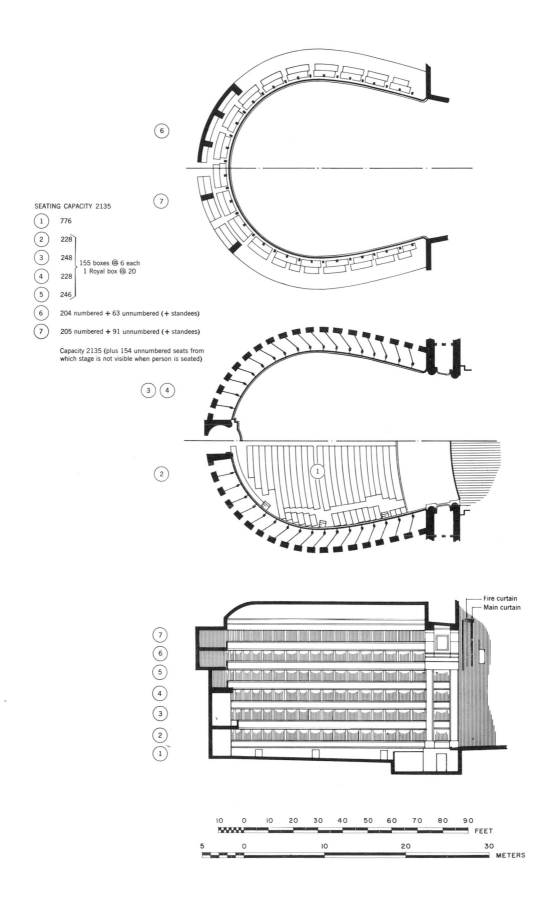

SEATING CAPACITY 2135

(1)	776
(2)	228
(3)	248
(4)	228
(5)	246
(6)	204 numbered + 63 unnumbered (+ standees)
(7)	205 numbered + 91 unnumbered (+ standees)

155 boxes @ 6 each
1 Royal box @ 20

Capacity 2135 (plus 154 unnumbered seats from which stage is not visible when person is seated)

Fire curtain
Main curtain

10	0	10	20	30	40	50	60	70	80	90

FEET

5	0	10	20	30

METERS

the sound more faithfully. The openings to the boxes are only 4½ feet square, so that the wall of the horseshoe is effectively the wall of the opera house, about 40-per-cent acoustically absorbent. The large reflecting faces of the boxes and the resulting small cubic volume of the house achieves an acoustical intimacy usually associated with a smaller house. The reverberation time is a little longer than in other large opera houses. The sound is clear, warm, and brilliant. The forestage is large enough to reflect energy into the hall from the singers' voices which would otherwise be lost in the pit.

Sound is returned to the stage from the faces of the boxes with an intensity that is not reached in any other large opera house. The vaulted ceiling returns the sound of the orchestra and the singers to the conductor, clear and loud. Both singers and conductors are enthusiastic about the acoustics of La Scala.

Could an opera house with these acoustics be built in the United States today? The answer seems to be negative for a number of reasons. The economics of opera in the United States requires that a house seat at least 3000 people. In contrast to La Scala's 5.5 square feet per person, today's American standards of comfort and safety require that an audience be allotted an area of about 7.5 square feet per person. Hence, an American house would require a seating area for its audience about double that of La Scala. Equally important, American audiences demand a full view of the stage, and a 60-per-cent closed "wall" at the line of the horseshoe would not be acceptable. For all these reasons, the acoustic response of a new American opera house—as heard by the singers and the conductor—would necessarily be below that of La Scala. A house with double the seating area would be deader, less intimate, and deficient in the necessary short-time-delay reflections. Other concomitants of modern stage design and lighting tend to reduce the area of the forestage and to increase the distance behind the proscenium opening at which the singers must stand. Thus, less of a singer's voice power is projected to the audience. Two hundred years of changing standards of comfort and safety, and the dearth of public funds for opera in the United States, combine to make it unlikely that the acoustics of any new American opera house will match the famous La Scala.

TECHNICAL DETAILS FOR OPERA*

$V = 397,300 \text{ ft}^3$ $T_{500-1000}(\text{Occup.}) = 1.2 \text{ sec}$ $S_P = 2400 \text{ ft}^2$

   $(318,200)\dagger$ $S_A = 14,000 \text{ ft}^2$ $S_T = 17,600 \text{ ft}^2$

$N_A = 2289 \text{ seats } \ddagger$ $(7700) \S$ $(11,300) \S$

$N_T = 2489$ $S_O = 1200 \text{ ft}^2$ $S_A/N_T = 5.6 \text{ ft}^2$

 $t_I = 15; 12 \text{ msec}$ $S_{OF} = 1350 \text{ ft}^2$ $V/S_T = 22.5 \text{ ft}$

                                                  (28.2)

* The terminology is explained in Appendix 3.

† Volume in the well only.

‡ Including 154 unnumbered seats from which the stage cannot be seen.

§ Main floor seating area only.

ARCHITECTURAL AND STRUCTURAL DETAILS

Uses: opera and ballet. *Ceilings:* vaulted (6 ft higher at the center than the sides), plaster on lath attached to 1 x 4-in. longitudinal boards; there are no irregularities (coffers) on the ceiling. *Walls:* box faces are of plaster 42 in. high; vertical columns at railings are plaster 6 in. wide; each box opening is 54 x 54 in. *Floors:* wood over 3-ft air space over concrete. *Pit floor:* wooden floor, flat, elevator type; often located about 10 ft below stage level. *Carpets:* on all floors. *Seating:* upholstered on front of the backrest and top of the seat-bottom; the rear of the backrest and the underseat are solid.

References: Drawings and photographs courtesy of Antonio Ghiringhelli, managing superintendent of La Scala. Details verified by author during visits. *Architect:* Giuseppi Piermarini.

A hall built in the tradition of Leipzig, Vienna, and Boston is Amsterdam's Concertgebouw, which seats 2206 persons. This concert hall, opened in 1888, has some unique architectural features that affect the acoustics.

The Concertgebouw is about a third wider than any of the six comparable halls discussed in this book (95 feet compared to 60 to 75 feet). Some of the audience is seated on steep stadium steps behind the orchestra. These seats were originally intended, not for the public, but for the large Concertgebouwkoor which has, since 1899, annually presented Beethoven's *Ninth Symphony,* Mahler's *Eighth,* and Bach's *St. Matthew Passion.* As audiences increased in size, these seats came to be sold. The ceiling over the orchestra is high, nearly 50 feet. The large, velvet-draped chandeliers shown above the orchestra in the photograph have been replaced by lighting fixtures near the ceiling. The stage floor is higher than that of any hall studied, 58½ inches.

The Concertgebouw houses all kinds of musical performances, but mainly orchestral concerts. The floor is flat and the seats are removable. The irregular walls produce good sound diffusion. The ceiling is deeply coffered. The balcony is high and shallow, and it does not shield the seats beneath it.

More than any other famous concert hall, the Concertgebouw has divided the conductors and music critics. One conductor who has had years of experience there said, "The Concertgebouw has marvelous acoustics. It is probably one of the best halls in the world." Another who has played there often in recent years said, "This house is very good, but it is not as good as the Musikvereinssaal in Vienna." A third, after months of conducting at the Concertgebouw, said, "This is the most overrated hall in the world. There is a jumble of sound and poor orchestral balance. The ceiling over the stage seems too high." To another conductor, "This is a wonderful hall." A concert violinist said, "This is an exciting hall to play in. The hall rings when you sound a note. Reverberation is a great help to a violinist, and this hall responds immediately."

Of the three American critics who know this hall well, one said, "The sound here is beautifully warm. The woodwinds, brass, and strings are mellow." The second said, "I know the Concertgebouw very well. It has

AMSTERDAM, CONCERTGEBOUW

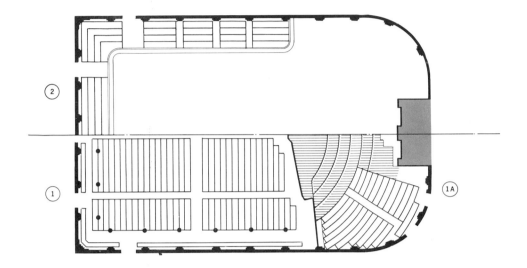

SEATING CAPACITY 2206

(1) 1366

(1A) 412

(2) 428

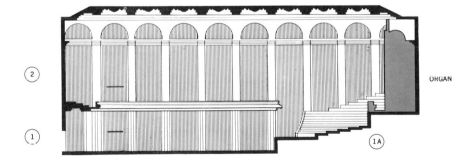

ORGAN

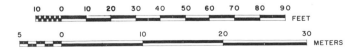

exceptional acoustics. It is a very **warm**, mellow hall and I have the impression that the sound does not change very radically from one location to another. Warm, to me, means that there is good solid sound at the lower, lower-middle and middle frequencies." And the third said, "This is a bad hall in many ways. There is a lack of resonance and blending. There is a dull separated tone."

I have attended several concerts in the Concertgebouw and I understand the reasons for the divergence of opinion. The hall is live—reverberant —which pleases the performers, and it is well suited to music of the Romantic period. The audience behind the orchestra reduces the loudness of the brass and the percussion, which is good for orchestral balance, but it also causes an unfortunate reduction in the loudness of the double basses; I was surprised at their weakness. The width of the hall and the high ceiling serve to increase the initial-time-delay gap on the main floor, with the result that there the sound loses some of its intimacy, brilliance, and clarity. On the other hand, in the balcony, particularly at the rear of the hall, the sound is well balanced, clear, and wonderfully live.

On the main floor, the reverberation in the hall and the music that produces it seem dissociated from each other. This gives the hall an aura of hugeness that is belied by its appearance. The reflections from the side walls heard in the center of the main floor are delayed almost long enough to sound like echoes. On the right side of the main floor the first violins are not loud enough, presumably because of the greater distance their sound has to travel over the heads of the audience to reach the listener's ears. In the balcony this is not true.

In the front half of the main floor, the double basses cause the seats to vibrate when they play fortissimo. These vibrations are pleasant and may contribute in some way to the fine reputation of the hall.

In my judgment, the Concertgebouw is excellent and ranks among the best halls described in this book. It is much better in the balcony than on the main floor, and on the main floor it is not as good as the Musikvereinssaal in Vienna or Symphony Hall in Boston. The Concertgebouw disappoints those musicians who are accustomed to a low ceiling over the orchestra, like that of the Philadelphia Academy of Music.

TECHNICAL DETAILS FOR CONCERTS*

$V = 663,000 \text{ ft}^3$ $\quad$ $T_{500-1000}(\text{Occup.}) = 2.0 \text{ sec}$ $\quad$ $S_T = 13,800 \text{ ft}^2$

$N_A = 2206 \text{ seats}$ $\quad\quad\quad\quad\quad$ $S_A = 12,200 \text{ ft}^2$ $\quad$ $S_A/N_A = 5.5 \text{ ft}^2$

$t_I = 21; 9 \text{ msec}$ $\quad\quad\quad\quad\quad\quad$ $S_O = 1600 \text{ ft}^2$ $\quad$ $V/S_T = 48.0 \text{ ft}$

* The terminology is explained in Appendix 3.

ARCHITECTURAL AND STRUCTURAL DETAILS

Uses: all types of music, with emphasis on orchestral. *Ceiling:* 1½-in. plaster on reeds, coffered and with ornamentation. There are deep "window" recesses around the top edges. *Side and rear walls:* below the balcony, plaster on brick; above the balcony, plaster on reed, which sounds dull or damped when tapped with the fingers. *Floors:* the main floor was of wood until recently, when it was replaced with 5-in. concrete, on top of which hardwood boards were nailed to 2 x 3-in. wooden battens. Two inches of sand were poured into the 3-in. space. *Stage floor:* wood over deep air space. *Stage height:* 58½ in. *Carpets:* on main floor aisles only. *Added absorptive material:* 400 sq ft of draperies over the front of the little room at the rear of the balcony and around the doorways. *Seating:* Upholstered in thick, hard-weave material.

References: Reverberation tapes from J. J. Geluk, Netherlands Radio. Details and photographs courtesy of the Council, Concertgebouw, Amsterdam. Details verified by author during a visit. *Architect:* A. L. van Gendt.

The Konserthus of Gothenburg, opened in 1935, is one of the world's most beautiful halls. It is the only orchestral hall described in this book that is finished entirely in wood. It is a small hall that has only 1371 seats. There is no balcony, and the floor is interestingly subdivided by elevated sections of seats at the sides and rear of the hall. Some small organ pipes are visible on a shelf above the orchestra.

The warm color of the wood, the lighting, the intimate contact between the audience and the stage, and the adequate reverberation time combine to make listening to music in this hall a rewarding experience.

Lest any reader jump to the questionable conclusion that wood accounts for its superiority, let me stress that the interior of the Konserthus is made of panels about 1 inch thick and 30 by 80 inches wide and long. The edge of each panel is fastened to wooden studs 2 inches deep, which in turn are secured to 3-inch battens, 3 feet on centers, that are bolted to the 7-inch concrete wall. Each panel is braced on its rear side with five or six 2 by 3-inch wooden stiffeners, each about 30 inches long and located differently on each sheet. And finally, each panel has wedged between it and the concrete wall a wooden block, 4½ inches thick, with ⅜-inch felt on both ends. Clearly, every attempt has been made to render the wood immobile and therefore non-resonant; consequently, the walls are inactive and, like plaster walls, serve only as effective reflecting surfaces.

The conductor, Igor Markevich, said, "This is one of the outstanding halls of the world. It is the most beautiful visually of those built in our century."

Bruno Walter, Eugene Ormandy, and Isaac Stern consider the acoustics of the hall very good, and all three comment favorably on its small size.

There has been some trouble with orchestral balance, because of the hard surfaces behind the players and the short shelf that covers, and perhaps reinforces too well, the instruments at the rear of the stage. When I heard a concert in the Konserthus some years ago, draperies had been hung on the rear wall to improve the balance.

My impressions at the concert were very favorable. On double forte

GOTHENBURG, KONSERTHUS

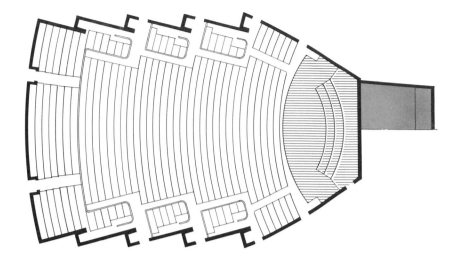

SEATING CAPACITY 1371

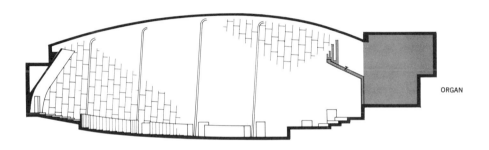

ORGAN

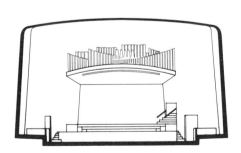

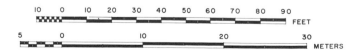

10 0 10 20 30 40 50 60 70 80 90
FEET

5 0 10 20 30
METERS

passages, with full orchestra, the music is very loud, as is to be expected in a small hall. However, the sound-absorbing material in the niches at the sides of the hall control this loudness somewhat and prevent it from becoming excessive.

The Konserthus illustrates one of the basic tenets of acoustics; in a hall for music, small size is attended by many of the desirable attributes of acoustic quality. The problems of acoustical design would be far simpler if all concert halls seated about 1500 people. In addition, the Gothenburg hall is not excessively wide, it has no balcony overhang, and it is high enough to provide a nearly optimum reverberation time for orchestral and chamber music. And the wood of the walls is not thin, so the warmth of the bass is preserved. When all these factors are combined with a pleasing appearance, the success of a concert hall is assured.

TECHNICAL DETAILS FOR CONCERTS[*]

$V = 420{,}000 \text{ ft}^3$ $T_{500-1000}(\text{Occup.}) = 1.7 \text{ sec}$ $S_T = 10{,}350 \text{ ft}^2$

$N_A = 1371 \text{ seats}$ $S_A = 8900 \text{ ft}^2$ $S_A/N_A = 6.5 \text{ ft}^2$

$t_I = 33; 22$ $S_O = 1450 \text{ ft}^2$ $V/S_T = 40.6 \text{ ft}$

[*] The terminology is explained in Appendix 3.

ARCHITECTURAL AND STRUCTURAL DETAILS

Uses: 85% orchestra, 10% soloists and chamber music, 5% organ. *Ceiling:* plywood affixed directly to a concrete sheet that is suspended from a steel overhead. *Side and rear walls:* described in the text above. *Floors:* linoleum. *Stage floor:* wooden planks over large air space. *Stage height:* 53 in. above the floor at the first row of seats. *Added absorptive material:* sound-absorbing materials are located in the overlaps of the panels on the side walls; a curtain is hung behind the orchestra to improve balance among sections of the orchestra. *Seating:* both sides of seat bottom, front of backrest and armrests are upholstered; underseats solid.

References: Drawings, photographs, and details from N. E. Eriksson. Details verified by author during visits. *Architect:* Nils Einar Eriksson.

Built in 1876, the Stadt-Casino at Basel is one of the pleasantest old halls of Europe. It is a small, rectangular hall with a flat coffered ceiling. Its reverberation time is relatively long, 1.7 seconds at mid-frequencies when the hall is fully occupied. It has for many years been considered the best Swiss concert hall.

The Stadt-Casino has every feature conducive to good acoustics. Because it is small—it seats 1400 people—the initial-time-delay gap is short. Irregular interior surfaces serve to diffuse the reverberant sound. The reverberation time is near optimum for a hall of its size. Its interior is plaster so that the bass is warm and the higher registers are brilliant. The hall responds well to the music and musicians love to perform in it.

Herbert von Karajan has said of the Stadt-Casino: "This is a typical rectangular hall—small, with a wonderfully clear and crisp resonance. It is almost perfect for Mozart. Although one can play nearly every kind of music in it, the volume of a very large orchestra is smashing."

Dimitri Mitropoulos thought the Stadt-Casino a very good hall but too small for full orchestra. A third conductor said that he failed to see anything outstanding about its acoustics.

In my judgment, all music that is properly scaled to the size of the Stadt-Casino sounds wonderful there. The enthusiasm of the musicians who know the hall well is fully merited.

TECHNICAL DETAILS FOR CONCERTS*

$V = 370,000$ ft^3 $T_{500-1000}$(Occup.) $= 1.7$ sec $S_T = 9650$ ft^2
$N_A = 1400$ seats $S_A = 8000$ ft^2 $S_A/N_A = 5.7$ ft^2
$t_I = 16; 6$ msec $S_O = 1650$ ft^2 $V/S_T = 38.3$ ft

* The terminology is explained in Appendix 3.

ARCHITECTURAL AND STRUCTURAL DETAILS

Uses: 85% orchestra, 5% lecture, and 10% soloists. *Ceiling:* plaster, coffered. *Side and rear walls:* plaster with a small amount of wood; baroque ornamentation and columns. *Stage floor:* wooden planks over large air space

BASEL, STADT-CASINO

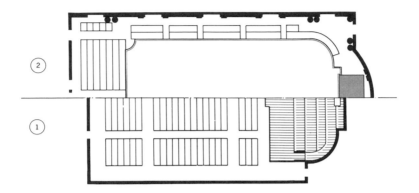

SEATING CAPACITY 1400

① 990

② 410

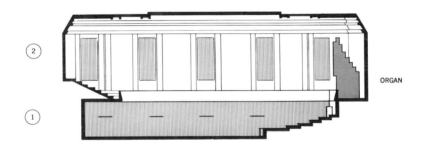

ORGAN

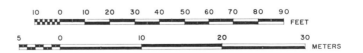

with wooden boxes for risers. *Stage height:* 43 in. above floor at first row of seats. *Seating:* upholstered on top of seat-bottom and both sides of backrests.

References: Drawings from W. Furrer, *Raum- und Bauakustik, Lärmabwehr,* 2nd Edition, Birkhäuser Verlag, Basel and Stuttgart (1961). Photographs courtesy of Swiss National Tourist Office. Details from W. Furrer. *Architect:* Johann Jacob Stehlin-Burckhardt.

The Salle Musica, which seats 1032 persons, was opened in June 1955. Built in the old tradition of the small-sized rectangular hall, it nevertheless reflects the state of the acoustic art of the 1950's. The sweep of the side walls is interrupted by protruding columns; the ceiling has deep coffers. Most of the main floor is flat and as a result the loudness of the high-frequency sound drops near the back.

None of the conductors or music critics whom I interviewed were familiar with the Salle Musica. The music director reports that many musicians—Ernest Ansermet, Carl Schuricht, Wilhelm Backhaus, Irmgard Siegfried, and Karl Münchinger—spoke favorably of the acoustics. They observed that the sound is carried without any distortion, that even the slightest pianissimo is perceptible, and that the musicians hear their own music well. There is no echo and the hall is free of noise.

The abundant use of paneling on the side walls tends to reduce the warmth of the bass. Thus the tone is rather dry and brittle, but very clear, in accordance with generally recognized French musical taste.

Organ music is less satisfying in the Salle Musica. It is often too loud, and the relatively short reverberation time limits the kinds of music that can be performed there successfully. As in many halls, the seats at the rear beneath the balcony are less desirable than those more exposed.

For chamber music and for orchestral music of the Baroque, Classical, and Modern periods, played by a medium-sized or small orchestra, this hall is excellent. For Romantic works and for organ music of the cathedral type, this hall is somewhat dry, and for large orchestras it may be too loud on fortissimo passages.

TECHNICAL DETAILS FOR CONCERTS[*]

$V = 278,000$ ft^3	$T_{500-1000}$(Occup.) $= 1.7$ sec	$S_T = 8350$ ft^2
$N_A = 1032$ seats	$S_A = 7000$ ft^2	$S_A/N_A = 6.8$ ft^2
$t_I = 14; 6$ msec	$S_O = 1350$ ft^2	$V/S_T = 33.3$ ft

[*] The terminology is explained in Appendix 3.

LA CHAUX-DE-FONDS, SALLE MUSICA

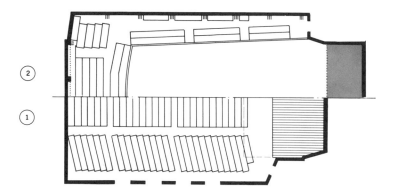

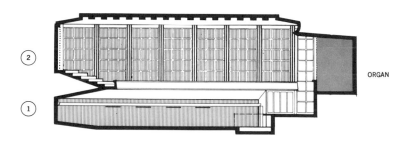

SEATING CAPACITY 1032

1   662

2   370

ORGAN

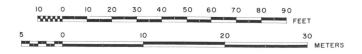

ARCHITECTURAL AND STRUCTURAL DETAILS

Uses: 70% orchestra, 30% other types of music. *Ceiling:* plaster on wire lath with 1½-ft coffers. *Side walls:* wood-fiber boards covered with thin-finish wood veneer; in order that all parts of the side walls not resonate at one frequency, air spaces of varying depths are provided behind the various wood-fiber panels. Wooden blocks of different density are glued at random to the back sides, and diffusion is provided by seven projecting wooden pilasters on each side wall, tapering from a depth of 2 ft at the ceiling to 1 ft at the balcony. *Rear walls:* mostly of glass covered with a folding wooden false wall. *Stage floor:* wooden planks over large air space with wooden boxes for risers. *Stage height:* 47 in. above floor at first row of seats. *Seating:* the top of the seat and both sides of the back are fully upholstered in mohair; the underseat is solid.

References: Drawings and photographs from W. Furrer, *Raum- und Bauakustik, Lärmabwehr,* 2nd Edition, Birkhäuser Verlag, Basel and Stuttgart (1961). Details from W. Furrer. *Architect:* H. Bieri and R. Chapallaz.

The Tonhalle, completed in 1895 and renovated in 1930, accommodates an audience of 1546 persons. Two glittering chandeliers hang beneath a series of oil paintings on the ceiling that portray Gluck, Haydn, Schubert, Brahms, Mozart, and Handel. The walls are a grayish ivory abundantly decorated with gold. Beneath the balcony, natural birch paneling gives the hall an appearance of being all wood, but this is not the case. Plaster forms more than 80 per cent of the walls and ceiling. The floors are wood parquet. The seats are not upholstered; during rehearsals the orchestra finds it necessary to have large curtains hung both above and below the balcony at the rear of the hall.

The Grosser Tonhallesaal was added to the halls analyzed in this book at a late date and, as a result, only four conductors were asked to express an opinion about it. Three of them rated it acoustically excellent. The fourth, who favors modern music, said, "This hall is not so good and not so bad. It is sort of in between."

W. Furrer, writing in the *Technische Mitteilungen* (pp. 3-11, 1937) said that in Switzerland this hall is not regarded as highly as the Stadt-Casino in Basel. He said that the Tonhalle is usually called "satisfactory"; he concludes that its ranking as second to the Stadt-Casino derives from its relatively deep side galleries and from its shorter reverberation time, which is 1.6 seconds, fully occupied, compared with 1.7 seconds for the Stadt-Casino.

My one musical experience with this hall was very pleasant. The program consisted of music of the Baroque and early Classical periods, and the reverberation time of the hall is nearly ideal for such music. The bass was not as satisfactory in the main floor as in the galleries, undoubtedly owing to the thin wood on the lower side walls. The violins sang forth clearly—their sound was intimate, live, and brilliant. Ensemble playing was good as was the balance among orchestral sections, with only a moderate tendency for the brass to dominate. The blend was excellent. The sound was not as good in the rear corners of the main floor and at the rear of the side balconies as on the main floor and in the rear balcony. All in all, it is a very good hall.

ZURICH, GROSSER TONHALLESAAL

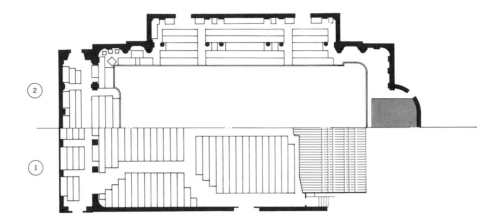

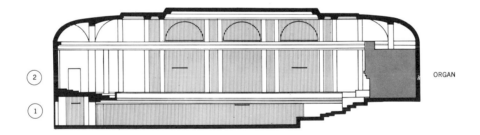

SEATING CAPACITY 1546

① 925

② 621

ORGAN

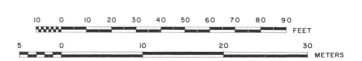

10 0 10 20 30 40 50 60 70 80 90
FEET

5 0 10 20 30
METERS

TECHNICAL DETAILS FOR CONCERTS[*]

V = 402,500 ft³ $T_{500-1000}$(Occup.) = 1.6 sec S_T = 11,000 ft²

N_A = 1546 seats S_A = 9440 ft² S_A/N_A = 6.1 ft²

t_I = 14; 6 msec S_O = 1560 ft² V/S_T = 36.6 ft

[*] The terminology is explained in Appendix 3.

ARCHITECTURAL AND STRUCTURAL DETAILS

Uses: symphonic music 200 days a year, piano and violin recitals, oratorio 12 days, and occasionally organ. *Side walls:* wood paneling beneath the balcony and on the soffit under the balcony; walls and decorations are of plaster above the balcony; balcony fronts are of plaster. *Ceiling:* plaster. *Floors:* wood, parquet on main floor and linoleum over solid in balcony. *Stage floor:* wood over air space. *Stage height:* 48 in. above floor at first row of seats. *Added absorptive material:* cloth curtains hang over the six clerestory windows; rehearsal curtains are used both above and below the balcony. *Seating:* all wood. *Note:* the doors at the rear of the main floor may be opened, exposing 200 additional seats in the Kleiner Tonhallesaal.

References: Drawings courtesy of W. Furrer. Photographs courtesy of Swiss National Tourist Office. Details and seating plan from H. I. Tobler, assistant to the general manager. Details checked by author during visits. *Architect:* Fellner and Helmer of Vienna.

Fantastico is the word that aptly describes the Great Hall of the University of Caracas. It is the only hall anywhere in which the work of a sculptor is so much in evidence. How this came about is an interesting story.

The architect won a competition for his design for the hall. His plans showed a very broad, fan-shaped room with a domed ceiling and a rear wall that formed a sector of a circle with its center of curvature at the rear of the stage. When the preliminary drawings were complete, the acoustical firm of Bolt Beranek and Newman Inc. was consulted. The curved ceiling and the circular rear wall presented serious problems of focused echoes, dead spots, and a general lack of uniformity in sound distribution. The acoustical consultants recommended an inner construction that would have greatly modified the shape of the hall, but by that time the shape had already been fixed.

An alternative solution was then explored. It was recommended that sound-reflecting panels, equal in area to about 70 per cent of the ceiling, be hung below the ceiling and on the side walls. These panels were originally recommended to be rectangular in shape. But the designers of the Aula Magna, hoping for a more satisfying solution, contacted Alexander Calder in Paris, a sculptor whose mobiles had made him famous, and invited him to participate in an unusual and rewarding collaboration of sculptor, architect, engineers, and acoustical consultant. The result is beautiful—in both form and color—an exciting array of "stabiles" suspended from the ceiling and standing away from the side walls. No photograph can do the hall justice. One must be inside the hall—inside the sculpture—to feel its rhythm and color.

The hall is a university auditorium and seats 2660 people. It is used for lectures, convocations, music, and drama. Its first use was to house the International Pan-American Congress of 1954.

Even though the Aula Magna serves many purposes and though its shape is basically unfavorable for music, it has received favorable comments from conductors and music critics. Music played there is clear and distinct. The string tone is brilliant. The bass is rich and warm. Short-time-delay

CARACAS, AULA MAGNA

reflections are provided by the hanging panels. The only shortcomings of the hall for music are its relatively short reverberation time and lack of sound diffusion. Thus, the hall is excellent for piano, modern music, and chamber music—for all music where clarity of detail is desired. The music comes to the listeners directly from the stage, since the very wide fan shape prevents a general mixing of the sound from cross reflections between the side walls.

On stage the sound is excellent, as a result of an effective canopy over the performers. Just after a tour around South America with the New York Philharmonic Orchestra in 1957, and again recently, Leonard Bernstein said to me, "This hall was the best in which I conducted in South America. After the concert I told reporters that on the stage the sound is excellent. I wished that I could take that part of the hall back to New York for the Philharmonic to use."

TECHNICAL DETAILS FOR CONCERTS[*]

V = 880,000 ft^3	$T_{500-1000}$(Occup.) = 1.35 sec	S_T = 22,500 ft^2
N_A = 2660 seats	S_A = 20,300 ft^2	S_A/N_A = 7.6 ft^2
t_I = 30; 10 msec	S_O = 2200 ft^2	V/S_T = 39.0 ft

[*] The terminology is explained in Appendix 3.

ARCHITECTURAL AND STRUCTURAL DETAILS

Uses: University auditorium. *Ceiling:* plaster on metal lath. *Side walls:* plaster on solid. *Rear walls:* highly absorbent to prevent echo. *Floors:* quarry tile. *Stage enclosure:* canopy of plywood, about 1 in. thick; rear wall of the stage and about 20 ft of the two side walls contiguous to the rear wall are of wood on solid concrete back. *Stage floor:* wood over air space. *Stage height:* 40 in. above the floor level at the front row of seats. *Carpet:* main aisles only. *Added absorptive material:* at the time the reverberation data were taken, 2770 sq ft of 1-in. glass fiber blanket had been installed on top of the stabiles to make the hall optimum for the Pan-American Congress; without this material, the mid-frequency reverberation time, fully occupied, would increase to about 1.7 sec, more nearly optimum for music. *Seating:*

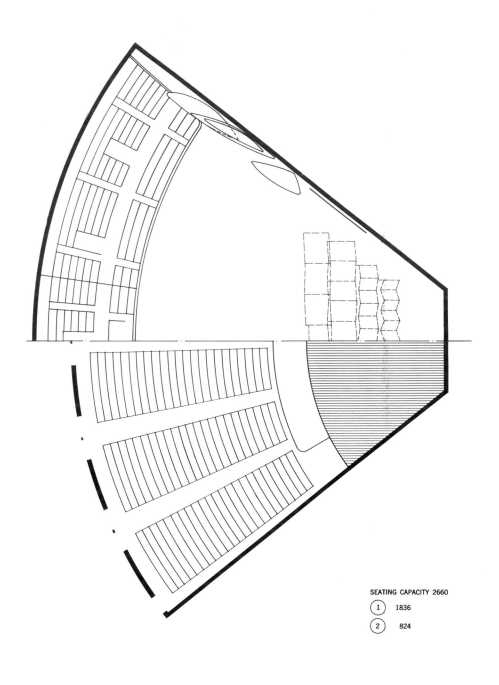

SEATING CAPACITY 2660

(1)   1836

(2)   824

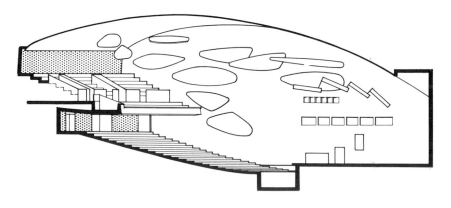

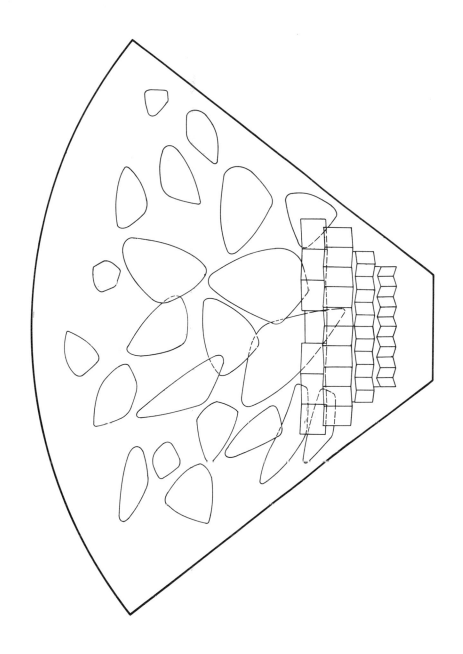

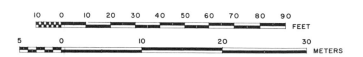

the top of the seat-bottom and the front of the backrest are upholstered in very porous, ribbed, hard cloth; the armrests are upholstered in leather; the underseat is perforated, with rock wool inside. *Hanging reflectors:* 30, each of which is 4 to 8 in. thick, made of two layers of ½-in. laminated wood on heavy framing. The total area is about 6500 sq ft.

References: Drawings and photographs from Santiago Briceño-Ecker. Acoustical details from Bolt Beranek and Newman Inc. Constructional details confirmed by author during visits. *Designers:* Carlos R. Villanueva, Santiago Briceño-Ecker, and Daniel Ellenberg.

Two thoughts emerge from the descriptions of the 54 halls. First, the halls can be assigned to several ordered categories; and second, except for the best and the worst halls there is a range of opinion on every one. No hall studied was entirely free of criticism, and no hall failed to win some praise. The variations come as no surprise. Conductors, music critics, and music listeners have individual preferences, in every hall some seats are better than others, and the blend of the sound on the podium may be very different from what the audience hears. Furthermore, we should not disregard the remark that the conductor Wilhelm Furtwaengler made some years ago to Claudia Cassidy, music critic of the Chicago *Tribune*, "The hall with the best acoustics is the hall with the best performance." Although Furtwaengler makes a telling point—witness the saving of Carnegie Hall—it is, of course, far from the whole story, as any listener who has followed the tour of a major orchestra or opera company can testify. There are differences in the acoustical quality of halls for music that can be perceived by any listener who focuses his attention on this problem.

Three observations that appeared in many of the interviews with musicians deserve special comment: (1) that small halls generally sound better than large ones; (2) that halls built to serve many purposes are inferior to halls built especially for concert or opera; and (3) that old halls sound better than new ones. These three widely held opinions provide clues to an understanding of the acoustical attributes of halls. Let us examine them in the context of the 54 halls.

CUBIC VOLUME

In order to determine whether small halls consistently outrank large halls, let us compare the cubic volumes of ten best-liked concert halls from the study in Chapter 6 with the ten halls liked least (see Table 7.1). The difference of 25 per cent between the two groups is hardly enough by itself to cause the great difference that listeners find in the acoustics of the halls they prefer and those they like less. The Grosser Musikvereinssaal (530,000 cubic feet) in Vienna and Symphony Hall (662,000 cubic feet) in Boston are undoubtedly better halls for symphonic music than either the Royal Albert Hall (3,060,000 cubic feet) in London or the Pudue University Hall of Music (1,320,000 cubic feet) in Lafayette, Indiana. But some other reason must account for the apparent superiority of the Tanglewood Music Shed (1,500,000 cubic feet) in Lenox, Massachusetts, to the Musikhochschule Konzertsaal (340,000 cubic feet) in Berlin. Obviously some large halls are acoustically preferable to some small ones.

Table 7.1 Cubic volumes of concert halls

	Median Cubic Volume	
	Cubic Feet	*Cubic Meters*
10 best-liked concert halls	620,000	17,600
10 least-liked concert halls	770,000	21,800

The problem is complicated. Although large size is always potentially detrimental to the acoustics of a hall, many of the negative effects of great size can be neutralized by special construction and by keeping the background noise level very low. In addition, it is not always easy to separate visual from acoustical impressions. Both contribute to our feeling of the quality of a hall. For example, the equivalent of the close visual rapport between musicians and audience in the Stadt-Casino (370,000 cubic feet) in Basel is achieved in the Fredric R. Mann Auditorium (750,000 cubic feet) in Tel Aviv through the clever architectural design.

Opera lovers invariably prefer small houses to large ones for several reasons, not the least of which is their being able to see better. I could hardly sleep after attending an opera performed in the very small eighteenth-century theater at Drottningholm, just outside Stockholm. The excitement left by the intimate relation of audience to performers made other opera performances seem cold, by comparison. As Rod Nordell said in *The Christian Science Monitor*, August 3, 1961,

> The Drottningholm Court Theater, built in 1766, fits into its setting as smoothly as, inside the theater, its stage fits into its auditorium. The interior is deliberately fashioned for continuity between the audience and the actors. The proscenium becomes not a line of demarcation but a meeting place.

SIZE, USE, AND AGE

Another and perhaps more important consequence of small size is the advantages to the singers. Harold C. Schonberg wrote in the New York *Times*, September 3, 1961,

The big, revelationary conclusion that I have arrived at may be very small stuff, but at least it is my own. . . . It is easier to sing in a small house than a large one.

For some three decades our ears have been conditioned to hearing opera singers in one of the largest houses in the world. Acoustics of the Metropolitan Opera are altogether different from acoustics at Bayreuth, or the Altes Festspielhaus in Salzburg, or the Prinzregententheater in Munich. Singers who sound one way at the Metropolitan Opera tend to sound different in smaller European theatres. They are less inclined to push, for one thing. They give the impression that they are more comfortable, as indeed they are. All this makes for more relaxed listening.

Finally music is louder in a small hall than in a large hall. Although the size of an orchestra can be adjusted somewhat to the cubic volume of a hall, a soloist does not have the same range. Isaac Stern, the violinist, elaborates, "The hall should bring the audience to you. The audience should sit on the edges of its chairs waiting to hear the faintest tones—and they must be loud enough or the listeners lose them and become restless. Then the magic effect is shattered."

The loudness of the reverberant sound, which is directly related to the reverberation time, is inversely related to the cubic volume. That is to say, loudness is some function of the ratio T/V where T is the reverberation time at mid-frequencies with audience and V is the cubic volume. This formula says that music in a hall may be too loud because the hall is either too small or too reverberant or a little of both. Bruno Walter cited an example of this, "I remember rehearsing Bruckner in the Tonhalle in Zurich one time. Empty, this hall gives the symphony enormous power, almost unbearable. The sound of full orchestra is overwhelming. But with an audience, this hall sounds very good." I calculate for the Tonhalle that the quantity T/V is 2.5 times greater without an audience than with one. No wonder that if the sound is at a comfortable level when the hall is filled, it is too loud for rehearsals. At the other extreme, the music in a hall may be too weak if the cubic volume is too great, or the reverberation time is too short, or both. Of course, outdoors, where the reverberation time is near zero, the loudness of an orchestra depends on the loudness of the direct sound alone, that is to say, on how near the listener is seated to the performing group.

INITIAL-TIME-DELAY GAP

The principal acoustical problem that is usually associated with a hall of large cubic volume is a too long initial-time-delay gap at the ears of many of the listeners. In illustration, let us study the two rectangular halls sketched in Figure 7.1. Both have high ceilings, say 60 feet, and thus long reverberation times. One hall is narrow, the other is wide. If the balconies are similar, the reverberation times for the two halls will be nearly alike because both ceilings are at the same height. The cubic volume and the potential size of the audience are greater, of course, in the wider hall.

A listener L hearing a violin V receives sound directly via path D and indirectly via path R_1 or R_2. If the distance D is the same in both halls, then path R_2 is longer than path R_1. Let us assume that the width W_1 of the first hall is 60 feet, the width W_2 of the second hall is 110 feet, and that D is equal to 55 feet. Then the path length R_1 is 76 feet, and R_2 is 110 feet. The initial-time-delay gap for the first hall is equal to the time it takes the sound to travel path R_1 minus the time needed to travel path D. Because the speed of sound is 1130 feet per second, the difference in travel time is $(76 - 55)/1130 = 0.019$ seconds, or 19 milliseconds. For the second hall the difference is $55/1130$ or 49 milliseconds.

With an initial-time-delay gap as short as 19 milliseconds, the acoustics may be first-rate, whereas with an initial-time-delay gap of 49 milliseconds, the acoustics will be less than adequate. It is mainly because of their great width that halls with a large cubic volume are liked less well than small halls. For this reason good acoustics cannot be achieved in a new hall simply by copying the proportions and materials of an excellent smaller hall. Because the initial-time-delay gap is longer in a large hall than in a small one—and most modern halls are larger than their predecessors—the acoustics of new halls will need special care if they are to measure up to the old.

Several antidotes have been developed for the acoustical ills associated with large halls. One solution calls for sound-reflecting surfaces, hung hori-

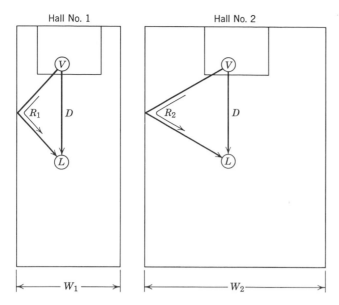

Figure 7.1. Drawings showing the effect of hall width W on the difference in path length of R and D. The direct sound travels path D from the violinist V to the listener L. The reflected sound travels path R. The distance $(R_2 - D)$ in Hall No. 2 is much longer than $(R_1 - D)$ in Hall No. 1. The ceilings of the two halls are assumed to be so high that reflections from the ceilings occur later than reflections from the side walls.

zontally between the ceiling and the main floor, to provide short initial-time-delay gaps at the listeners' ears—particularly those listeners seated on the main floor. Sound-reflecting panels were employed by Lothar Cremer in the 1953 reconstruction of the Herkulessaal in Munich [*Die Schalltechnik,* Vol. 13 (1953)], by Bolt Beranek and Newman Inc. in the Aula Magna in Caracas, Venezuela, dedicated in March 1954, and again by Bolt Beranek and Newman Inc. in the Kresge Auditorium in Cambridge, Massachusetts, opened in 1955. They were also used by Gunnar Sundblad in the 1954 modification of the Konserthuset in Stockholm [*Gravesaner Blätter,* Nos. 2/3, pp. 34–36 (January 1956)]. In these halls the panels were employed either to shorten the initial-time-delay gap or to prevent the unfortunate focusing of sounds from curved ceilings, or, as in the Herkulessaal, to direct the upper registers of the strings over the heads of an audience seated on a flat floor to the listeners at the back.

As acoustic techniques and measures are refined, our understanding of the degree to which acoustical quality is affected by various lengths of initial-time-delay gap can be more precisely specified. For example, Cremer's 1953 article on the Herkulessaal said, "The task has been done well when the difference in path length *via* the reflectors [initial-time-delay gap] is less than 56 ft." As a consequence of the findings of Chapter 9, however, we now know that, unless the initial-time-delay gap is smaller than about 25 milliseconds, a hall cannot take its place among the best halls of the world.

Cremer now designs reflectors to decrease the differences in path length to under 54 feet. For example, beneath the ceiling of the new opera house in West Berlin, he has had lamp-shaped panels hung, 5 feet in diameter.

There now seems to be sufficient evidence—notably the installations at the Tanglewood Music Shed, Lenox, Massachusetts, and at Philharmonic Hall, New York—to warrant the conclusion that hung reflecting panels, or a partly open ceiling, between the main ceiling and the floor improves the acoustics of halls whose initial-time-delay gap would otherwise be too large. Well-designed suspended panels will produce the necessary short initial-time-delay gaps at listeners' positions throughout the hall. Thus for the first time acoustics is able to provide an alternative to building a narrow hall with its attendant small seating capacity.

REVERBERATION TIME

Cubic volume does not provide an unambiguous cue to the effectiveness of an acoustical design. The acoustics are poorer in a hall with a small cubic volume than in a hall with a large volume if the reduction in volume is achieved by lowering the ceiling and, hence, shortening the reverberation time. The basic formula for auditorium acoustics is Sabine's equation [Eq. (1), Appendix 1], which says that the reverberation time increases in direct proportion to the cubic volume and in inverse proportion to the total area of sound-absorbing surfaces—area of the audience, carpets, draperies, sound-absorbing materials, and so forth. A hall with a low ceiling has a low ratio of volume to audience area, and, hence, its reverberation time will be short, and its acoustics poor for today's typical symphonic repertoire. In order to lengthen the reverberation time, the ceiling height must be raised. In a narrow hall, raising the ceiling may improve the acoustics since the initial-time-delay gap will still remain small (see Figure 7.1). Thus a hall whose reverberation time is too short may benefit from an increase in its cubic volume provided either that it is narrow or that it has hanging panels to provide a short initial-time-delay gap. It also follows from Sabine's equation that, if the cubic volume is to be kept as small as possible for a given reverberation time, carpets, draperies, and sound-absorbing materials must be eliminated from the hall, and the audience must be seated in as small an area as possible.

SEATING CAPACITY

Early in this study I concluded that audiences do not absorb sound in proportion to the number of people in them. For example, in the following halls nearly the same amount of sound absorption results from the presence of quite different numbers of people; Bayreuth, Festspielhaus, 530 people; Boston, Symphony Hall, 440 people; Vienna, Staatsoper, 380 people; Caracas, Aula Magna, 330 people. I first reported before the Acoustical Society of America in May 1958 (see Appendix 1) that an audience absorbs sound the way a thick carpet does—in proportion to the area it covers and not in proportion to the number of tufts comprising it. Although the number of people in the four halls above differ, they have one thing in common—they occupy the same amount of floor area, 2500 square feet.

Widely spaced seats make the audience more comfortable, but usually at the expense of acoustical quality and high building costs. If the seats in a hall are to be generously spaced, the architect is likely to design a wide hall in order to obtain the extra floor area. As a result, the initial-time-delay gap at the listeners' ears may be too long.

If, in order to accommodate the oversized seating, the architect selects the alternative of adding balconies rather than widening the hall, other acoustical problems arise. In order for the reverberation time to be long, the ceiling must be high, and even then some of the audience will be hemmed in by a balcony over their heads.

The wide hall or the high ceiling necessitated by balconies—either one —may result in a large cubic volume, but it is achieved at a disproportionately high cost. The combined defects of poor acoustics for music and inflated costs should serve as effective deterrents to unnecessarily large row-to-row or seat-to-seat spacing.

USES FOR HALLS

Except in the largest cities, most American auditoriums serve a variety of purposes. Even in halls with permanent seating, the uses may include concerts by symphonic and chamber music orchestras, jazz bands and brass bands, performances of grand opera and musical comedy, instrumental and vocal recitals, choral concerts, dramatic productions, lectures, conventions, panel discussions, cinema, and church services. In most European halls that are designed for opera or concert, such a range of activities would be unthinkable. In order for a hall to book the touring Metropolitan Opera or the Bolshoi Ballet, the management must be able to guarantee an audience of over 4000 persons. Actually, many auditoriums in the United States have more than 6000 seats. One large city in the Midwest is now planning a multi-purpose hall to seat more than 10,000 people. Many multi-purpose halls have stagehouses that rival the largest opera houses in size and complexity. Ray Berry, editor of *The American Organist*, wrote,

> But music always takes a beating in favor of other uses; events like sports, lectures, drama, automobile shows, what have you?

And Howard Taubman of the New York *Times*, in an admirable understatement, said,

> One must feel that multi-purpose acoustics are not the ideal solution for strictly musical purposes.

What can we do to make the multi-purpose auditoriums more hospitable to music? The floor area occupied by each person should be kept to a minimum. Novel designs will be needed to meet conflicting requirements—a small stage for lectures, a large stage for opera, a tall stagehouse for drama, and a much smaller acoustical enclosure or shell for concerts. Some of these topics are discussed in Chapter 14.

AGE OF HALLS

According to one of the myths of acoustics, old halls have better acoustics than new halls, and the acoustics of concert halls mellow with age. Many of the interviews made me aware that the myth is still current. I have never seen evidence that Carnegie Hall, the Metropolitan Opera House, Symphony Hall in Boston, or the Royal Festival Hall have changed at all with age. The music reviews written in the first two years of their existence differ little from those that I see in the current newspapers, and acoustical tests reveal no changes. Still, it is incontrovertible that the median age of the best-liked halls in this study is 70 years, whereas the median age of the halls liked least is 11 years. What is the source of this difference?

Table 7.2 lists some important reasons why old halls are better liked than new ones. The examples are limited to some of the best halls surviving from the nineteenth century and some less satisfactory halls built in the twentieth century.

Table 7.2 Comparison of some 19th- and 20th-century halls: seven 19th-century halls with excellent acoustics; eight 20th-century halls with mediocre acoustics. All numbers are median values.

	19th-Century Halls	*20th-Century Halls*
Seating and orchestral areas	14,000 sq ft	23,000 sq ft
Ceiling height	60 ft	52 ft
Width	70 ft	128 ft
Initial-time-delay gap	20 msec	30 msec
$T_{500-1000}$(Occup.)	1.7 sec	1.5 sec
Substantial amount of thin wood in interior?	no	yes

Clearly, there are several important differences. The median floor area occupied by seats and orchestra is 65 per cent greater in the new halls and the median ceiling height is 8 feet lower, so that the median mid-frequency reverberation time is only 1.5 seconds, a value too short for today's typical symphonic repertoires. Most twentieth-century halls are lined with thin wood, which causes a serious loss of bass tones. Most damaging of all, the median width for the twentieth-century halls is 83 per cent greater, yielding a median initial-time-delay gap 50 per cent longer than for the nineteenth-century halls. The reasons for the better acoustics in the good nineteenth-century halls is to be found in their architecture, not in their age. The myth that acoustics improve with age is nonsense. Let us bury it and be done with it.

8

Categories of Acoustical Quality
and a Numerical Rating System

"Come into this hall with me, please," invited Erich Leinsdorf, "and listen to the strings during the overture. You will hear the lack of brilliance and the poor balance with the brass. The pit is impossible." Experiences like this one, which I shared with Maestro Leinsdorf during a tour of the Metropolitan Opera Company, are as rewarding as they are infrequent. How does an acoustical engineer go about establishing communication with knowledgeable musicians? It is not easy; these men are very busy and often inaccessible. But without their cooperation, this study could not have been made. In addition to seeking interviews with as many musicians as time permitted, my colleagues and I wrested precious moments during rehearsals and interposed questions into planning sessions in architects' offices. We tried to correlate the musicians' judgments with the architectural features, the acoustical data, and our own listening experiences. By carefully accumulating evidence, sifting fantasy from fact, and sorting idiosyncrasy and bias from general consensus, we have learned to recognize many of the architectural and acoustical features that affect the music and consequently are crucial to the design of the concert hall. Now the reader may ask, was not most of this information already known?

Actually, the technical literature on architectural acoustics offers very little concrete help to the designer of a concert hall or opera house. Musicians have long known that the halls that sound best have relatively long reverberation times, and some acoustical texts have agreed that 1.7 seconds or longer is a reasonable minimum for excellence; and yet the Leipzig Neues Gewandhaus had a reverberation time of 1.55 seconds and the revered Philadelphia Academy of Music has a reverberation time of 1.4 seconds. Some writers on acoustics have advocated a very short reverberation time, contrary to what musicians prefer. F. R. Watson in *Acoustics of Buildings*, Third Edition [John Wiley and Sons, New York, 1947, p. 63] states, "Auditors should have the listening conditions as satisfactory as outdoors, that is, with very little reverberation. The acoustics advances during the past ten years . . . appear to confirm the principles underlying this ideal."

Another dictum in the technical literature has called for irregularities on the surfaces of the ceiling and side walls of opera houses and concert halls. But many good halls are almost without irregularities; for instance, the "relief" on the ceiling of La Scala is actually the trompe d'oeil of a gifted painter. And what modern architect would clutter up his designs with the gee-gaws of the past century ?

The textbooks agree that the ceiling and side walls should reinforce the sound reaching the audience, especially toward the rear of the hall. But the seven nineteenth-century halls represented in Table 7.2—all of which have excellent acoustics—have no special architectural provision for directing sound to the rear.

Though acoustical engineers agree that fluctuations in the growth and decay of sound may control the quality of the after-ring, to my knowledge no one has done a systematic study that would provide exact specifications that could be used by a builder. Of course, there has never been any doubt among musicians or architects that a hall should be free of noise and echo, or that separate performers must hear each other if they are to play in perfect ensemble.

For the architect planning a concert hall, acoustics has not provided quantitative procedures—or over-all guiding formulas—with which he could evaluate acoustical quality or predict the effect of architectural features. The formula for computing reverberation time, developed by Sabine in 1898, has stood almost alone as a numerical acoustic guidepost. But even the computation of the reverberation time of large auditoriums has lacked the necessary accuracy. Since Sabine's time, the formula has been based on the number of people in the audience instead of the area they occupied— a difference that can lead to a 100-per-cent discrepancy in the calculations. (The computation of reverberation time is explained in detail in Appendix 1.) No wonder some of my skeptical friends have suggested that acoustics is more an art than a science.

CATEGORIES OF ACOUSTICAL QUALITY

In order for acoustical science to provide direction to architecture in the interests of music, a scale is needed against which the quality of a hall can be gauged, and the importance of a particular acoustic attribute weighed.

The following chapters attempt a tentative formulation of such a scale. The ingredients are the attributes of acoustical quality, defined in Chapter 4, and the assessments of the 54 concert halls, discussed in Chapter 6.

Of first importance, the 54 halls must be reduced to a manageable number of categories, each one containing halls that are roughly equivalent in total acoustical effectiveness. With the help of the interviews with musicians and critics and my own notes made while listening in almost all the halls, I have been able to assign 53 of the 54 halls into five categories of quality—A^+, excellent; A, very good to excellent; B^+, good to very good; B, fair to good; and C^+, fair—on the basis of their effectiveness for symphonic music and non-Wagnerian opera. The 54th hall, the Bayreuth Festspielhaus, is especially suited to Wagnerian opera and must be rated on a different basis.

This study has purposely omitted poor halls; their gross defects are easily identified and detailed study of them seemed fruitless. Only one hall classified as fair is included, the Royal Albert Hall in London. And some sections of the Royal Albert deserve a higher rating than fair would indicate, for example, the section on the main floor between 30 and 60 feet from the stage, and the part of the balcony that is directly opposite the stage.

It is more than likely that no two listeners would make exactly the same assignment of these halls into five categories. A listener may never have sat in the best or poorest part of the house, or in a location of average quality. Someone with many years of listening in a particular hall may no longer be aware of its acoustical blemishes, because he has long since accustomed himself to pay attention only to the performance. It is also possible in some of the newer halls that have not yet established themselves that the musicians, the critics, and I may have judged them more severely than we judged the more familiar older halls. Consequently, it is probable that any particular hall could be ranked one category higher or one category lower than its present assignment. An error of three categories is almost impossible, and an error of two categories is highly unlikely.

The assignment of the 53 halls to categories was made in the following way. After interviewing the 50 conductors and music critics and completing my visits to the halls, I tentatively assigned each hall to one of the five categories. Then I sent the compilation, with a request for criticism, to most of the men interviewed. A small number of adjustments to an adjacent category resulted from their comments, but the majority wrote as did Howard Taubman of the New York *Times*, "On the whole I agree with you about the halls that I know anything about."

Another problem now becomes apparent. Although science might be served by identification of the halls in the comparisons that follow, both art and commerce plead for circumspection. With reluctance, I have not identified the halls by name in the succeeding analyses.*

DEFINITIONS OF THE FIVE RATING CATEGORIES†

Category A+

The halls in this category were rated "excellent" for symphony orchestra concerts or for the typical repertoire of non-Wagnerian opera by nearly every musician or critic interviewed. These halls received few adverse comments. Six concert halls and seven opera houses fall in this category.

Category A

These halls were generally rated "very good" to "excellent." They are all deficient in one or two of the important acoustical attributes. Each hall is highly treasured by the community it serves and is spoken of favorably by the majority of the musicians who perform there. There are nineteen concert halls and eight opera houses in this category.

Category B+

The halls in this category were rated "good" to "very good." They received more favorable than adverse comment. These halls are not mediocre; any negative criticism received came in response to a request made to the persons interviewed that their assessment include both the good and bad

---

* Identification of the halls may be requested on a confidential basis by research workers.

† Twelve of the halls in the study are used for both opera and concerts, which accounts for the total of 66 concert halls and opera houses in the five categories.

features. Some of the halls are better suited to the music of the Baroque period than to either Classical or Romantic music. Others may be deficient in one or more of the attributes of acoustical quality. Some are very large, and large size is inimical to excellent acoustics. All but three of these halls were built to serve many uses—music, speech, dance, conference—and they suffer from the compromises that so often downgrade the acoustics of a hall for concert or opera. There are fourteen concert halls and four opera houses in this category.

Category B

The halls in this group were rated "fair" to "good." They received more adverse than favorable criticism in the interviews, but they are not poor or unsatisfactory halls. Of the seven concert halls in this category, all but two were built to serve many different purposes.

Category C+

The Royal Albert Hall in London is the only hall in Category C+. Its chief defects are its large lateral dimensions and its huge cubic volume. It is a satisfactory hall for organ and choral music of the cathedral type and for ceremonial orchestral and band music. It is non-uniform acoustically. In his comment on the original assignment of the halls into five categories, Sir Adrian Boult wrote: "I think I agree with the categories at which you arrive in every case, except that I would like to put in a word for the Royal Albert Hall. It is unpredictable anywhere around the ground floor and the first two tiers of boxes, but above that, although one gets a great impression of distance, the quality is lovely throughout, and I really think on that account it might figure higher in your scale. In other words, I agree to C+ for the lower half, but would, I think, vote for B+ or A upstairs."

One question deserves consideration: under controlled conditions, just how well do qualified listeners agree on the acoustical quality of a hall in which music is played? I find that they agree very well indeed. During the week of May 27, 1962, in which Philharmonic Hall in New York was "tuned," a listening group was formed to judge the acoustics of the nearly completed hall. The group was made up of the musical director and three

407

assistant conductors of the New York Philharmonic Orchestra, several other leading American conductors, a recording engineer, several musicians from the Juilliard School of Music, and five of my colleagues and myself from Bolt Beranek and Newman Inc. The New York Philharmonic Orchestra performed works of all musical styles during nine two-hour "rehearsals" in the new hall. Adjustments in the acoustics were made daily. The members of the listening team, all of whom were in remarkable agreement in their judgments, were able to detect the effect on the acoustics of subtle architectural adjustments in the hall, for instance, variations in the height and angle of the stage canopy or the installation of additional sound-reflecting panels. All of us felt that the final state of adjustment of the hall was the best one tried during the week, just as we had all agreed on which of the earlier adjustments was the worst. Acoustical evaluations under controlled conditions need not be a matter of guesswork.

TOWARD A NUMERICAL RATING SYSTEM

The ultimate goal of this study of the acoustics of concert halls and opera houses is to derive a system that will give a numerical rating to the acoustical quality of a hall from information available from drawings alone. It is not difficult to rate a hall after it is built and has been in use for some time. At that point, opinions gathered from trained listeners may correlate highly with measures of the acoustical qualities that they mention. It often turns out, however, that these acoustical qualities by themselves do not provide a sufficient yardstick on which to evaluate other halls. For example, a musician rating Symphony Hall may say that it is acoustically live and has brilliant sound for violins and good attack. He may note also that it is old, rectangular, has a plaster interior, niches, and statues, and that in his opinion these three qualities are important for good sound.

An acoustician, attempting to find the acoustical features that correlate with this musical description may measure the reverberation time of Symphony Hall. It is fairly long, 1.8 seconds at mid-frequencies when the hall is fully occupied. He can also measure the time required for the sound to build up on the stage or in the seating area of the empty hall; in Symphony Hall there is a reasonably rapid buildup of sound, which confirms the musicians' judgment of a "good attack." The hall is, as the musician said, old and rectangular, and its irregular plaster walls and ceiling diffuse sound.

Now, have the musician and the acoustical analyst made any contribution to acoustical knowledge that will help us to evaluate another hall? Can the yardstick on which Symphony Hall has been measured be applied to, say, the Academy of Music in Philadelphia, which also stands high on the musicians' list of favorite halls?

The reverberation time of the Academy of Music is quite low, 1.4 seconds; the hall is horseshoe-shaped rather than rectangular; it is older than the Boston hall; the musicians find its attack good; its interior finish is chiefly wood of medium thickness. Clearly, our picture is incomplete, our yardstick provides an insufficient measure. In order to distinguish among good concert halls on acoustic grounds, we must evaluate a larger number of acoustical variables, and, most important, we must find a way to quantify our findings.

WHAT ARE THE IMPORTANT VARIABLES?

In order to establish a numerical scale of acoustical quality, against which our concert halls can be compared, let us return to the attributes of acoustical quality, defined in Chapter 4. First among these attributes, in the judgment of most musicians, are cubic volume, which is often correlated with intimacy, and reverberation time, which is related to liveness.

Cubic volume

The range of cubic volumes from the best-liked halls to the least-liked halls is not great (see Table 7.1). Within certain limits, cubic volume does not, by itself, appear to provide a measure against which acoustical quality can be gauged. Cubic volume is, however, one of the determinants of the initial-time-delay gap. Since a short initial-time-delay gap, and thus intimacy, is more readily achieved in a hall of small cubic volume than in a large hall, cubic volume is one important variable.

Reverberation time

Ideally, the reverberation time of a hall should be adjusted to suit the style of music most often played in it. But most present-day concert halls must serve for a wide variety of music. The architect must seek a best compromise. The following analyses, given in Table 8.1 and Figure 8.1, show the mid-frequency reverberation times of the 47 halls used primarily for symphonic music in terms of the categories of acoustical quality. In Category A^+ there are six halls with reverberation times between 1.7 and 2.05 seconds—a median of 1.9 seconds. In the three categories of A, B^+, and B the reverberation times range between 1.0 and 2.0 seconds, with median values of 1.5 and 1.6 seconds.

Table 8.1   Mid-frequency reverberation times of the
47 concert halls, divided into five categories of acoustical quality

Categories of acousti- cal quality	Mid-frequency reverberation times—in seconds	Median reverberation times—in seconds
A^+	1.7, 1.8, 1.8, 2.0, 2.05, 2.05	1.9
A	1.2, 1.3, 1.4, 1.4, 1.5, 1.5, 1.5, 1.6, 1.6, 1.6, 1.6, 1.7, 1.7, 1.7, 1.7, 1.7, 1.8, 1.9, 2.0	1.6
B^+	1.0, 1.3, 1.4, 1.4, 1.5, 1.5, 1.5, 1.5, 1.5, 1.6, 1.7, 1.7, 1.7, 1.9	1.5
B	1.3, 1.4, 1.5, 1.6, 1.6, 1.6, 1.8	1.6
C^+	2.45	2.45

Four tentative conclusions can be drawn from Table 8.1:

1. In order for a concert hall to fall in the A^+ category, its reverberation time must be at least 1.7 seconds.

2. A reverberation time as long as 1.7 seconds does not ensure that a concert hall will fall in Category A^+ and, therefore, reverberation time alone does not distinguish an excellent hall from an inferior hall.

3. Let us assume that the only reason those seven halls in Category A

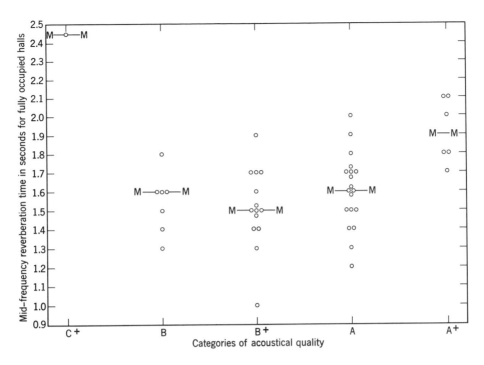

Figure 8.1. Mid-frequency reverberation times (average of the reverberation times at 500 and 1000 cycles per second with full occupancy) plotted against the subjectively determined categories of acoustical quality for 47 concert halls.

whose reverberation times are shorter than 1.6 seconds do not fall in A^+ is their short reverberation time, since, if they were deficient in additional ways, they would fall in a still lower category. Then it follows that the difference between the median of the A^+ group (1.9 seconds) and the median of the seven halls with short reverberation time (1.4 seconds) is one rating category.

4. Thirteen halls in Categories A, B^+, and B have reverberation times between 1.7 and 2.0 seconds. Perhaps deviation in only one acoustical attribute is responsible for their falling into a category below A^+.

The age and shape of the hall

Chapter 7 made the point that among both old and new halls there will be found both good and poor halls. Nor does a hall need some particular shape to have excellent acoustics. Of the six concert halls in Category A^+, four are rectangular, one is horseshoe-shaped, and one is fan-shaped. Seven of the concert halls in Category A are rectangular, seven are fan-shaped, two are horseshoe-shaped, and three have other shapes. Of the opera houses in the two top categories, A^+ and A, seven are horseshoe-shaped, six are fan-shaped, and one is rectangular. Obviously, there must be other more critical attributes to explain their acoustical ratings.

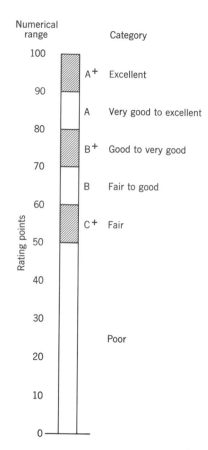

Figure 8.2. Range of numerical values arbitrarily assigned to the five categories into which the concert halls of this study are divided, plus the category "poor."

THE RANGE OF THE RATING SCALE

The next step in establishing a rating scale is to choose arbitrarily a maximum and minimum value such that each category of acoustical quality can be assigned a range of values on the scale. If our arbitrary scale runs from 0 to 100, we can arrange the five categories along it in the manner shown in Figure 8.2. The ranges shown in the figure have been selected as a reasonable representation of the 54 halls included in this study. Remember that this study deals with no poor halls—no circular, or elliptical, or very long and narrow, or very short and wide halls; no halls with focusing domes, or large amounts of draperies, or very low ceilings; no halls with severe echoes.

According to Figure 8.2, the halls that are called excellent—those assigned to Category A⁺—are given a numerical rating between 90 and 100; those in Category A, between 80 and 90; and so on, down to the category "poor," which would include halls whose numerical ratings fell below a score of 50 (none of which are included in this study). This chart says, in effect, that to be reasonably acceptable for concerts or opera a hall needs a rating of better than 50 points.

In order to determine the relative weight of each of the 18 acoustical attributes of Chapter 4, let us first separate them into three categories: (1) the independent attributes that contribute positively to the acoustical quality of a hall for music; (2) the independent acoustical blemishes—those attributes that contribute negatively to the acoustical rating; and (3) the dependent attributes that are a function of combinations of independent attributes. The acoustical attributes fall into these three categories as shown in Table 8.2.

Table 8.2   Separation of the attributes of acoustical quality into three categories

Independent positive attributes	*Independent negative attributes*	*Dependent attributes*
Intimacy	Echo	Clarity
Liveness	Noise	Brilliance
Warmth	Distortion	Attack
Loudness of the Direct Sound	Hall Non-uniformity	Texture
Loudness of the Reverberant Sound		Dynamic Range
Diffusion		
Balance and Blend		
Ensemble		

By this division, the eight attributes in the first column, when rated numerically, can add to a maximum total of 100 points. The four independent negative attributes in the second column may subtract from the total rating. For example, a hall that rated 85 points when its air-conditioning system was turned off, might become so noisy with the air conditioning operating that its rating would drop by 40 points to a level unacceptable for musical performances. No points are assigned to the five attributes in the third column since they are dependent on the attributes in the other two columns.

A most difficult question is whether the eight independent attributes in Table 8.2 are linearly additive. For example, if each of two attributes, taken separately, is 10 points less than the optimum, does their combined effect reduce the total rating by 20 points? Or does the presence of one of the attributes lessen the effect of the other in reducing the total rating? We can not give a definitive answer, but the evidence that is available indicates that the eight attributes each contribute independently, and that additivity should be assumed in the application of the rating system to the 54 halls.

LIMITATIONS IN THE RATING SYSTEM

There are limitations in the rating system. First of all, a coarse scale of this kind cannot be applied to a hall of unusual design. For example, in subsequent chapters, a 10-point range is assigned to the acoustical quality of the orchestra enclosure. If a drastic change were made in the enclosure, say, if the main curtain between the orchestra and the audience were lowered to within 3 feet of the stage, the change in acoustics would be greater than 10 points. Consequently, so unusual a situation could not be handled by this rating system.

The rating system applies primarily to the seats commonly occupied by professional music critics and visiting conductors. After all, the numerical system is correlated with their judgments. Music critics normally occupy seats on the main floor, at one side of center, and about halfway between the stage and the front of the lowest balcony or ring. Though the conductors may have occupied balcony seats during their student years, they now generally listen from the very good seats reserved for visitors. Consequently, they have little experience with seats under deep balcony overhangs or far to the side, at the very rear of the main floor or in a balcony. In a horseshoe-shaped opera house, the management's seats may be in a box in the first ring above the main floor, fairly well off the center line, but not too near the proscenium opening. This location gives a clear view of the performance but does not deprive subscribers of choice seats. For these reasons, the evaluation of the halls is limited to two locations. One location is at one side of center on the main floor, about halfway between the balcony front farthest forward and the stage. The other location is about halfway between the front of the balcony and the last row of seats. The initial-time-delay gaps given in Chapter 6 are for these two positions. Other seats in the hall may have better or worse acoustics than these two locations, but the interviews with musicians make it clear that these locations exert a preponderant influence on the reputation that a hall acquires.

It goes without saying that the numerical rating system can report on the presence or absence of the components of good acoustics, but it cannot, in its present form, assess whether they are fully effective. During the "tuning week" of Philharmonic Hall, a group of musicians, architects, and acousticians had the exciting experience of observing how the acoustics changed with minor tuning and adjustment of the architectural details of the hall—adjustments that we judged raised the hall one full category, without any structural change taking place. The tuning of Philharmonic Hall is discussed in detail in Chapter 15.

9

Acoustical Intimacy and Liveness

The preceding chapter established that neither cubic volume nor reverberation time nor age nor shape qualifies as the single ingredient that separates the excellent halls from the ordinary. On the theory that variation in only one acoustical attribute may be primarily responsible for dropping many live halls into categories of acoustical quality below A^+, let us continue the effort to identify the one crucial attribute of acoustical quality.

ACOUSTICAL INTIMACY: THE INITIAL-TIME-DELAY GAP

Table 8.1 listed 20 concert halls with reverberation times of 1.7 seconds or longer that fall in all five categories of acoustical quality. Perhaps a detailed look at the acoustical data will suggest wherein the differences among these halls lie. In all but three of the 20 halls, the ratios of the reverberation times at both low and high frequencies to those at mid-frequencies are about the same; there is no observable distortion; there is almost no noise; balance and blend are good; sound diffusion is adequate, and ensemble good. The listeners in the middle of the main floor of these 17 halls are nearly the same distance from the concertmaster, approximately 60 feet. The only obvious attributes that vary among these 17 concert halls are the initial-time-delay gap and the cubic volume. Cubic volume has already been eliminated as the crucial variable, except insofar as it is related to other attributes. Consequently, we must now test the notion that the attribute responsible for the variation in quality of the 17 halls is acoustical intimacy. What the musician calls intimacy can be measured by the initial-time-delay gap, which was defined in Chapter 4 as the interval at the listener's ear between the arrival of the direct sound and that of the first reflected sound. Let us first study this attribute in concert halls.

Concert halls

The initial-time-delay gap at the ears of a listener sitting on the main floor of a concert hall can be determined from drawings of the hall. Detailed procedures for making this measurement are given in Appendix 3. All of the sound reflections are considered in the measurement (see Figure 2.12), that is to say, reflections from the side walls, the ceiling, the balcony faces, the rear walls, the box faces, and the stage enclosures.

The range of initial-time-delay gaps for the 47 concert halls of this study is, as shown in Figure 9.1, from 8 to 71 milliseconds. The 17 halls that differ only in cubic volume and initial-time-delay gap lie within the blocks with solid boundaries. One other hall with slightly low bass reverberation also falls in this group. Of the 18 halls, the 6 in Category A^+ have initial-time-delay gaps, measured at the center of the main floor, of between 8 and 21 milliseconds; the 8 in Category A, between 22 and 34 milliseconds; the 2 in Category B^+, between 35 and 46 milliseconds; the one in Category B, between 47 and 58 milliseconds; and the one in Category C^+, between 59 and 71 milliseconds. In each category, the range of initial-time-delay gaps seems to be about 12 milliseconds. The remaining 29 concert halls are plotted in the blocks with dashed boundaries. These 29 halls fall one or more categories below what would be expected if the initial-time-delay gap alone could determine the excellence of a concert hall.

If a hall could be classified by this single attribute, 11 halls in Category A would move to Category A^+; 11 halls in B^+ would move to Category A, and one to Category A^+; 4 halls in B would move to Category B^+, one to Category A, and one to Category A^+. Apparently, these 29 halls have deficiencies in some other acoustical attributes. Let us see if this is so.

Of the 26 concert halls of Figure 9.1 that fall one category below the solid blocks, 9 have short reverberation times, 7 are slightly deficient in each of a number of the acoustical attributes, 5 have somewhat short reverberation times and are also deficient in the ratio of bass reverberation to mid-frequency reverberation, 4 have distortion combined with fairly short reverberation times, and one is seriously deficient in the ratio of bass reverberation to mid-frequency reverberation.

Of the 2 concert halls of Figure 9.1 that fall two categories below the solid blocks, both have short reverberation times, both are somewhat deficient in bass reverberation, and both are wanting in balance and blend.

The one concert hall of Figure 9.1 that falls three categories below a solid block has a short reverberation time, a deficiency in bass reverberation,

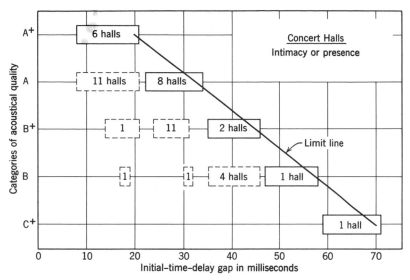

Figure 9.1. The relation of the subjectively determined categories of acoustical quality to the initial-time-delay gaps of 47 concert halls measured at a center seat on the main floor, for sound emanating from the concertmaster's position. The heavy diagonal line indicates the highest category in which one expects to find a hall with a given initial-time-delay gap. In the solid blocks are 17 concert halls, similar in many respects, but with different cubic volumes and initial-time-delay gaps, plus an eighteenth hall; in the dashed blocks are the remaining 29 concert halls.

poor balance and blend, some distortion, and some echo.

From this recital of deficiencies, we can make certain deductions about concert halls:

1. A relatively short reverberation time, of about 1.4 seconds, causes a drop of about one category. This was also suggested by tentative conclusion 3, relating to Table 8.1.

2. A serious deficiency in ratio of bass to mid-frequency reverberation produces a drop of one category.

3. Poor balance and blend account for a drop of about one-half a category.

4. Distortion to the extent found in these halls causes a drop of about one-half a category.

Obviously, a short initial-time-delay gap is necessary to ensure excellence in a concert hall, but it alone is not sufficient to effect it.

Opera houses

A similar graph for opera houses, shown in Figure 9.2, suggests that longer initial-time-delay gaps are tenable in opera houses than in concert halls. Initial-time-delay gaps as long as 24 milliseconds are found in opera houses rated excellent. With an initial-time-delay gap of 55 milliseconds, the rating of an opera house drops only to the B+ category. The difference

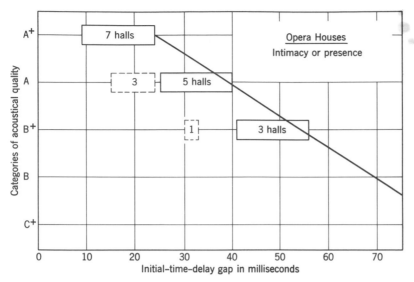

Figure 9.2. The relation of the subjectively determined categories of acoustical quality to the initial-time-delay gaps of 19 opera houses measured at a center seat on the main floor for sound emanating from principal singer's position. In the solid blocks are 15 opera houses, similar in many respects, but with different cubic volumes and initial-time-delay gaps; in the dashed blocks are the remaining 4 opera houses.

in the importance of intimacy to a concert hall and to an opera house must arise from the different natures of the human voice, whose movement is slow and legato, and the symphony orchestra, which is frequently called upon to emit rapid discrete sounds. Only 4 halls of the 18 that house opera lie one category lower than their initial-time-delay gap would predict, and none of them drop by more than one category. Let us investigate the acoustical attributes in which these 4 halls are deficient.

Of the 4 opera houses of Figure 9.2 that fall one category below the solid blocks, 2 have very short reverberation times, about 1.1 seconds, and are somewhat deficient in the ratio of bass to mid-frequency reverberation; 2 have fairly large cubic volumes, between 650,000 and 750,000 cubic feet, and of this pair of halls, one has a somewhat short reverberation time and the other is somewhat deficient in bass reverberation.

These data, though meager, suggest two tentative conclusions:

1. An opera house for Italian opera music should probably have a reverberation time longer than 1.3 seconds, but no longer than 1.6 seconds. On the strength of the successful Bayreuth Festspielhaus, I would risk the opinion that an opera house for Wagnerian music should have a fairly long reverberation time, say, 1.5 to 1.8 seconds.

2. A first-rate opera house apparently should be small. La Scala is 397,000 cubic feet, Vienna is 377,000 cubic feet, Bayreuth is 364,000 cubic feet, and the Philadelphia Academy of Music is 530,000 cubic feet. On the other hand, the Teatro Colón in Buenos Aires and the Baltimore Lyric

Theatre, both of which have volumes of about 730,000 cubic feet, are successful despite their size, apparently because of their excellence in other respects.

Psychoacoustic experiments and the initial-time-delay gap

In Figure 9.1, a heavy diagonal line intersects the right-hand end of each of the five solid blocks. This line delimits the highest category into which a concert hall can fall for any initial-time-delay gap. For example, a concert hall with a gap of 44 milliseconds cannot attain a category higher than B^+, even if it is superior in every other acoustical attribute. But it may drop several categories lower if it has other acoustical deficiencies.

The solid diagonal line of Figure 9.1 is based on evidence that is confirmed by two researches on the psychoacoustic effects of adding a delayed reflection to music. H. Haas of the University of Göttingen, Germany, published his results in *Acustica* in 1951 (Vol. 1, pp. 49–58); a later study by R. W. Muncey, A. F. B. Nickson, and P. Dubout of the Laboratories of the Commonwealth Scientific and Industrial Research Organization of Australia, published in *Acustica* in 1953 (Vol. 3, pp. 168–173) agrees well with Haas's findings. Let us review the experiment of the Australian group. They presented music, through loudspeakers, to a group of 20 listeners. In order to produce the equivalent of a reflection from a surface in a room, they used a magnetic tape recorder that added to the original transcription of the music the same music delayed by an amount of time up to 1000 milliseconds. The amount of the delay could be varied and the intensity of the delayed or "reflected" music could be adjusted. Two of the melodies used are shown in Figure 9.3. Each passage took 14 seconds to play. The music was recorded by a string quartet playing outdoors.

During the period of silence between repetitions, the listeners were asked to report whether they were disturbed by the added reflection, not just whether they could perceive it. At each session one sample of music was repeated about 18 times, with various combinations of time delay and intensity.

The listeners were disturbed most by reflections added to fast music played by stringed instruments, the kind of music that forms the foundation

Figure 9.3. Melodies played in the Australian studies of the annoyance of delayed single reflections: (*a*) string music at fast tempo, (*b*) string music at slow tempo.

of present-day symphonic concerts. When the intensity of the reflection was about 5 decibels below the intensity of the direct sound, fewer than 20 per cent of the listeners were disturbed by delays of 15 to 30 milliseconds. Nearly all the listeners were disturbed by reflections that were delayed by 100 milliseconds.

In these experiments the experimental subjects who did the listening were laboratory staff members chosen without concern for whether they were regular concert-goers; there were no professional musicians among them. If we assume that those 10 to 20 per cent of the listeners who found delays of 15 to 30 milliseconds disturbing were critical listeners, then it should be reasonable to conclude that an initial-time-delay gap in excess of about 20 milliseconds detracts from musical quality. The results of the tests imply also that, the greater the time delay of the reflection, the less pleasant the music becomes. In the experiment, when the time-delay gap reached 70 milliseconds, about 80 per cent of the listeners found it disturbing. It seems safe to conclude that acoustical intimacy cannot survive an initial-time-delay gap in excess of 70 milliseconds, particularly if the first reflection has an intensity within 10 decibels of that of the direct sound. Thus both the Australian experimenters and Haas confirm the thesis illustrated in Figure 9.1.

According to Figure 9.1, since an initial-time-delay gap of 70 milliseconds or more corresponds to a rating of C^+ or lower, it contributes no points to the rating of a concert hall. Since an initial-time-delay gap of 20 milliseconds or less can place a hall four categories higher, it must account for a contribution of 40 points. Therefore the scale for intimacy ranges from

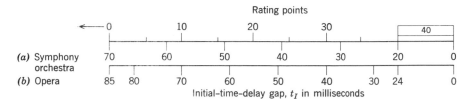

Figure 9.4. Rating scale of intimacy as a function of initial-time-delay gap, t_I: (a) for concert halls, (b) for opera houses. If the time-delay gap between the first and second reflections exceeds the initial-time-delay gap, that measure should be substituted in rating acoustical intimacy.

0 to 40 points. If we assume that the relationship between acoustical intimacy and the duration of the initial-time-delay gap is linear, we can draw the rating scale for the attribute of intimacy in concert halls shown in (a) of Figure 9.4.

The rating scale for opera houses, shown in (b) of Figure 9.4, covers a range of 24 to 85 milliseconds. Again, a 40-point maximum is assumed.

Although these scales are derived from initial-time-delay gaps measured at the test location at the center of the main floor, the validation in Chapter 13 suggests that the scale can also be applied to the second test location in the center of the balcony. By extrapolation, the method should apply to any seat that is neither too near the stage nor too far from the centerline of the hall, provided it is not under a balcony overhang, deep in a box, or at any other location that is shielded from either the direct sound from the orchestra or the reverberant sound.

Thus far, only the first reflection has received attention. What about the second? It seems obvious that the gap between the first and second reflections should also satisfy the relation of Figure 9.4, although insufficient evidence is available to prove this contention. The essence of the problem is that in the ear two reflections tend to merge into one if they are separated by less than about 20 milliseconds. Whenever two reflections are separated by as much as 70 milliseconds, the ear hears the second sound as an echo. At intermediate separation there is a progressively deleterious effect on music. In obtaining the initial-time-delay gaps of Chapter 6, I have disregarded any reflection of a sound that arrived within a few milliseconds of the direct sound, since it would be heard as part of the direct sound. Thus I have measured the gap between the direct sound, so defined, and the first following reflection. Also, whenever the time-delay gap between the first and second reflections exceeds that between the direct sound and the first reflection, I have used it in conjunction with Figure 9.4 for rating the attribute of intimacy.

Although the initial-time-delay gaps given in this book come from measurements on architectural drawings of the various halls, several experimenters have investigated the measurement of reflection patterns directly in the hall. Three studies have been published from the Physikalishes Institut III at Göttingen University. R. Thiele [*Acustica*, Vol. 3, pp. 291–302 (1953)] explored a method for measuring reflection patterns in existing halls; E. Meyer and R. Thiele [*Acustica*, Vol. 6, pp. 425–444 (1956)] measured the reflection patterns of 31 different rooms; and G. Schodder [*Acustica*, Vol. 6, pp. 445–465 (1956)] made detailed measurements on several radio studios, concert halls, theaters, and churches. Unfortunately, in each of the studies the halls measured were unoccupied.

It is interesting to compare their measurements with the data taken from drawings that are presented here. In the Royal Festival Hall in London (see Chapter 6), Schodder measured initial-time-delay gaps on the main floor of 36 milliseconds and in the balcony of 15 milliseconds. The values obtained from the drawings at reasonably comparable positions are 34 and 14 milliseconds. However, there is one important difference between his measurements and the data presented here. All the reflection patterns measured in the unoccupied hall show a prominent reflection from the low rear wall of the stage at about 25 milliseconds. If the stage were occupied by a full orchestra, this reflection would not occur. The data taken from the drawings, presented in Chapter 6, include only those reflections that would occur with a full audience and with the orchestra on stage.

The principal advantage of making measurements on drawings is that a hall can be evaluated before it is constructed. This procedure is essential to the architect if a number of alternate drawings are to be compared before the final design is selected. If only one design is to be evaluated, an accurate scale model can be made and tested. In our experience, a scale model yields little information that cannot be obtained directly from drawings, and the cost of constructing a good model is considerable.

Another procedure for evaluating the reflection pattern has been published by V. Jordan of Copenhagen [*Proceedings of the Third International Congress on Acoustics*, Stuttgart, 1959, Vol. II, Elsevier Publishing Co., Amsterdam, pp. 922–925 (1961)]. Jordan's method calls for either measurements made in the completed hall without an audience, or the use of a model with the audience simulated. His system, like that of the Göttingen group, offers no guidance to the architect or his acoustical consultant during the early stages of the design of a hall. Nor does either system solve the problem of simulating an orchestra.

LIVENESS: REVERBERATION TIMES AT THE MIDDLE AND HIGH FREQUENCIES

Liveness is the subjective impression of reverberation. Music sounds louder in a hall that has a long reverberation time, particulary in the rear of the hall. Reverberation increases the fullness of tone; it enhances the bass; it contributes to the blending of the instruments; it increases the range of crescendo and decrescendo; and it diffuses the sound so that it seems to be distributed throughout the room rather than emanating from one direction only.

From the musician's point of view, reverberation is a component of music. It takes an active part in the performance by increasing the fullness of tone and the blend, and it is often a component of the composer's tonal palette. In interpreting some styles of music, musicians prefer a concert hall with a fairly long reverberation. A reverberation time that is too long leads to a loss of clarity, the blending of incompatible chords, and inordinate loudness.

In its technical sense, liveness in a hall is related to the reverberation times at the middle and high frequencies, above 250 cycles per second. The separate term warmth describes the reverberation at low frequencies, at the bass. Thus a hall can sound live and yet be deficient in bass, and thus lacking in warmth.

In the discussion that follows, reverberation times given without qualification refer specifically to the mid-frequency reverberation in a fully occupied hall. They consist of the arithmetic average of the reverberation times at 500 and 1000 cycles per second, measured in a hall that contains a full audience and orchestra. Any reverberation times that refer to other frequencies, or to a hall incompletely occupied, will be labeled explicitly.

425

Dry halls

Liveness is often mentioned by musicians and trained listeners as an important aspect of the concert hall. A room that is not live enough is usually described as "dry" or "dead." Table 9.1 gives the mid-frequency reverberation times of six halls known for their dryness.

Table 9.1   The mid-frequency reverberation times of six dry halls, with audience

	Reverberation time in seconds
Old Festspielhaus, Salzburg*	ca. 1.0
Orchestra Hall, Chicago	ca. 1.3
Kleinhans Music Hall, Buffalo	1.32
Academy of Music, Philadelphia	1.4
Kresge Auditorium, Cambridge	1.47
Royal Festival Hall, London	1.5

* The Salzburg hall, though not one of the 54 halls discussed in this book, is included here as an example of extreme dryness.

Erich Leinsdorf describes the sound in the Old Festspielhaus as "dead dry" or "straw dry."

Of Orchestra Hall, Chicago, Alfred Frankenstein says, "This hall has no life when the audience is in it; it is as dead as any I know." Fritz Reiner says, "When Orchestra Hall is fully occupied, the reverberation time is too short." Roger Dettmer says, "When the hall is full, there is almost no reverberation."

Reiner calls Kleinhans Hall "completely dead." William Steinberg says, "Kleinhans is dry." Tauno Hannikainen calls it "a little dry."

Pierre Monteux says of the Academy of Music, "This hall is too dry; the tone stops instantly." Eugene Ormandy says, "The Academy is a little dry." Reiner speaks of halls with a horseshoe shape and many balcony rings, of which the Academy of Music is one, as "the dry Italian type."

Of Kresge Auditorium, Cyrus Durgin says, "For a full symphony orchestra, the reverberation is too short, the sound is too dry." Harold Rogers adds, "The sound is somewhat too clear for full orchestra, but the hall is excellent for chamber music and piano." Izler Solomon says, "With just this small orchestral group and chorus, it [Kresge] was very charming."

Munch, Monteux, and Ormandy consider the Royal Festival Hall too dry. Each of them has mentioned that there is no resonance, even when the hall is empty. Alexander Gibson writes of the Royal Festival Hall, "The dry acoustics of this hall make for a clinical effect." Sir John Barbirolli comments, "Everything is sharp and clear and there is no impact, no fullness on climaxes."

I could cite many more authorities, but suffice it to say that, for the repertoires of today's symphony orchestra, conductors and trained listeners consider a reverberation time under 1.6 seconds to be too short, and a hall with so short a reverberation too dry.

Live halls

Table 9.2 shows the reverberation times of some highly praised halls.

Table 9.2   The mid-frequency reverberation times of seven very good to excellent halls with full audience

	Reverberation time in seconds
Grosser Musikvereinssaal, Vienna	2.05
Tanglewood Music Shed, Lenox	2.05
Concertgebouw, Amsterdam	2.0
Symphony Hall, Boston	1.8
Teatro Colón, Buenos Aires	ca. 1.8
Stadt-Casino, Basel	1.7
Carnegie Hall, New York	1.7

Commenting on a number of these halls, Igor Markevich says, "I prefer a bit more reverberation than Symphony Hall has. The Musikvereinssaal has a longer reverberation time than the Boston hall, but I would not want a longer time than that of the Musikvereinssaal. The Concertgebouw has very good acoustics. I think the Teatro Colón is a very good house, both for opera and symphony concerts. Carnegie Hall is too muted."

Herbert von Karajan says of the Grosser Musikvereinssaal, "The sound in this hall is so full that the technical attack of instruments—bows and lips—gets lost. Also successive notes merge into each other. I consider Symphony Hall a little better than the Musikvereinssaal."

Dimitri Mitropoulos commented, "The Musikvereinssaal rings too much. Carnegie is good; it is not overly reverberant. Symphony Hall has good acoustics."

Monteux says, "The Concertgebouw has marvelous acoustics. The Musikvereinssaal too is very good. I find Carnegie a little dead with audience. Symphony Hall I like very, very much, and Tanglewood is also extremely good."

Charles Munch says, "The Musikvereinssaal has a beautiful quality of sound. Carnegie could use more reverberation. Symphony Hall is excellent. Tanglewood is also excellent, especially for large orchestra and violin."

George Szell observed, "The Musikvereinssaal in Vienna and Symphony Hall in Boston are excellent halls—the reverberation times in both of them are about right."

Ormandy says, "The Musikvereinssaal is just right acoustically. Boston has one of the world's best halls. Carnegie is not as reverberant as it might be."

Sir Adrian Boult writes, "Symphony Hall is our ideal."

Reiner says, "The Musikvereinssaal and Symphony Hall are the two best halls. I do not consider the Concertgebouw as good."

Hermann Scherchen says, "The Musikvereinssaal is very good for Romantic music, but not for Bach. The Concertgebouw is not as good."

Isaac Stern says, "The Concertgebouw is marvelous for the violin; it rings when you sound a tone. Symphony Hall is excellent. Carnegie is better in rehearsal than with audience. The Teatro Colón is the best of all halls. Tanglewood has brilliant, warm, singing sound."

Leopold Stokowski says, "The Musikvereinssaal is excellent."

Bruno Walter said, "The Musikvereinssaal has beauty and power, and I consider it better than Carnegie. Boston is very fine, more live than Carnegie. I like the Concertgebouw; it is really a live hall. The Gewandhaus in Liepzig [whose reverberation time was 1.55 seconds] was not as good as the Musikvereinssaal; it was not as live or as noble."

Both these musicians and the critics, recording engineers, and performers whom I have consulted arrive at the same specification: for Romantic music, today's audience seems to prefer a reverberation time at mid-frequencies of 2.1 to 2.3 seconds; for the average symphony orchestra program, a reverberation time between 1.8 and 2.0 seconds; for Baroque and Classical music, a reverberation time between 1.4 and 1.8 seconds.

As Hermann Scherchen remarked, "With such a range in reverberation time depending on the type of music, how can one say what is a good hall?" There may be some truth in this, but fortunately the building has to satisfy only today's musicians and today's audiences. Tomorrow's musicians and listeners may choose to listen differently, but how could we try to predict their taste?

Although reverberation time at the mid-frequencies has proved to be a reliable indicator of the liveness of a hall, reverberation time at higher frequencies has been found to have surprisingly little relation to liveness. A comparison of the reverberation times at 2000, 4000, and 6000 cycles per second to those at the mid-frequency, 500 to 1000 cycles per second, shows that these ratios are about the same for reverberant halls and dead halls, halls with good bass and halls with poor bass. Table 9.3 shows this clearly.

Table 9.3 Ratios of reverberation times at high frequencies
(2000, 4000, and 6000 cps) to those at mid-frequencies (average of 500 and 1000 cps)

Classification of Halls	T_{2000}/T_{mid}	T_{4000}/T_{mid}	T_{6000}/T_{mid}
Short reverberation times at mid-frequencies	0.93	0.83	0.75
Long reverberation times at mid-frequencies	0.91	0.80	0.67
Halls deficient in bass	0.97	0.83	0.72
Halls with medium bass	0.95	0.83	0.73
Halls with strong bass	0.93	0.83	0.76
MEDIAN	0.93	0.83	0.73

The ratio T_{6000}/T_{mid} was slightly smaller in halls with long reverberation times than in halls with short reverberation times. Appendix 1 shows that this slight difference has a fundamental physical explanation. Its implication for the concert hall is that differences among materials and audiences have little effect on the reverberation times at high frequencies relative to those at mid-frequencies. This would not be true, of course, if large amounts of sound-absorbing tiles or heavy draperies were installed in a hall, but these materials seldom grace good concert halls or opera houses.

Liveness scale

Several inferences follow from these facts about reverberation. A concert hall that is to be used for symphony orchestra concerts should have a reverberation time at mid-frequencies of about 1.9 seconds in order to be live enough for today's repertoires. If the reverberation time in a hall is as short as about 1.4 seconds, the rating of the hall drops by one category, or 10 points. Reverberation adds very little to the liveness of a concert hall if it lasts less than about 1.1 seconds. If a change in reverberation time in the sensitive region between 1.9 seconds and 1.4 seconds equals a change in rating of 10 points, then the additional difference of 0.3 seconds between 1.4 and 1.1 seconds must equal about a 5-point change. Thus, the spread in rating between the optimum reverberation time of 1.9 seconds and a reverberation time of 1.1, which is so short that it is of no significance to the music, is 15 points.

Let us now formulate a scale of reverberation time that can be applied to symphonic music in a concert hall. A reverberation time shorter than 1.1 seconds is rated zero; 1.4 seconds is rated 5 points; 1.9 seconds is rated 15 points. If the reverberation time is longer than 1.9 seconds, the rating decreases but not as rapidly as it does at the low end of the scale. The rating scale, so derived, is shown in *(a)* of Figure 9.5.

Musicians seem to be agreed that in a hall intended for Romantic music alone each rating score should correspond to a reverberation time at mid-frequencies about 0.3 second longer than the values given for average symphonic orchestral music in *(a)* of Figure 9.5. A hall intended for Classical music only should have about 0.2 second subtracted from all the reverberation times. And a hall intended for Baroque music only should have about 0.4 second subtracted from all reverberation times of Figure 9.5, scale *(a)*.

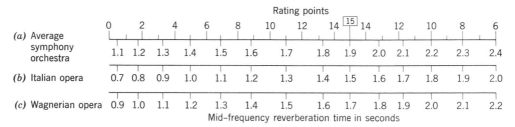

Figure 9.5. Rating scale for liveness as a function of mid-frequency reverberation time, for occupied halls, for (a) average symphony orchestra, (b) Italian opera, and (c) Wagnerian opera.

The evidence at hand confirms that Italian opera requires about the same reverberation time as Baroque music [see Figure 9.5, scale *(b)*], probably because Italian opera has continued to be written in the Baroque tradition and to be presented in the horseshoe-shaped houses so appropriate to music of the Baroque style.

Wagnerian operas, particularly those composed for the Festspielhaus in Bayreuth, need about the same reverberation time as Classical orchestral music, as is shown in scale *(c)* of Figure 9.5.

SUMMARY

Acoustical intimacy and liveness emerge as the two most important attributes of acoustical quality. Intimacy, which is related to the initial-time-delay gap, contributes a maximum of 40 points to the rating of a concert hall or opera house. Liveness, which is related to the reverberation times at mid and high frequencies, is closely tied to the style of music and cannot be prescribed except in relation to the intent of the composer. Liveness contributes a maximum of 15 points to the rating of a concert or opera house. Because music of different periods and types requires different degrees of liveness, a separate rating scale is needed for each style of symphonic music and for the two principal types of opera.

We turn now to the scaling of the four acoustical attributes next in importance—warmth, loudness, clarity, and brilliance.

10
Warmth, Loudness, Clarity, and Brilliance

On a winter day in 1960, Leopold Stokowski sat with me in a conference room high in a skyscraper in the center of New York for the explicit purpose of lending his years of experience as a musician and his keen interest in acoustics to the cause of this book. Stokowski opened the discussion with his analysis of what he believes is wrong with most modern concert halls. I shall attempt to reproduce his words from my scribbled notes.

In my opinion the most serious acoustical problem in modern concert halls is the lack of bass. The double basses by their nature are problems because their fundamentals are so weak that only the harmonics are heard. It requires more energy by the players to produce good low-frequency sound in a concert hall than is required to produce good middle-frequency sound.

One should think of the frequency range of music as divided into five zones: extreme lows, lows, middles, highs, extreme highs.

One has serious trouble with the extreme lows; some trouble with the lows; no trouble with the middles and highs; and the extreme highs can easily become brittle. Let me take an example of a modern hall, the Royal Festival Hall in London, to illustrate.

In Festival Hall the double basses simply cannot be heard. I have conducted there a number of times and during rehearsals I have gone into the stalls in the audience area to listen. I could hear absolutely no bass. I have returned to the stage and asked the double bass players to use their maximum effort. Still I couldn't hear the bass in the audience. As a result the sound in the Royal Festival Hall is metallic and brittle. There is no warmth. A hall must transmit the sound from the orchestra to the listener naturally. The lows should be in balance with the middles, and the highs should not be metallic.

In the Academy of Music in Philadelphia the sound is natural. The lows are in good relation to the middles. In the Grosser Musikvereinssaal in Vienna the bass is very good, but it could be better. Carnegie should have more lows.

Sir John Barbirolli too had criticized Festival Hall for its lack of acoustical color and its weak bass. Frank Howes, music critic for the London *Times,* wrote to me:

The Royal Festival Hall is too dry. More detailed criticism is that the bass frequencies are extinguished too rapidly. Wagner and Elgar are starved in it.

The single most important need for the Royal Festival Hall seems to me to be for more bass. The acoustical consultants for the Festival Hall also expressed this view when they wrote in *Acustica* [Vol. 3, pp. 1–21 (1953)]:

> The only criticisms which have been at all serious are those concerning lack of fullness. . . . It might be that a greater increase [of reverberation time] at low frequencies, or even an increase only at low frequencies, would be the most effective way of increasing the fullness.

W. A. McNair of the Bell Telephone Laboratories wrote on the importance of a high ratio of bass reverberation to mid-frequency reverberation as early as 1930 in the *Journal of the Acoustical Society of America* [Vol.

Table 10.1   Ratio of reverberation times at low frequencies (67, 125, and 250 cps) to that at mid-frequencies (500 to 1000 cps) for four groups of concert halls

Concert hall	T_{250}/T_{mid}	T_{125}/T_{mid}	T_{67}/T_{mid}	Thin wood
EXCELLENT BASS				
Tonhalle, Zurich	1.12	1.31	1.44	Little
Symphony Hall, Boston	1.11	1.22	1.28	None
Tanglewood, Lenox	1.22	1.27	—	None
Stadt-Casino, Basel	1.18	1.29	1.29	None
Binyanei Ha'Oomah, Jerusalem	1.14	1.25	1.37	None
GOOD BASS				
Grosser Musikvereinssaal, Vienna	1.07	1.12	1.17	None
Carnegie Hall, New York	1.05	1.05	1.35	None
Academy of Music, Philadelphia	1.21	1.00	—	Some
Salle Musica, La Chaux-de-Fonds	1.06	1.00	1.06	Much
FAIR BASS				
St. Andrew's Hall, Glasgow	0.95	0.95	0.84	Much
Fredric Mann Auditorium, Tel Aviv	0.97	1.00	0.97	Much
Alberta Jubilee Auditoriums, Edmonton and Calgary	1.00	0.90	—	Much
POOR BASS				
Royal Festival Hall, London	0.90	0.86	—	Much

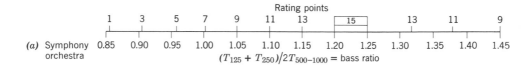

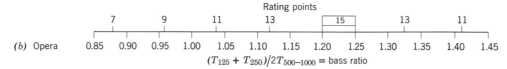

Figure 10.1. Rating scales for warmth as a function of the ratio of average reverberation time at 125 and 250 cycles per second to that at mid-frequencies for (a) concert halls and (b) opera houses.

1, pp. 243–248]. Many later writers have also emphasized the importance of bass reverberation. This evidence is an adequate basis for considering acoustical warmth as one of the principal attributes of acoustics. Let us now develop a rating scale for it.

WARMTH: RATIO OF REVERBERATION TIMES AT 125 AND 250 CYCLES PER SECOND TO THOSE AT MID-FREQUENCIES

The degree to which acoustical warmth varies from one hall to another can be demonstrated by tabulating, for a number of halls, the ratios of reverberation times at 250, 125, and 67 cycles per second to the reverberation time at mid-frequencies (the average of the reverberation times at 500 and 1000 cycles per second). The halls divide into four groups: (1) those with excellent bass; (2) those slightly deficient in bass, called good; (3) those substantially deficient in bass, called fair; and (4) those seriously deficient in bass, called poor. The analysis is shown in Table 10.1.

The median values of each reverberation ratio for the halls in each category of acoustical quality are given in Table 10.2.

In the section on Intimacy in Chapter 9, a deficiency in bass was found to correspond to a drop of one category, or a loss of 10 rating points.

Table 10.2   Acoustical warmth in concert halls: summary of Table 10.1

Median Values

Category	T_{250}/T_{mid}	T_{125}/T_{mid}	$(T_{250} + T_{125})/2T_{\mathrm{mid}}$	Assigned Rating Points
Excellent Bass	1.14	1.27	1.21	15
Good Bass	1.06	1.03	1.05	9
Fair Bass	0.97	0.95	0.96	5
Poor Bass	0.90	0.86	0.88	2

Warmth appears to be about equal in importance to liveness in its effect on the quality of a concert hall. Let us therefore assign a maximum of 15 rating points to an average bass ratio of 1.2 to 1.25, and 2 rating points to an average bass ratio of 0.88. The ratings for concert halls with other bass ratios are then located evenly between these numbers along the scale shown in Figure 10.1, scale *(a)*.

In opera, although rich bass is desirable, a deficiency is less noticeable since the orchestra is subordinated to the vocal parts. For opera houses, 15 rating points corresponds to an average bass ratio of between 1.2 and 1.25, and 7 rating points to an average bass ratio of 0.88. The scale of Figure 10.1, part *(b)* applies to opera houses.

Cause of loss of bass

What factors cause the loss of bass in a concert hall? In modern halls, thin wood with an air space behind it is the material most commonly responsible for a deficiency of bass. I realize that this dogmatic assertion goes

Table 10.3   Construction materials in eight "very good" to "excellent" halls

Hall	Construction
Symphony Hall, Boston	All walls and ceiling are of plaster, except the stage enclosure, which is of wood that averages more than ¾ of an inch in thickness.
Carnegie Hall, New York	All walls and ceiling are of plaster, including the stage enclosure.
Teatro Colón, Buenos Aires	All walls and ceiling are of plaster.
Grosser Musikvereinssaal, Vienna	All walls and ceiling are of plaster, except around the stage, where there is wood of medium thickness.
La Scala, Milan	All balcony faces and ceiling are of plaster. The box openings are highly sound-absorbent at all frequencies, owing to people, chairs, and draperies.
Concertgebouw, Amsterdam	All walls and ceiling are of plaster.
Stadt-Casino, Basel	All walls and ceiling are of plaster.
Binyanei Ha'Oomah, Jerusalem	Ceiling is of plaster. Side walls are wood directly affixed to plaster.

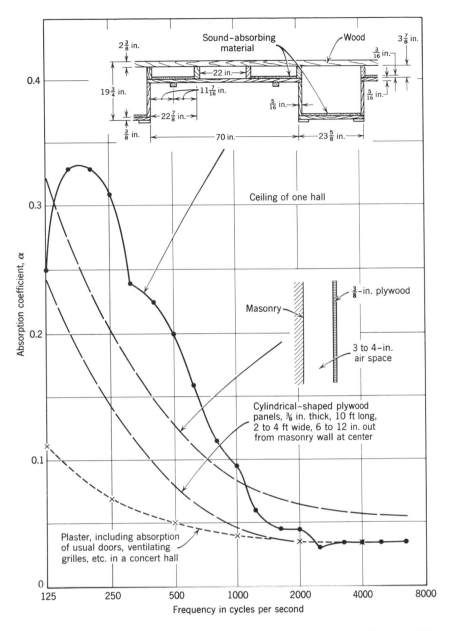

Figure 10.2. Sound-absorption coefficients for walls and ceilings made of thin wood (¼ inch to ⅝ inch thick) or plaster.

contrary to one of the most prevalent myths in acoustics—that wood is good. Table 10.3 describes the finishing materials of eight well-known very-good-to-excellent halls.

Technical data on the absorbing effect of thin wood with air space behind it are readily available in books on acoustics. Some typical data are given in Figure 10.2. The curves in the figure show that, at 125 cycles per second, ⅜-inch plywood with 3 to 4 inches of air space behind it absorbs about ³⁄₁₀ of the intensity from a sound wave every time the wave reflects from it. In a concert hall whose ceiling and side walls are made of wood, a sound wave traveling around the room at the rate of 1130 feet per second strikes a wood surface about 10 times each second. The sound intensity remaining in a 125-cycle-per-second wave after 10 reflections is $\frac{1}{35}$ of the original intensity. A plaster wall, on the other hand, reduces the sound intensity of a 125-cycle-per-second wave to only $\frac{1}{3}$ of its original intensity after 10 reflections. Thus, 1 second after it has sounded, a low-frequency sound wave is 10 times more intense in a plaster hall than in a hall lined with thin wood. Above 1000 cycles per second both wood and plaster absorb sound to about the same degree. Figure 10.2 also shows the sound absorption of a kind of cylindrical-shaped plywood panels often used in radio broadcasting studios, and of the special type of ceiling construction employed in the Herkulessaal in Munich.

The eight halls analyzed in Table 10.3, none of which have thin wood interiors, all have very good to excellent acoustics; on the other hand, the five halls in the bottom two categories of Table 10.1, all of which have considerable amounts of thin wood, all suffer from a weak bass. Can there be any doubt, then, that a hall lined with thin wood will be deficient in bass? On the other hand, thick wood, plaster, or wood of any thickness, provided it is securely cemented to smooth plaster, is acoustically satisfactory, and the architect may choose freely among these three materials.

LOUDNESS OF THE DIRECT SOUND

For good acoustics the music that travels directly from the performers to the listener must be comfortable to listen to. If the direct sound is too weak, it may be masked by the audience noise, or by the reverberant sound, and the result is a loss of clarity. If it is too loud, it seems overwhelming and may even cause discomfort to the ear. The loudness of the direct sound is a function of the distance from the performer to the listener, the nature of the sound-reflecting surfaces at the sending end of the hall, the presence or absence of intervening heads (which contribute to the difference in loudness between the rear of the main floor and the front of the balcony), and the size of the performing group. The discussion that follows assumes as the performing group a large symphony orchestra of 90 to 100 pieces.

In the best-liked concert halls, listeners prefer the seats in the center of the main floor. This preference is due partly to the visual impression. But in a first-rate hall the main-floor seats also have acoustical advantages. There the music reaches the listener at a pleasing loudness; the reverberation seems to surround him, the balance between direct and reverberant sound is satisfactory, and both the middle and the ends of the orchestra are at approximately the same distance from him. In nine good-to-excellent halls, the distance between a listener at the center of the main floor and the concertmaster of an orchestra or a vocal soloist in an opera is about as follows:

Symphony Hall, Boston	64 feet
Tanglewood, Lenox	68 feet
Carnegie Hall, New York	60 feet
Teatro Colón, Buenos Aires	72 feet
Musikvereinssaal, Vienna	56 feet
Staatsoper, Vienna	62 feet
Sender Freies, Berlin	48 feet
La Scala, Milan	64 feet
Concertgebouw, Amsterdam	48 feet

The average distance is about 60 feet, and to this distance we may assign a maximum rating of 10 points.

In a large fan-shaped hall that has no special reflecting surfaces to direct sound to the rear but that has no other acoustical deficiency, seats located 130 to 160 feet from the concertmaster are inferior in musical quality by about one category or 10 points. Thus, the rating scale for the loudness of the direct sound ranges from 10 points to 0 as the distance from the test location to the stage increases from 60 to 160 feet. The rating scale for clarity or loudness of the direct sound is shown in Figure 10.3.

Correction in the rating for balconies

The rating scale of Figure 10.3 applies to seats on the main floor of the hall. The loudness in the hall is affected also by reflecting surfaces that are specially designed to direct sound toward the back of the hall. Any contribution that these reflections make to the sound on the main floor has

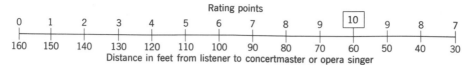

Figure 10.3. Rating scale for loudness of the direct sound, applicable to seats on the main floor. Balcony seats must be rated by a combination of this scale and the corrections given in Table 10.4. The resulting rating cannot exceed a total of 10 points.

already been taken into account in the rating scales for intimacy (Figure 9.4). This is true also for contributions to the sound reflected into the balcony from a non-directive ceiling. But we need to give special attention in the ratings to sound reflections from balcony faces and from ceilings that are designed specifically to reflect sound to the back of the balcony. Thus, when the rating scale for the loudness of direct sound is applied to balcony seats, corrections must be made to take into account the differences in acoustical conditions. These corrections are shown in Table 10.4.

Table 10.4   Corrections to the rating scale of Figure 10.3 for loudness of direct sound, to be applied to balcony seats only

Conditions	Rating points to be added to those of Figure 10.3
Favorable reflections (under 35 milliseconds delay) from a pair of balcony fronts	2
Favorable reflections (under 35 milliseconds delay) from a pair of side walls	4
Highly directive ceiling	4
Maximum possible increment to Figure 10.3	8

Note: Total of Figure 10.3 plus Table 10.4 limited to 10 points.

The combined rating for the loudness of the direct sound in the balconies, made up of the rating from the scale of Figure 10.3 to which is added the correction given in Table 10.4, cannot exceed 10 points. No correction is added for a flat ceiling—only for a specially directive ceiling. Provided the time delay is under about 50 milliseconds, early reflections from flat ceilings and from side walls also add to the loudness of the direct sound. However, since the contribution of these reflections to the total rating has already been included in the scale of acoustical intimacy, they cannot be considered a second time.

In Chapter 13, which contains some examples of the application of the rating scale, some halls are discussed whose total rating is as much as 20 points better for the balcony than for the main floor. There are also halls in which the rear of the main floor is as much as 10 points lower than the center. These differences usually corroborate the experience of listeners in those halls.

LOUDNESS OF THE REVERBERANT SOUND

Both the direct sound and the reverberant sound contribute to the total loudness of music in a hall. The only rating scale dealing with reverberant sound that has been presented thus far is the scale of liveness, in Figure 9.5, and that scale concerns only the effect of reverberation time on the integrity of the musical composition. Now we must consider how much the reverberation contributes to the loudness. Another factor that has not yet been analyzed is the effect that the cubic volume of the hall has on the loudness of the music.

When is music too loud or too faint? Like all the other attributes of acoustical quality, preferred loudness varies somewhat with taste. For me, the reverberant sound is too loud if my ears are tickled by a fortissimo passage. And music is too soft if it fails to hold my attention in the presence of audience noise. Unfortunately, many halls suffer from one or the other of these defects—small, highly reverberant halls at one extreme, and large, dead halls at the other.

Lothar Cremer has devised a formula that relates the loudness of the reverberant sound in a room to the cubic volume, the reverberation time, and the energy in the sound [L. Cremer, *Statistische Raumakustik*, S. Hirzel, Stuttgart, Germany, p. 231 (1961)]. Cremer defines the loudness of a tone, either steady or staccato, in terms of the relation NT/V, where N is the energy in the tone, T is the reverberation time, and V is the cubic volume. In other words, the longer the reverberation time and the smaller the cubic volume, the greater the loudness of the tone, and vice versa. Thus, the loudness of a tone of a certain strength is related to T/V.

Because the reverberation times of most halls lie between 1 and 2 seconds, and the cubic volumes between 300,000 and 1,500,000 cubic feet, let us multiply T/V by 1,000,000 so that our numbers lie between 1 and 6.

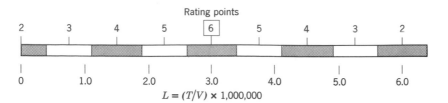

Figure 10.4. Rating scale for loudness of the reverberant sound defined by the equation $L = (T/V) \times 1{,}000{,}000$, where $T =$ mid-frequency reverberation time in seconds, and $V =$ volume of the room in cubic feet.

We can now define the quantity L as a correlate of the loudness of the reverberant sound, and calculate it by the equation

$$L = (T/V) \times 1{,}000{,}000$$

where V is measured in cubic feet.

If we use as a standard of satisfactory loudness the concert halls of Boston, Philadelphia, Bristol, Bonn, Stuttgart, Glasgow, Liverpool, Amsterdam, Brussels, and Buenos Aires, the optimal value of L lies between 2.5 and 3.5. Let us assign 6 points as the upper limit to the rating scale for loudness of the reverberant sound.

At the other extreme, a hall with very low reverberation time may be good, though not excellent, for orchestral music—witness some outdoor amphitheaters. So let us assign 2 rating points to an L of zero. At the other extreme, the loudest halls in our study have values of L between 5.5 and 6. If a 4-point deficit is assigned to an L in this range, we now have enough data to form the entire rating scale for the loudness of reverberant sound, given in Figure 10.4.

CLARITY OR DEFINITION

Music played in a hall with good definition sounds clear; played in a hall with poor definition, it sounds blurred or muddy. Actually, there are four factors other than the speed of the music that affect the clarity of sound in a hall. First, the initial-time-delay gap should be short; if the delay is short enough, the first reflection adds strength to the direct sound. Second, the direct sound must be sufficiently loud at each seat; therefore no listener should be seated too far from the performers, nor should the floor be so flat that heads intervene between performer and listener. Of course, wall and ceiling shapes that direct sound to seats at the rear of a hall can compensate partially for loss of sound with distance, but the danger of directing too much sound to the rear is that the initial-time-delay gap at seats in the front of the hall may become too long, or echoes may develop. Third, the reverberant sound must not be so loud as to mask out the direct sound. Fourth, there must be no echoes; the absence of echo ensures greater definition.

Some of the rating scales already established have dealt with the effects on clarity of the initial-time-delay gap (Figure 9.4), the loudness of direct sound (Figure 10.3), and the loudness of reverberant sound (Figure 10.4). Echoes are treated separately in a later chapter. Thus, no new rating scale need be established for clarity.

BRILLIANCE

A very common word in the vocabulary of musicians and listeners alike is "brilliance." When I asked Erich Leinsdorf for his definition he answered without hesitation, "The high frequencies are stressed and their decay is slow." Webster's defines a brilliant musical tone as "bright, clear and ringing: rich in high harmonics" [*Webster's New International Dictionary*, Third Edition, Unabridged]. An analysis of musicians' use of this term shows that a hall is called brilliant when:

1. Its intimacy rating is high, that is, the initial-time-delay gap is short.

2. Its liveness rating is high, that is, the reverberation times at frequencies 500 cycles and above approach the ideal.

3. The loudness of the direct sound rates high.

No special rating chart is needed for brilliance since it is made up of elements already reckoned in the three rating scales for intimacy, liveness, and loudness of the direct sound.

11

Diffusion, Balance and Blend, Ensemble, Attack, and Texture

Chapters 9 and 10 have dealt with the principal attributes of acoustics, which account for 86 out of the possible 100 points on the rating scale for halls for music. Now we come to secondary attributes—attributes that in themselves are not prominent but that in the aggregate account for 14 rating points, or nearly a category and a half.

DIFFUSION

Concert music sounds better to a listener when its origin seems to be diffuse, that is to say, when the sound arrives at his ears from many directions—from overhead and from the sides, as well as from in front of him. In order for the diffusion of sound to be good, two conditions must be met. First, the reverberation time must be fairly long. Second, the ceiling and walls of the hall must be irregular so that the sound waves are scattered when they reflect from these surfaces.

Many of the finest concert halls in the world—halls built in the nineteenth century in Baltimore, Boston, Vienna, Munich, Glasgow, Basel, and Zurich—have coffers or deep beams on the ceiling, and columns, niches, or statues on the side walls. These irregularities help to diffuse the sound. But a more important contribution to diffusion is the long reverberation time. Diffuse sound arrives at a listener's ears from all directions. In order for it to do so, it must have traveled around the room many times. But unless the room is quite reverberant the wave will have died out after relatively few traversals. The contributions of reverberation time to the general acoustical quality of a hall have already been rated by the scales of Figures 9.5 and 10.4. Thus the factor of reverberation time should not be considered in the rating scale for diffusion.

If a concert hall lacks irregularities on its walls and ceiling to scatter the sound waves in many directons, its rating is lowered by close to one-half a rating category.

In opera houses, diffusion appears to be of little importance because the listener concentrates on the action and music directly in front and does not expect to be "bathed in sound." And also the circular shape of most opera

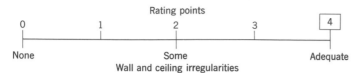

Figure 11.1. Rating scale for sound diffusion. Since sound diffusion is not important in opera houses, this scale is *not* applied to them.

houses and the tiers of boxes and balconies that rise almost to the ceiling make it impossible for the walls to have the same kinds of irregularities as a concert hall. As for their ceilings, the sculptured effects often turn out to be painted.

Rating scale

If a concert hall has irregularities on its walls and ceiling in the quantity and degree found in the seven halls named above, the amount of diffusion is "adequate" and is rated at 4 points. Less effective diffusing elements can be assessed on the scale of Figure 11.1. Diffusion is not rated in opera houses.

BALANCE AND BLEND

The attributes of balance and blend are dependent on the architectural design of the sending end of the hall and the information that the conductors and musicians get back from the hall. The sending end of the hall includes the stage and the sound-reflecting surfaces overhead, at the sides, and at the rear of the stage. It also includes portions of the ceiling and side walls of the hall at the front of the audience. In the opera house the pit must also be considered. The sending end of the hall should mix or blend the sounds from the various performers in such a way that they are heard harmoniously by the listeners. It should also contribute to the balance among the various sections of the orchestra or between the soloists and the orchestra or in an opera house, between the singers and the pit orchestra. Stage and pit design are dealt with separately in Chapter 14.

In the assessment of the potentialities for good balance and blend in a hall under design, maximum rating should be given if the stage, pit, and surfaces at the front of the hall conform to the schemes described in Chapter 14. Radically different, unproved designs should be rated low until their merit is demonstrated. In a hall that is already built, of course, the rating for balance and blend can be based on judgments made in the hall by qualified listeners.

For concert halls, a maximum of 6 points is assigned to balance and blend in the upper scale of Figure 11.2. Opera houses are assigned 10 points

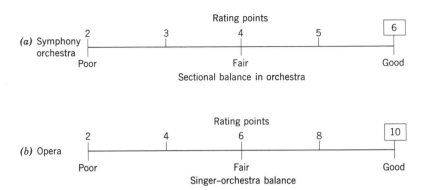

Figure 11.2. Rating scales for balance and blend for (*a*) symphony orchestra, and (*b*) opera. The maximum values are different for the two scales.

for the balance between singers and pit orchestra, as is shown in the lower scale of Figure 11.2.

ENSEMBLE: THE EASE WITH WHICH PERFORMERS CAN PLAY TOGETHER

When a group of performers play together in perfect unison we speak of good ensemble. Ensemble is partly a matter of the skill of the conductor and the performers and partly a matter of the design of the stage enclosure or the reflecting surfaces at the sides and above the stage. Good ensemble depends also on the sound that the conductor and musicians hear from the hall itself. In a well-designed hall there must be some means for reflecting in proper proportion the sound of each section of the orchestra to other players and to the conductor. Among the strings, the violas and cellos depend for certain cues on the sound from the first violins, often across the stage from them. The sound of the woodwinds must reach the conductor. The woodwinds and horns also must hear the violins. The brass and percussion frequently play together and so must hear each other.

A maximum of 4 points is assigned to ensemble on the rating scale shown in Figure 11.3.

ATTACK: RESPONSE OF THE HALL TO A TONE

Musicians speak of attack to describe the response of a hall to the sounding of a tone. The attack is called good when sound is reflected to the stage from the auditorium without sounding like an echo. Good attack results from good total design and is dependent on the reverberation time, the initial-time-delay gap, freedom from echo, the diffusion of sound, and a satisfactory sending end. Ideally, some surfaces in the hall should return

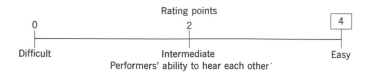

Rating Scale for Ensemble

Rating points

0   2   4

Difficult   Intermediate   Easy
Performers' ability to hear each other

Figure 11.3. Rating scale for ensemble, the performers' ability to hear each other on the stage.

sound directly to the performers. Attack is not designed for separately from the other attributes. When the hall is good, the attack is good. Thus, attack is not given a separate rating scale.

TEXTURE: DETAILED PATTERN OF REFLECTIONS

In Chapter 4 texture was defined as the subjective impression of the way in which the sequence of sound reflections arrives at the ears of a listener after the direct sound. Figure 11.4 shows typical sound-reflection patterns for five halls of each of the three most common shapes—rectangular, horseshoe, and fan. These reflection patterns were taken from drawings, and the intensity of each reflection was not determined. However, in analyses of completed halls where data are available, all reflections whose intensity is within about 10 decibels of the direct sound should be considered. Some differences are discernible among the reflection patterns in the three types of architecture most common for halls in which music is played.

Rectangular halls

Each of the five rectangular halls in Figure 11.4 has an initial-time-delay gap of 22 milliseconds or less, primarily because these are narrow halls with balconies on their side walls. Each hall has about five reflections, approximately uniformly spaced, within 60 milliseconds of the arrival of the direct sound.

Horseshoe halls

The five horseshoe-shaped halls have initial-time-delay gaps of less than 20 milliseconds, primarily because of the relatively small distance between opposite balcony faces. However, because of the high ceiling in most horseshoe-shaped halls, there are only two other reflections within 60 milliseconds.

Fan halls

The principal difficulty with fan-shaped halls is the long initial-time-delay gap for listeners on the main floor. In Figure 11.4, except for the Tanglewood Music Shed, whose first and second reflections are at 11 and

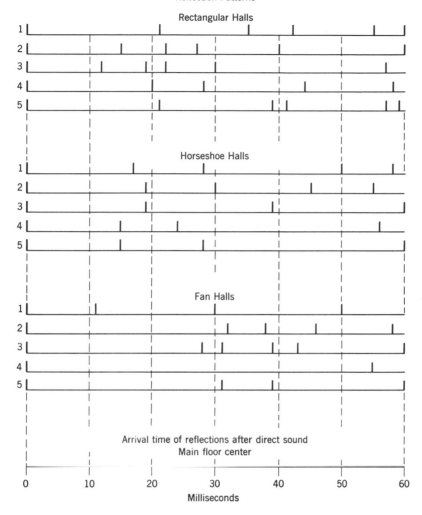

Figure 11.4. Reflection patterns for 5 rectangular, 5 horseshoe, and 5 fan-shaped halls. Only the first fan-shaped hall has an initial-time-delay gap of less than 27 milliseconds, and that hall, the Music Shed at Tanglewood, has a low-hung ceiling with about 50 per cent open area. Because the second time-delay gap is greater than the first, 19 versus 11 milliseconds, it becomes the controlling one in rating the attribute of acoustical intimacy.

30 milliseconds, the initial-time-delay gaps of these halls are of the order of 30 milliseconds. These halls have no more than three other reflections within 60 milliseconds.

Texture is not easily separated from the initial-time-delay gap; its importance in determining the acoustics of a hall is not rated separately on the scale of acoustic quality. Halls from each of the three groups of Figure 11.4 are in category A⁺, as well as in each of the three categories A, B⁺, and B. The principal factor that correlates with the subjective assignment of halls to the various categories is the initial-time-delay gap, that is to say, the acoustical intimacy. Although the present study does not provide definitive demonstrations, it seems necessary that the time-delay gap between the second and third reflections should be substituted for the initial-time-delay gap when it is the longer of the two. In other words, the longer of the two gaps should be used with Figure 9.4 in rating the acoustical attribute of intimacy.

The three shapes of hall analyzed in Figure 11.4 obviously have different tonal textures, and one type of reflection pattern may be preferable to another. But until listeners make subjective judgments of the various reflection patterns in controlled experiments, we can only speculate about their preferences. On the basis of what is known today, I am not prepared to propose a rating for the acoustical attribute of texture. It should be noted, however, that narrow rectangular halls are rated highest by musicians and critics. Such halls exhibit five or more nearly evenly spaced reflections in the first 60 milliseconds of a reflection pattern, with an initial-time-delay gap less than 22 milliseconds long.

The eight positive independent attributes of acoustics listed in Table 8.2 have now received rating scales. The relative contributions of each attribute, shown in Table 11.1, illustrate the overwhelming importance of acoustical intimacy in the total rating of a concert hall or opera house, a result that has not received appreciable attention in the technical literature before now.

Table 11.1   Rating scale of acoustical quality

| | Maximum Points | |
Attribute	Concert Halls	Opera Houses
Intimacy	40	40
Liveness	15	15
Warmth	15	15
Loudness of Direct Sound	10	10
Loudness of Reverberant Sound	6	6
Balance and Blend	6	10
Diffusion	4	0
Ensemble	4	4
TOTAL	100	100

Of course, echo, noise, and distortion, separately or in combination, can render an otherwise fine hall unfit for musical performances. Thus in the scaling of the quality of a concert hall the topics in the following chapter take on all the importance that textbooks on acoustics have for over half a century assigned to them.

12

Echo, Noise, Distortion, and Non-uniformity

A motion picture artfully conceived and movingly acted would never be submitted to the Cannes Festival if the film were overexposed. Nor would the most noble gastronomic effort of the chef at the Tour d'Argent surmount the addition of an extra spoonful of salt. The whitened scene and the briny taste of acoustics are echoes, noise, tonal distortion, and non-uniformity of hearing conditions. These attributes can only detract from the beauty of the music; they add nothing.

ECHO

In acoustics an echo is defined as a long-delayed reflection, sufficiently loud to become annoying to a listener (Chapter 4). For the purposes of this study the definition is limited to those reflections that are delayed by more than 70 milliseconds after the direct sound (Chapter 9). According to the Australian studies referred to in Chapter 9, an echo is disturbing if it is within 15 decibels of the level of the direct sound when the time delay is 100 milliseconds; within 20 decibels when the time delay is 200 milliseconds; or within 30 decibels when the time delay is 300 milliseconds or more.

The musical instrument that most often produces an echo in a hall is the trumpet, because of its piercing staccato tones and because its bell can direct the sound onto a reflecting, focusing surface. A usual solution to a trumpet echo is to reseat the brass section so that the bells of the trumpets do not point toward the offending surface.

The rear wall of a narrow rectangular hall seldom causes an echo if there are balconies, even shallow ones, in front of it. The echo from a high, bare rear wall can be avoided by breaking up the surface of the wall into a number of sections, some tilted up, some down, and others to the sides, so that the sound is scattered and prevented from returning directly to the front of the hall. The angle and amount of tilt of the several sections of the wall depend on the dimensions and shape of the hall, the rake of the main-floor seating, and other factors.

Echoes resound from focusing domes, semi-circular walls, and other

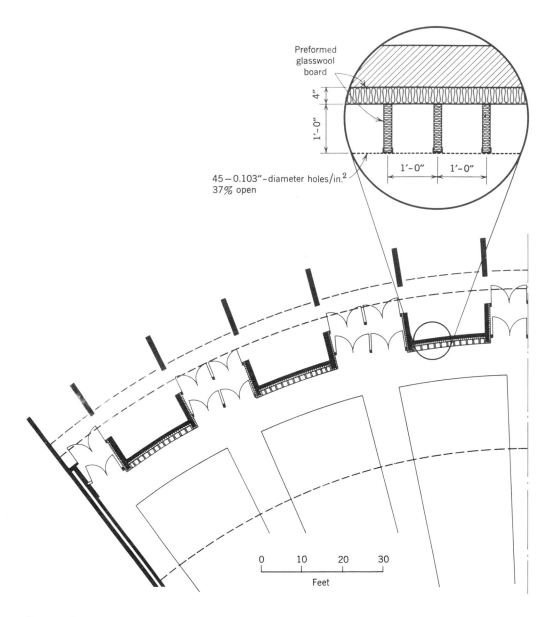

Figure 12.1. To prevent echo, a highly absorbing surface was created at the rear of the Aula Magna, Caracas, an auditorium with a long circularly curving rear wall whose focal point is on the stage. Sound-absorbing material is also inserted in the perforated metal faces of the doors.

acoustically difficult shapes, and great care must be taken to avoid them in the design.

An echo that is difficult to suppress occurs in a fan-shaped hall whose rear wall is a sector of a circle with its center of curvature on the stage. Two such halls are the Aula Magna in Caracas and the Music Shed at Tanglewood. In the Aula Magna, the echo was suppressed by applying highly absorbent materials to the rear wall and doors and by splaying the doors so they would not return sound directly to the front of the hall (see Figure 12.1 and Chap-

ECHO, NOISE, DISTORTION, AND NON-UNIFORMITY

ter 6). In Tanglewood (see Chapter 6) echoes were avoided by tilting the top half of the rear wall forward so that the sound energy is reflected downward into the audience and absorbed before it becomes an echo. The lower half of the wall at Tanglewood is already highly absorbent since it is open to the outdoors. In both Caracas and Tanglewood, disturbing echoes would have been present had these precautions not been taken in the original design.

Echoes may also occur if inadequate ceiling and side-wall diffusion is coupled with a short reverberation time. Let me elaborate: when a tone is sounded, the members of the orchestra and the listeners at the front of a hall expect to hear a response. If the reverberation time is not very long, the hall responds immediately only if there are irregularities on the walls and ceiling to reflect some acoustic energy back to the front. If there are no irregularities, the first reflection comes from the rear wall. This reflection stands out like a black spot on a white surface: it is heard as an echo. In the Salle Pleyel in Paris, which has a parabolic longitudinal section, most of the sound from the stage is channeled to the rear of the hall by the smooth, flaring walls and ceiling. The strongest reflections returned to the front are from the balcony fronts and the back wall, and these reflections have traveled over 250 feet and are delayed in time by about 200 milliseconds. Instead of giving useful support to the direct sound, they produce echoes. Except for what is reflected from the high ceiling, the sound is channeled to the back of the hall. Thus in the seats at the center and front of the main floor, the initial-time-delay gap is long and the intimacy is correspondingly low.* The parabolic shape also causes noises that originate in the audience to be focused toward the stage, to the annoyance of the performers. It is no surprise that, ever since its construction in 1927, the Salle Pleyel has had adverse criticism or that efforts have persisted to suppress the echo, noise, and lack of intimacy that obscure the good features of the hall.

Three changes in design may lead to solution of the problem of annoy-

* In 1932 V. O. Knudsen wrote of the Salle Pleyel [*Architectural Acoustics*, John Wiley and Sons, New York] "[The first ceiling reflections] are not delayed enough to produce an echo, but because of the great height of the ceiling some of the reflected sound is delayed enough to produce a slight interfering effect in the central portions of the parquet . . . detected . . . during very rapid movements." Knudsen's analysis describes clearly the phenomenon that is identified in our study as lack of intimacy.

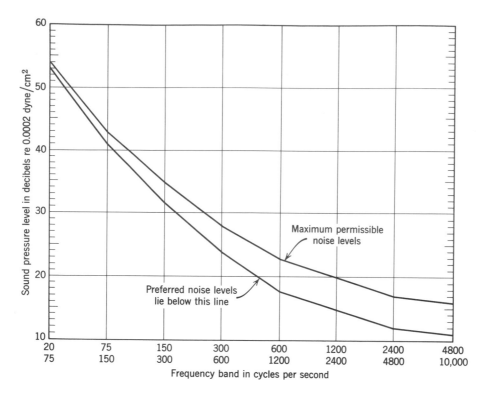

Figure 12.2. The range of acceptable noise levels in concert halls and opera houses. The lower curve is the recommended limit for the noise. The upper curve represents the upper limit beyond which noise levels would be seriously disturbing. Those curves are established for measurements made with an American Standard sound level meter and octave band analyzer in a hall without audience.

ing echo. First, not too much of the sound should be guided directly to the rear of the hall. Second, medium time-delay reflections should be provided for the orchestra and the listeners at the front of the hall by means of irregularities on the ceiling and walls. And third, in a wide hall, a short initial-time-delay gap should be created, either by hanging a partly open false ceiling below the main ceiling, or by creating its acoustic equivalent by hanging sound reflecting panels.

Suitable irregularities can be provided by coffers in the ceiling or niches in the side walls, as in Symphony Hall, Boston, or by a ceiling of irregular construction, as in Binyanei Ha'Oomah in Jerusalem (see Chapter 6).

NOISE

Noise is a serious nuisance in a hall. It may arise from ventilation openings, machinery, subways, trains, aircraft, or traffic. Vibrations too may be troublesome, especially if their source is machinery beneath the main floor.

In order for a concert hall or an opera house to be adequately quiet, its noise level, measured without audience with an American Standard sound level meter and octave band analyzer, should lie below the lower curve in Figure 12.2. The noise levels should under no circumstances be permitted to exceed the levels of the upper curve.

Air-conditioning machinery and fans should be placed in a separate building, preferably below the ground and completely isolated from the concert hall. A most desirable acoustical condition results when the spans of acoustically lined ducts are long and there are discontinuities in the paths over which the noise and vibrations travel.

A recent inspection of the technical literature has failed to uncover any standards for permissible vibration levels in buildings. Until new information is available, the architect and acoustic designer would do well to try to reduce single-frequency vibration levels at the floors on which the musicians and audience are seated to below an acceleration of 1 centimeter per second per second.

The reduction of noise and vibration is a subject too vast to be more than touched on here. A technical treatment of these matters can be found in such texts as: L. L. Beranek, Editor, *Noise Reduction,* McGraw-Hill Book Company, New York (1960), and C. M. Harris, Editor, *Handbook of Noise Control,* McGraw-Hill Book Company, New York (1957).

DISTORTION

Tonal distortion is a special kind of acoustical fault that may take many forms. Distortion in the hall may inject into the music sounds that have not been played, or it may suppress tones that the musicians have sounded. Proper initial acoustical design can eliminate these problems on the drafting board, but they are almost impossible to solve in the completed hall.

Selective sound absorption

The most common instance of tonal distortion occurs when the side walls or ceiling resonate to some particular frequency and in so doing remove from the music some of the energy near that frequency. Three

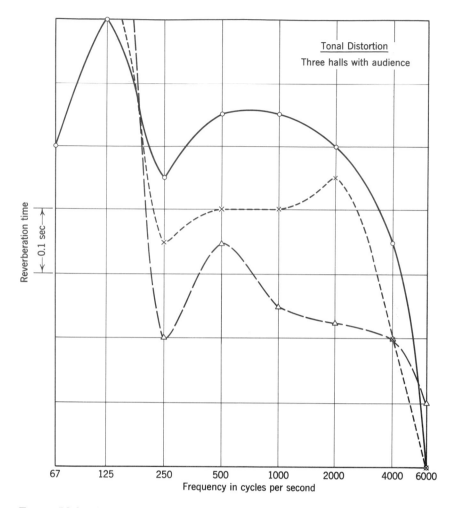

Figure 12.3. The curves illustrate tonal distortion at frequencies near 250 cycles per second. The reverberation time is about 0.2 second shorter at 250 cycles per second than it would be if there were no distortion.

examples are presented in Figure 12.3, in which reverberation times are plotted against frequency for three halls with full audience. In all three halls, the ceiling is designed so that it absorbs the tones near 250 cycles per second—close to middle C—and vitiates the loudness of the first few harmonics of the viola and the higher harmonics of the cellos and double basses. Most noticeable is the lack of richness in the tone of the cellos.

It is not uncommon for an unoccupied hall to have a high absorption of sound at frequencies around 250 cycles per second. Eight of the halls of this study show a peak in their sound-absorbing power which results from the design of their seats (see Figure A1.10 of Appendix 1). In each hall, the undersides of the seats are not perforated and the cloth used in the upholstery is nearly impervious to the flow of air. The construction leads to a "bubble" resonance in the seat cushion, which renders it highly

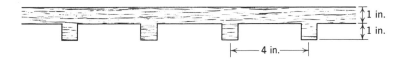

Figure 12.4. A side-wall construction illustrating an acoustic diffraction grating.

sound-absorbent at a particular frequency. Consequently, these halls are unsuitable for recording on disks or tapes. Chairs with permeable coverings and perforated underseats would eliminate this problem.

A rare type of tonal distortion affects the upper frequencies of the violins. This distortion arises when thin, brittle materials are used in a hall, which, through a phenomenon known as wave coincidence, absorb the energy from the high frequencies.* In halls with this distortion, the brilliance of the violin tone is dulled.

Sympathetic ringing tones

I know of two halls in which ringing tones can be heard following the sharp cut-off of a musical chord that contains a frequency equal to the frequency of whatever is set into sympathetic vibration. In one of these halls, the organ grille is made of hollow, square metal bars that ring loudly in sympathetic vibration whenever a tone of 580 cycles per second—about the D an octave above middle C—is sounded. The response of this hall is so unusual as to be disturbing to any critical listener, and the ringing makes it impossible to record music properly there on disk or tape. The solution would require the application of a vibration-deadening material to each metal bar.

In the second hall a singing tone is heard as part of the reverberation. The tone is produced by an acoustical resonance between the uniformly spaced beams of the exposed structure of the ceiling. The remedy would be to enclose the exposed beams with a heavy, hung, irregularly coffered concrete ceiling.

Acoustic diffraction grating

In one hall, the side walls are covered with a decorative series of vertical projecting slats (see Figure 12.4) up to a height of between 12 and 20 feet above the main-floor level, giving the effect of a dado. This series of vertical projections constitutes what is known as an acoustic diffraction grating. It has the power to reflect a single tone, and in doing so it imparts an

* See L. L. Beranek, *Noise Reduction*, McGraw-Hill Book Co., New York (1960), pp. 280–359; and L. Cremer, *Die Wissenschaftlichen Grundlagen der Raumakustik:* Band III—*Wellentheoretische Raumakustik*, S. Hirzel, Leipzig (1950), pp. 169–182.

odd tonal distortion to music containing that tone. This kind of structure is better avoided, but, if it is employed, the depth and spacing of the projecting members should be varied in a random manner.

Flutter echo

A good place to demonstrate a flutter echo is between the two parallel plaster walls of a 20-foot-wide corridor. If you stand in the center and clap your hands once, you will hear immediately afterwards a succession of claps in a very rapid sequence, creating a sort of "flutter." A flutter echo may occur in any hall that has two opposite surfaces that are parallel. It sounds like a "buzz," distorting the music, and it is usually heard with staccato tones. The obvious remedy is to avoid opposing large parallel surfaces. Even a slight splay between opposing walls prevents the formation of flutter echo.

It is not easy to formulate a scale for the acoustical blemishes, because they can vary over so wide a range, and because any one of them can nullify the acoustical effectiveness of a hall. A noisy air-conditioning system, for example, can decrease the rating of a hall by 40 or 50 points—dropping it from an excellent rating to a poor one. Nevertheless, some correction for the acoustical negatives must be brought into the numerical rating system. Table 12.1 applies ratings to three of the four blemishes—echo, noise, and distortion.

Table 12.1   Correction to the rating scales
for echo, noise, and distortion

Amount of negative attribute	Correction to rating points
None	0
Some	−5
Substantial	−10
Bad	−15 to −50

NON-UNIFORMITY IN HALLS

One of the most unfortunate acoustical flaws is non-uniformity of the sound in a hall. There are a number of ways in which the music may be distributed unevenly to the various sections of a hall; each one wears away

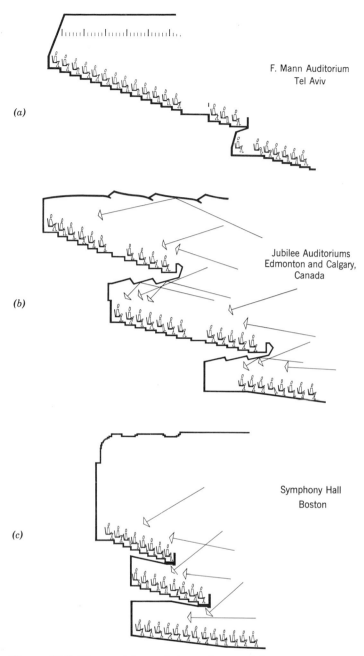

Figure 12.5. Three satisfactory balcony designs: (*a*) excellent, no overhang; (*b*) very good, little overhang and wide openings; (*c*) center balcony is good except for last three rows, which do not receive sound from the upper part of the hall.

one's expectation of an evening of pleasant entertainment. Almost every hall has some poor seats; these poor locations are known to the architect and owner, but pecuniary realities necessitate the use of every possible space. The rationale is that, when an outstanding performance comes to the hall, everyone possible should have a chance to attend, even if the acoustics or the sight lines are inferior in some places. Of course, the listeners who are

461

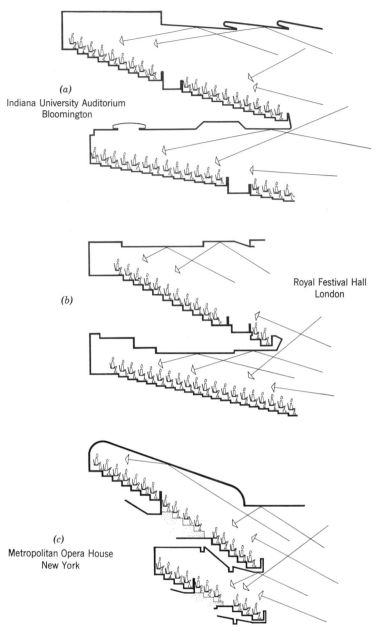

Figure 12.6. Three fair balcony designs: (*a*) fair, large overhang; (*b*) fair, large overhang and small opening; (*c*) lower balcony is poor, receives little sound from upper hall and opening is small.

seated in these inferior locations often judge the whole hall by its weakest spots.

Balcony overhangs

Balconies are used in large halls to reduce the distance between the stage and the farthest row of seats. The architect chooses between one large balcony and a number of smaller ones. Whichever he selects, he is faced with the problem that people seated underneath a deep overhang do not receive sound reflected from the upper part of the hall. If the balcony is deep and the mouth of the opening is not very high, even the sound that travels directly from the stage will be muffled.

Figure 12.5 shows three relatively satisfactory designs for balconies. The overhang in the Mann Auditorium in Tel Aviv covers only one row of seats, which is an ideal arrangement. The well-designed overhangs in the Jubilee Auditoriums in Edmonton and Calgary, Alberta, Canada, cover only six rows of seats. In addition, the openings are high and the soffits are shaped to direct the sound toward the listeners' heads. Sound from the upper ceiling is reflected into the last row. The third example, Symphony Hall in Boston, does not provide the listeners below the lower balcony with very good sound, although listeners beneath the upper balcony near the center of the hall have relatively good conditions. However, sound that is reflected from the ceiling does not penetrate very far under either overhang, and the extreme back corners of the hall under the two balconies have quite poor acoustics.

Figure 12.6 shows three very deep balcony overhangs. Deep overhangs are more damaging to symphonic music than to opera, since many styles of symphonic music require the overhead reverberation of the hall to convey the full effect of the composition. The balcony overhang in the Indiana University Auditorium in Bloomington has a relatively high mouth, and the forward part of the soffit helps to direct sound to the heads of the listeners. Sound reflected from the ceiling penetrates nearly halfway back under the overhang. The people in at least the first six rows would not find this overhang objectionable. The rear part of the main floor of the Royal Festival Hall is much the same as the Bloomington hall, except that the height of the mouth is lower at Royal Festival. The back rows hear only the direct sound. The lower of the two balconies shown for the Metropolitan Opera House would not be very satisfactory for symphonic music, although the direct sound from the stage can be heard quite well. The soffit does nothing toward reflecting the direct sound to the rear, and the overhang cuts off the ceiling reflections from six of the eleven rows. The upper balcony is much better; the sound in the front and back five rows is excellent.

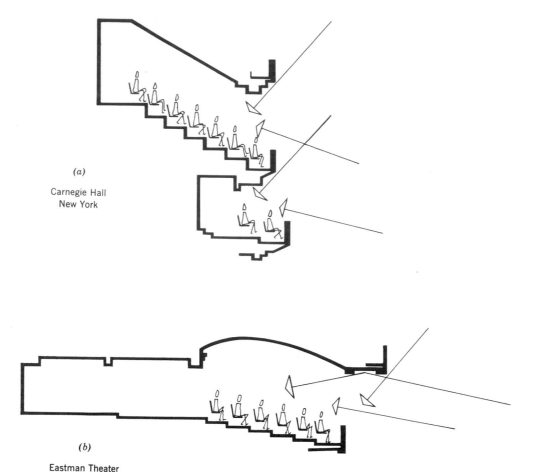

(a)

Carnegie Hall
New York

(b)

Eastman Theater
Rochester

Figure 12.7. Two poor balcony designs: (*a*) upper balcony is poor, receives little sound from upper hall and opening is small; (*b*) poor balcony, very small opening and large carpeted area behind listeners.

Two less desirable plans for balconies are shown in Figure 12.7. In the large balcony of Carnegie Hall, the ceiling reflections do not penetrate well, although the sound in the shallow ring beneath the balcony is quite good. The balcony design shown in part (*b*), Figure 12.7 is particularly inadequate; the ceiling reflections do not penetrate even to the first row, and the small height of the mouth means that even the direct sound is muffled in the last four rows of seats.

Recommendations: A study of overhangs suggests two general recommendations, which are illustrated in Figure 12.8.

1. For *concert halls*, the distance D in Figure 12.8, part (*a*) should not exceed the height H. In addition, the soffit should be shaped to reflect the direct sound to the heads of the listeners.

2. For *opera houses*, the distance D in Figure 12.8, part (*b*) should

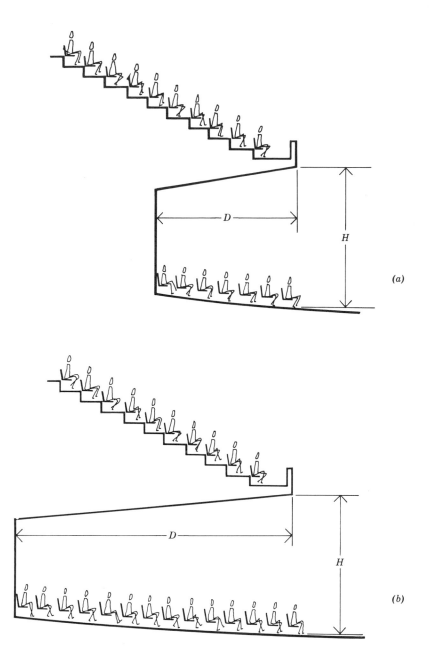

Figure 12.8. Recommended designs for excellent balconies: (*a*) In a concert hall, *D* should not exceed *H*. (*b*) In an opera house, *D* should not exceed 2*H*. Note that the under-balcony shaping is not shown here, since it is specific to each hall and depends on the location of the stage and the rake of the floor beneath the seats.

not exceed *twice* the height *H*. Here also the soffit should be shaped to reflect the direct sound toward the heads of the listeners.

The depth of overhang recommended for a concert hall is half what is recommended for an opera house because symphonic music has greater need for reverberant sound and for diffusion of the sound. A person listening

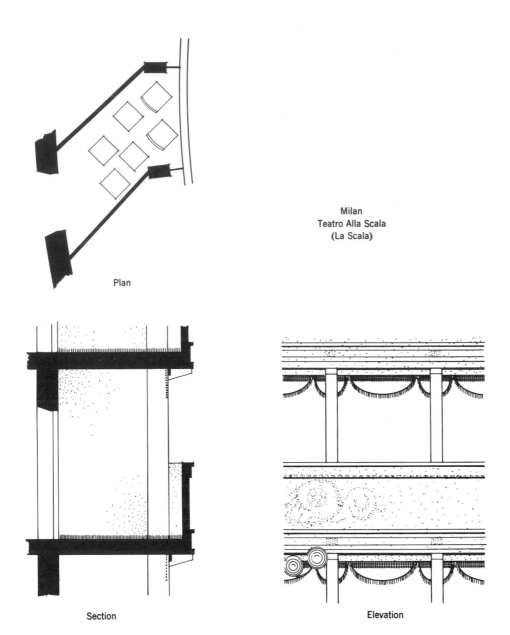

Milan
Teatro Alla Scala
(La Scala)

Plan

Section

Elevation

Figure 12.9. Sketches of a typical box in La Scala in Milan. Note the small opening to the house at the front of the box.

to orchestral music does not get the "feel of the hall" if he is seated far under a balcony overhang. The drawings of the 54 halls in Chapter 6 show that many halls do not meet these specifications. The pressure for a vast seating capacity is so great that additional depth under a balcony is frequently provided in spite of the sacrifice of acoustical quality.

Boxes

In some opera houses, the acoustics in the boxes are quite good, especially if the boxes are in effect only balconies with semi-dividers separating

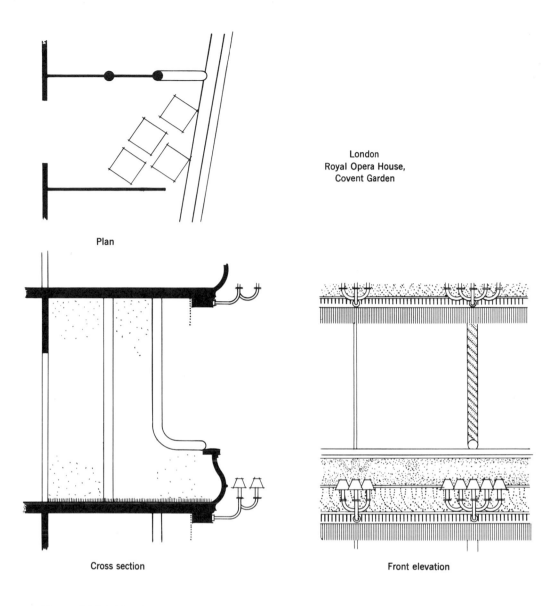

London
Royal Opera House,
Covent Garden

Plan

Cross section

Front elevation

Figure 12.10. Sketches of a typical box in the Royal Opera House of London. Note the relatively large opening to the house at the front of the box.

the units. On the other hand, in an opera house like La Scala, the box front openings are so small that only the three people sitting at the front of the box enjoy the acoustics of the house. Those in the rear of the box hear something much less satisfactory.

A comparison of Figures 12.9 and 12.10 shows that in La Scala a box opening constitutes about 40 per cent of the total surface in which it is cut, whereas in the Royal Opera House the opening occupies about 60 per cent of the total face. As a result, people sitting in the back of a box in the London Opera house hear much better than those in similar seats at La Scala.

Variations in acoustical intimacy

Why are the acoustics in concert halls often so much better in the balcony than on the main floor? There are two answers. One, the initial-time-delay gap is generally shorter in the balcony and the improved intimacy that results is one of the most important elements of good concert-hall acoustics. Two, often all side-wall surfaces, ceilings, and balcony faces are shaped to guide sound to the balconies rather than to the main floor. A comparison of ratings in the balcony and on the main floor of a number of halls, presented in Chapter 13, shows that balconies often have the superior sound, particularly in halls in categories B and B$^+$.

Seats with poor sight lines

In most halls, seats that have poor sight lines also have defective acoustics. Sounds whose frequencies are above 1000 cycles per second—for example, violin tones—do not bend around corners or obstructions. If a listener is seated behind the heads of other people, or in a side seat high in an upper balcony where he does not get a full view of the stage, the music will sound muffled to him and will lack brilliance and tonal balance. The un-numbered seats in the upper two rings of La Scala have this defect. As a result, the people in those locations stand during the performance, in order both to hear and to see.

Seats at front sides of wide halls

Wide halls usually have the acoustic disadvantage of a long initial-time-delay gap on much of the main floor. Another defect occurs in a hall that widens abruptly at the proscenium opening. People seated at the front of the hall on either side of the opening are deprived of the direct sound because the proscenium opening does not project it through a wide angle.

Seats near the stage

Seats very close to the stage are undesirable. With one's nose beneath the cellos it is only to be expected that the distant violins will sound out of balance. Of course, these front seats may compensate in their perspective on the conductor for what they lack in tonal quality of the orchestra. Ideally it would be desirable to have at least a 12-foot gap between the front row of seats and the edge of the stage, but this is a luxury that the box office is unlikely to sanction.

Rating of non-uniformity

The two attributes that vary most from seat to seat are intimacy and loudness of the direct sound, and the ratings scales for these two attributes take into account a large part of the non-uniformity. None of the other attributes vary significantly from one part of a hall to another, except in seats under deep balcony overhangs or in other unfavorable locations.

The numerical ratings have been developed to apply to the theater as a whole and have not been refined sufficiently to afford ratings for atypical locations. The rating charts are best applied to seats from which the listener experiences both the direct sound and the general reverberation of the hall. It is certainly conceivable that a hall might have such severe non-uniformity that a negative rating would be called for. However, since all the measurements on the 54 halls discussed here were made from locations at which the sound was satisfactorily uniform, no scale for non-uniformity was developed in this study.

13

Validation of the Numerical Rating Scale

The formulation of the numerical rating scale is now complete. The next question to be broached is, does the scale satisfy—that is to say, predict—the musical judgment about the 54 halls that is based on the interviews? By superimposing the numerical scale on the subjective category rating for individual halls, we can see how well they match.

In Chapter 8 the five rating categories for concert halls and opera houses were assigned the following numerical equivalents:

Subjective rating category	Numerical rating
A+ Excellent	90 to 100
A Very Good to Excellent	80 to 89
B+ Good to Very Good	70 to 79
B Fair to Good	60 to 69
C+ Fair	50 to 59
— Poor	Below 50

THE NUMERICAL RATING CHARTS

Two summary rating charts are presented in this chapter—Figure 13.1 for symphony orchestra concerts, and Figure 13.2 for opera. For concert halls, there are eight positive attributes, whose maximum values add up to 100 points; for opera, seven positive attributes total 100. Each of the figures contains two tables of corrections—one for the negative attributes of echo, noise, and distortion, and the other (Table A) for ratings in the balcony of the loudness of direct sound. The loudness of direct sound in the balcony may receive as many as eight additional points if there are especially favorable reflections or a specifically directive ceiling (see also Table 10.4).

SAMPLE RATING FOR A HYPOTHETICAL CONCERT HALL

Let us try out the rating chart on a hypothetical hall with the physical characteristics listed at the top of page 474.

RATING SCALES FOR ORCHESTRAL CONCERTS

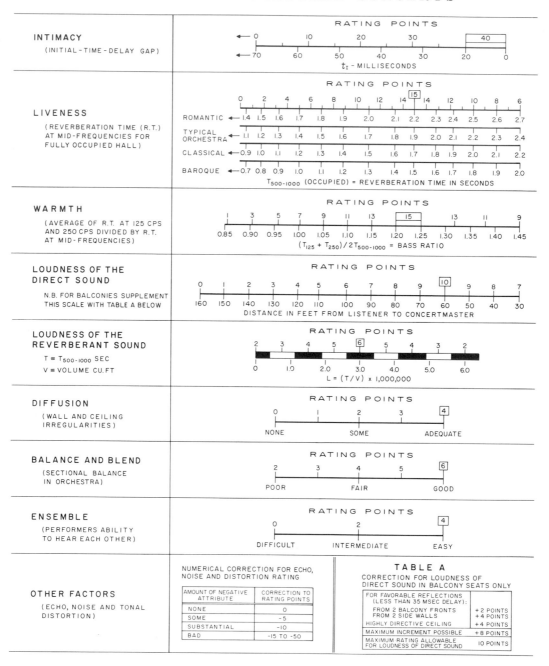

Figure 13.1

RATING SCALES FOR OPERA

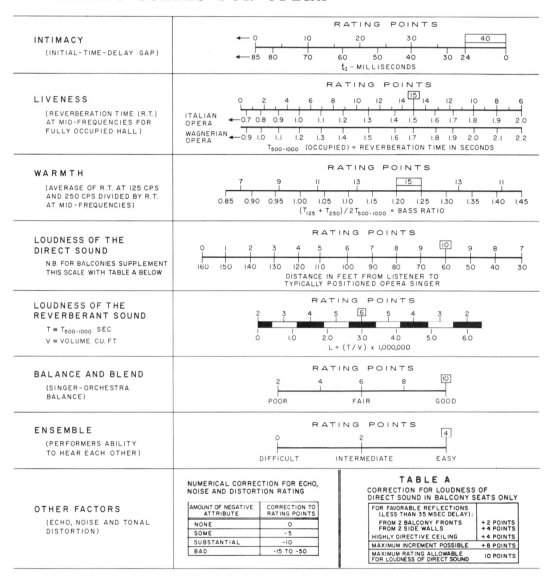

Figure 13.2

Initial-time-delay gap at the ears of the listener*	$\begin{cases} 29 \text{ msec on main floor} \\ 16 \text{ msec in balcony} \end{cases}$
$T500-1000$cps (Occupied)	1.6 sec
Distance between the listener and the concertmaster	$\begin{cases} 50 \text{ ft on main floor} \\ 104 \text{ ft in balcony} \end{cases}$
Average bass ratio $(T_{125} + T_{250})/2T_{500-1000}$	1.0
Loudness of the reverberant sound $T/V \times 10^6$	3.7
Diffusion	Adequate
Balance and blend	Good
Ensemble	Excellent
Echo	None
Noise	None
Distortion	None

* The initial-time-delay gaps for the 54 halls are taken from the technical details of Chapter 6; the reverberation times are taken from Chapter 6 or the measurements listed in Appendix 2, or they can be calculated by the means of Appendix 1. The other attributes are either judged by listening in the hall or are estimated from drawings.

From the summary rating chart of Figure 13.1 and the correction for balcony given in Table A of that figure, we obtain the following ratings:

	Main floor	Balcony
Intimacy	33	40
Liveness	9	9
Warmth	7	7
Loudness of the direct sound:	9	6
correction for balcony	–	4
Loudness of the reverberant sound	5	5
Diffusion	4	4
Balance and blend	6	6
Ensemble	4	4
Echo	0	0
Noise	0	0
Distortion	0	0
TOTAL	77	85
TOTAL RATING (average of totals)		81

With this total rating, the hall of the example would qualify for Category A, as a very-good-to-excellent concert hall. In the hypothetical hall, the attributes that exhibit deficiencies are intimacy (the initial-time-delay gap on the main floor is 9 milliseconds longer than optimum), liveness (the reverberation time is 0.3 second shorter than optimum), and warmth (the bass ratio is 0.2 lower than optimum). For music of the Baroque period this hall has a desirable degree of liveness, and for the music of Bach the low bass ratio would be no handicap (see Figure 13.1). Hence, if this hall were intended for limited use—say, the music of Bach and his contemporaries—it would receive the rating excellent (A^+) from musicians and critics. For the typical symphonic repertoire, however, it falls in Category A.

CORRELATION OF THE SUBJECTIVE AND NUMERICAL RATINGS

The 54 halls of the study are made up of 47 halls used for orchestral concerts and 19 for opera; the 12 halls that house both concert and opera are rated separately for each use.

The halls were first divided into categories on the basis of the opinions expressed in the interviews. When these tentative assignments were then submitted to the 50-odd musicians for their recommendations about final adjustments (see Chapter 8), 13 halls were shifted, 9 upward by one category and 4 downward by one category. The category assignments of the other 41 halls remained unchanged. All 13 halls that were shifted had straddled a border line; they were the halls that had been most difficult to place initially in an appropriate category.

Since no hall of the 54 is considered a poor hall, the sixth category—poor—remains unused.

Orchestral halls

In Table 13.1 the 41 concert halls are shown in the categories in which the musicians' judgments placed them. Within each category the halls are listed by the average calculated numerical rating, in descending order.

The agreement between the numerical rating scores and the subjectively determined categories is very close: in not a single instance is the descending order of the average rating violated by the assignment into category. Only

Table 13.1   Correlation of numerical and subjective ratings of 47 concert halls

Each of the 47 concert halls is shown in the category to which it has been assigned on the basis of the interviews with musicians and critics. The numerical score is based on the rating scales for the acoustical attributes, determined for the test locations on the main floor and in the uppermost balcony.

Subjectively determined categories of acoustical quality	*No. of halls*	TOTAL RATING SCORE		
		Main floor	*Balcony*	*Average*
A+ Excellent	6	96	95	96
		95	94	95
		94	93	94
		92	94	93
		92*	—	92
		90	92	91
A Very Good to Excellent	19	89	89	89
		88	89	89
		86	91	89
		87	89	88
		87	88	88
		87	87	87
		85	87	86
		85	85	85
		84	84	84
		84	84	84
		83	84	84
		81	87	84
		84	82	83
		82	84	83
		82	82	82
		78	85	82
		78	86	82
		82*	—	82
		80	83	82

* Hall has no balcony. Rating is for center of the main floor.

Table 13.1   (continued)

Subjectively determined categories of acoustical quality	No. of halls	TOTAL RATING SCORE		
		Main floor	Balcony	Average
B+	14	80	82	81
Good		75	84	80
to		76	82	79
Very Good		77	80	79
		74	81	78
		71	83	77
		76*	—	76
		75	76	76
		69	81	75
		69	79	74
		71	74	73
		70	74	72
		66	78	72
		69	74	72
B	7	67	75	71
Fair to		64	76	70
Good		61	76	69
		68	70	69
		58	78	68
		63	68	66
		58	71	65
C+	1	40 to 65	35 to 60	50
Fair				

* Hall has no balcony. Rating is for center of the main floor.

four halls have been assigned to a category that would not be predicted by the calculations, and each of these disagreements is by one category only. The two halls at the top of Category B$^+$ seem by the rating to belong in Category A, and the two halls at the top of Category B to belong in the B$^+$ category. But the differences are small, no more than 2 points for any of the four halls. In spite of these small discrepancies, it is clear that the numerical rating system separates the 47 concert halls into five categories in almost precisely the way in which they were subjectively divided by the musicians and music critics.

Halls for opera

Similar ratings for opera houses are calculated from the rating scale for opera houses in Figure 13.2, plus the appropriate corrections. The comparison of the category assignments by the musicians with the numerical ratings calculated from the rating scales are presented in Table 13.2.

The opera houses, like the concert halls, show a high correlation between the calculated rating and the subjectively determined categories. Perhaps the only ambiguity lies at the dividing line between Categories A$^+$ and A, where three opera houses, whose ratings are identical, are assigned to two different categories by the musicians' judgments.

SIGNIFICANCE OF THE RATING SCALE

What is the significance of the numerical ratings? Can we depend on their accuracy, the precision of the measurements? The correlations of the subjective category classifications with the numerical ratings promise great usefulness in the design of halls for concert and opera. The purpose of the numerical rating system is to provide the architect and the acoustician with guidelines that will assist them in the design of halls for musical performances. Although the rating scales of Figures 13.1 and 13.2 and the calculations based on them are susceptible of refinements, they serve as a general index of a hall's acoustic effectiveness and they enable the acoustical consultant to determine whether modifications of special features of the architecture might bring about improvement in the acoustics.

Table 13.2   Correlation of numerical and subjective ratings of 19 opera houses

Each of the 19 opera houses is shown in the category to which it has been assigned on the basis of the interviews with musicians and critics. The numerical score is based on the rating scales for the acoustical attributes, determined for the test locations on the main floor and in the uppermost balcony.

Subjectively determined categories of acoustical quality	No. of halls	TOTAL RATING SCORE		
		Main floor	Balcony	Average
A+	7	95	93	94
Excellent		93	91	92
		91	90	91
		92	89	91
		89	91	90
		88	88	88
		88	88	88
A	8	88	88	88
Very Good		87	87	87
to		85	87	86
Excellent		86	83	85
		79	85	82
		77	85	81
		79	80	80
		81	79	80
B+	4	70	85	78
Good		72	77	75
to		63	83	73
Very Good		66	78	72

The numerical ratings are not precise in the sense that the measurement of the speed of light is precise, since the factors that make up the numerical scale derive from the aesthetic judgments expressed by the musicians and music critics in the interviews. And indeed, there is a range of opinion among listeners on the relative merits of the halls studied, and the subjective category assignments based on these opinions show some variability. But in spite of differences of opinion, the judgments of the musicians and music critics about the best of the halls and those liked least were in remarkable accord. Only the halls that were ranked in the middling categories, A and B^+, were subject to divergent judgments.

The reasons for the differences in subjective ranking are probably as many as the number of experts expressing opinions. Some of the halls in Categories A and B^+ were deficient in liveness, some in warmth, some in intimacy, and some in several attributes. Each deficiency assumes a different importance to a different listener. Liveness, for example, looms larger to Pierre Monteux than it does to Herbert von Karajan. And warmth is mentioned more often by Leopold Stokowski than by any of the British conductors. Eugene Ormandy expressed this point of view in a recent letter, "I feel that each performer looks for something different in a hall and, therefore, it would be almost impossible . . . to express [a more precise] opinion on the [final] ratings without getting involved in discussions. For this reason, I am afraid I cannot add anything beyond what I told you in Philadelphia."

14

Some Considerations in the Design
of Concert Halls and Opera Houses

Fortunately, our experience and the studies of this book have verified that there is no single, ideal architectural solution to the acoustical design of a hall. Successful acoustics for music have been achieved with rectangular, fan or wedge, horseshoe, and even asymmetrical plans. Of the halls rated "excellent" and "good to excellent" in this study, some are of each shape. But though this is true, the many attributes of musical-architectural acoustics are so closely interrelated that, if a hall is to be successful, the architect must solve all requirements simultaneously. And the fact that the solution comes most readily in narrow, rectangular halls accounts for many of the acoustical successes of the nineteenth century.

Designers of early concert halls and opera houses often merely duplicated the size and shape of previous halls that were regarded as acoustically successful. In many cases the model halls were those very halls for which the music of their era had been composed. Today, halls must not only accommodate a musical repertoire extending over centuries but they often must seat so large an audience that they become an entirely new type of space in which to perform music. The multi-purpose character of today's halls introduces further complexities. If a hall must house drama, ballet, lectures, and a multitude of other non-musical uses, the design of the stage and its integration with the hall itself can tax the ingenuity of even the most clever architect.

Acoustical planning for a concert hall or opera house must begin early, at the time when such considerations as seating capacity and the pattern of use are being determined. The planning should encompass both the selection and the development of the site, so that exterior and interior noises will be at a minimum. If there is a subway or a busy airport nearby, additional expenditures for vibration and noise control will probably be imperative. In the development of the design of a hall, the acoustics dictate the cubic volume and strongly influence the orientation of every sound-reflecting surface, the interior materials, and even the seating. Each element of a hall has its effect on the ultimate acoustical result, and many elements cannot be corrected once they are built into the basic shape.

481

The acoustical complexities involved require the combined talents of the architect, the acoustical consultant, and other engineering specialists who collaborate to produce a successful solution in the finished building. And the participation of the building owner, as well as the musicians and other performers, is required in the planning stages if the acoustics of the hall are to satisfy their needs.

Because of the myriad of architectural possibilities for design, this chapter cannot hope to contain specific recommendations applicable to halls of every design. Instead we shall review here for the architect the more important parameters of acoustical design and point out some of the major pitfalls that may occur between the day the architect's contract is signed and the first time a conductor's baton is raised in the completed hall.

SEATING CAPACITY AND SEATING DENSITY: CRUCIAL EARLY DESIGN DECISIONS

The architects and acoustical consultants who have practiced in Western Europe, particularly during the great period of reconstruction following World War II, have been fortunate in having to design only relatively small halls. Because states and cities have long subsidized orchestra and opera groups in continental Europe, the presentation of music has had to depend for its support only partly on the sale of tickets. Thus European halls have generally been built to accommodate audiences of only 600 to 1800; a few halls seat approximately 2000. Consider, for example, some of the halls in use today (Table 14.1).

It is a great deal easier to design good acoustics into a hall with fewer than 2000 seats than one with 2500 or more seats—numbers that are demanded outside of Continental Europe, where there is no government tradition of subsidizing the arts. Consider, by comparison, the halls (Table 14.2) in which major opera groups and symphony orchestras perform in the Western Hemisphere and elsewhere. Of the 52 halls listed only two have seating capacities below 2000!

These lists help to answer the question why so many halls on the European continent have turned out well compared to many larger halls in the rest of the world. The answer is, for most halls, directly related to size—

Table 14.1   Seating capacities for 47 Continental European halls

	No. of seats
AUSTRIA	
Salzburg, Neues Festspielhaus	2158
Vienna, Grosser Musikvereinssaal	1680
Vienna, Staatsoper	1658
BELGIUM	
Brussels, Palais des Beaux-Arts	2150
DENMARK	
Aarhus, Koncertsal	817
Aarlborg, Aarlborghallen	1800
Copenhagen, Tivoli	1840
FINLAND	
Helsinki, Kulttuuritalo	1500
Turku, Konserttisali	1002
GERMANY	
Bad Orb/Spessart, Konzerthalle	800
Bayreuth, Festspielhaus	1800
Berlin, Benjamin Franklin Kongresshalle	1220
Berlin, Deutsche Oper	1900
Berlin, Grosser Sendesaal	1120
Berlin, Musikhochschule Konzertsaal	1360
Berlin, Städtische Oper	1533
Bonn, Beethovenhalle	1407
Cologne, Bühnen der Stadt Köln, Opernhaus	1346
Cologne, der Neue Gürzenich, Festspielssaal	1070
Duisburg, Stadttheater	1183
Dortmund, Städtische Bühnen, Opernhaus	642
Düsseldorf, Opernhaus	1041
Frankfurt, Städtische Bühnen, Grosses Haus	1430
Gelsenkirchen, Stadttheater	1000
Hamburg, Hamburgische Staatsoper	1649

	No. of seats
Hannover, Landestheater Oper	1084
Karlsruhe, Badisches Staatstheater, Grosses Haus	1055
Kassel, Staatstheater, Grosses Haus	950
Kiel, Bühnen der Landeshauptstadt, Stadttheater	1044
Mannheim, Nationaltheater, Grosses Haus	1200
Munich, Herkulessaal	1287
Nuremberg, Städtische Bühnen Nürnberg-Fürth, Opernhaus	1456
Stuttgart, Liederhalle	2000
Stuttgart, Württembergisches Staatstheater, Grosses Haus	1400
Wuppertal, Wuppertaler Bühnen, Opernhaus	870
ITALY	
Catania, Teatro Massimo Bellini	1400
Genoa, Teatro Carlo Felice	1400
Milan, Teatro alla Scala	2135
Palermo, Teatro Massimo	2228
Rome, Palazzo Pia	2000–2500
Rome, Teatro dell'Opera	2212
SWEDEN	
Gothenburg, Konserthus	1371
Halsingborg, Konserthus	1000
Stockholm, Konserthus	1110
SWITZERLAND	
Basel, Stadt-Casino	1400
La Chaux-de-Fonds, Salle Musica	1032
Zurich, Grosser Tonhallesaal	1546
MEDIAN NUMBER OF SEATS IN 47 HALLS	1400

Table 14.2   Seating capacities of 52 halls outside of Continental Europe

	No. of seats		*No. of seats*
UNITED STATES		New York, Proposed	
Atlanta, Fox Theater	4663	Metropolitan Opera House	3800
Atlanta, Municipal Auditorium	4853	Omaha, City Auditorium	4000
Baltimore, Lyric Theatre	2616	Philadelphia, Academy of Music	2983
Bloomington, Indiana University		Rochester, Eastman Theatre	3347
Auditorium	3788	San Francisco, War Memorial	
Boston, Municipal Auditorium	5900	Opera House	3198
Boston, Music Hall	4600	St. Louis, Kiel Auditorium	3500
Boston, Symphony Hall	2631	Washington, Constitution Hall	3810
Buffalo, Kleinhans Music Hall	2839		
Chicago, Arie Crown Theatre	5081	**ARGENTINA**	
Chicago, Civic Opera House	3625	Buenos Aires, Teatro Colón	2487
Chicago, Orchestra Hall	2582		
Cleveland, Severance Hall	1890	**CANADA**	
Dallas, McFarlin Auditorium,		Edmonton and Calgary, Alberta	
Southern Methodist University	2500	Jubilee Auditoriums	2697
Dayton, Memorial Hall	2502	Montreal, Cultural Center	3000
Detroit, Fisher Theater	2202	Toronto, O'Keefe Auditorium	3155
Detroit, Henry and Edsel Ford		Vancouver, Queen Elizabeth	
Auditorium	2926	Theatre	2800
Houston, Music Hall	3100		
Jacksonville, Municipal		**GREAT BRITAIN**	
Auditorium	3200	Bristol, Colston Hall	2180
Kansas City, Municipal		Edinburgh, Usher Hall	2760
Auditorium, Music Hall	3000	Glasgow, St. Andrew's Hall	2500
Lafayette, Purdue University		Liverpool, Philharmonic Hall	1955
Hall of Music	6107	London, Royal Albert Hall	6080
Lenox, Tanglewood Music Shed	6000	London, Royal Festival Hall	3000
Los Angeles, Greek Theater	4407	London, Royal Opera House	2180
Los Angeles, Philharmonic		Manchester, Free Trade Hall	2569
Auditorium	2670		
Los Angeles, Shrine Auditorium	6600	**ISRAEL**	
Minneapolis, Cyrus Northrop		Jerusalem, Binyanei Ha'Oomah	3142
Memorial Hall	5300	Tel Aviv, Fredric R. Mann	
New Orleans, Municipal		Auditorium	2715
Auditorium	2750		
New York, Carnegie Hall	2760	**VENEZUELA**	
New York, Metropolitan Opera		Caracas, Aula Magna	2660
House	3639	MEDIAN NUMBER OF	
New York, Philharmonic Hall	2644	SEATS IN 52 HALLS	3000

a median number of 3000 versus 1400 seats. The concert halls on the continent of Europe are mainly small, and thus they can be narrow, with the result that the most important acoustical attribute—acoustical intimacy—is seldom far from optimum. European opera houses are also low enough in cubic volume so that singers can fill the space without straining their voices.

Audience count

The architect's first concern in the design of a new hall should be, therefore, the total seating capacity, since this is the factor that fixes the size of the hall. He should make certain that the number of seats called for by the owner is actually what is needed. A hall should not be built to accommodate the largest anticipated audience.

Ideally, a new hall should accommodate an audience very little larger than the audience which the principal musical use, be it opera or symphony orchestra, can draw. No musical group performs its best in a half-filled house, and half the acoustical battle is won if the hall is small.

Audience density

Once the total seating capacity is established, the next important consideration is the density with which the audience is seated. Most good halls for music have walls and ceilings made of plaster or thick wood, and very few draperies and carpets; thus the audience is the principal sound-absorbing element. The absorption of an audience is not related simply to the number of persons comprising it. One of the important findings of our study of 54 halls shows that an audience absorbs sound in proportion to the total area of floor it covers plus part of the area of the aisles surrounding or contained within the seating area.* An audience does *not* absorb sound in proportion to the number of people in it (assuming that the hall is fully occupied). In other words, the more the audience is spread out, the more sound it absorbs in the hall. Consequently the spacing of the seats is as important as the total number of seats.

The architect must keep to a minimum the floor area that the audience

---

* This idea was first presented at the Spring meeting of the Acoustical Society of America in 1958 in Washington in a paper entitled "Audience and Seat Absorption in Large Halls," which is reproduced with additions in Appendix 1.

covers if he is to achieve the required liveness within a reasonable cubic volume. He should keep the center-to-center spacing and the row-to-row spacing of the seats as small as possible, consistent with current standards of audience comfort and safety, as well as make certain that the number of seats needed is not overestimated. Some typical areas per person in halls built since 1930 are given in Table 14.3.

Architects sometimes ask why it is that, if a new hall is to seat no more than, say, the 2631 people of Boston's Symphony Hall, a cubic volume nearly 20 per cent greater is needed in order to achieve the same reverberation time. The answer lies in the larger size of the seats, the generous spacing, and today's more protective building codes, which require very wide aisles and access ways. The standards of comfort and of safety have come a long way from those of 60 to 100 years ago. Perhaps we cannot force nineteenth century standards on present-day builders, but for every square foot of added seating area, approximately 40 cubic feet of volume must be added to the hall.

Table 14.1 shows that the range of areas per person extends from 5.1 to 8.0 square feet with a median value of 6.6 square feet per person. Remember that aisles up to 3.5 feet of their width, located within or surrounding the seating area, are included in the computations of area per seat. Anything over 7 square feet per person is quite generous from the standpoint of comfort. Even in halls where the area per person is between 6.5 and 6.8 square feet, there are complaints about comfort only from very large people.

Total sound-absorbing area

The total audience area S_A is computed by multiplying the area per seat by the total number of seats. Although the audience itself contributes the most significant part of the sound absorption in a hall, the absorption, and hence the area, of the orchestra S_0 must also be considered in the computation of the liveness. The area S_A plus the area S_0 gives the total sound-absorbing area S_T. In opera houses the area of the proscenium opening is included in the total sound-absorbing area S_T, since the acoustical characteristics of the stagehouse and the auditorium are two separate matters.

Table 14.3   Audience area per person for post-1930 halls

	Audience area per person including part of the aisles* S_A/N_A*	
	ft^2/person	m^2/person
AMERICA		
Buffalo, Kleinhans Hall	7.4	0.69
Chicago, Arie Crown Theatre	6.5	0.60
Lenox, Tanglewood Music Shed	5.1†	0.47
New York, Philharmonic Hall	6.5	0.60
San Francisco, War Memorial Opera House	6.5	0.60
AUSTRIA		
Salzburg, Festspielhaus	6.9	0.64
Vienna, Grosser Musikvereinssaal	6.3	0.58
Vienna, Staatsoper	6.6	0.61
CANADA		
Vancouver, Queen Elizabeth Theatre	6.9	0.64
GERMANY		
Bonn, Beethovenhalle	8.5	0.79
Stuttgart, Liederhalle	7.0	0.65
GREAT BRITAIN		
Bristol, Colston Hall	5.6	0.52
London, Royal Festival Hall	7.1	0.66
ISRAEL		
Tel Aviv, F. R. Mann Auditorium	6.7	0.62
SWEDEN		
Gothenburg, Konserthus	6.5	0.60
SWITZERLAND		
La Chaux-de-Fonds, Salle Musica	6.8	0.63
Zurich, Grosser Tonhallesaal	6.1	0.57
VENEZUELA		
Caracas, Aula Magna	7.6	0.71

* See Appendix 3 for definitions of terminology and directions for figuring the area of aisles to be included.

† Unupholstered metal chairs without arms.

LIVENESS AND CUBIC VOLUME

Reverberation time

Having determined the total areas that will contribute sound absorption to the hall, we next choose the appropriate mid-frequency reverberation time. The preferred reverberation time for various styles of music has been discussed in Chapter 9. As a factor of safety in design, it is wise to add 0.05 second to the value chosen if there are to be no carpets in the aisles and no draperies on the walls. Add 0.2 second if the aisles are fully carpeted or if there is a substantial area of draperies. The value that is selected for reverberation time, including the factor of safety, is designated by the letter T.

Cubic volume

From the value of T that has been selected, we can now determine the ratio V/S_T from Table 14.4. The quantity V—the required cubic volume of the hall—is found by multiplying the ratio V/S_T by S_T.

Table 14.4 Value of the ratio V/S_T as a function of the reverberation time at mid-frequencies T for a fully occupied hall (T includes a safety factor). The table is derived from Figure A1.2 in Appendix 1.

$T_{500-1000}$(Occup.) Seconds	V/S_T Feet	V/S_T Meters
1.1	21.6	6.6
1.2	24.0	7.4
1.3	26.4	8.1
1.4	28.9	8.9
1.5	31.4	9.6
1.6	34.0	10.4
1.7	36.6	11.1
1.8	39.2	11.9
1.9	41.8	12.7
2.0	44.5	13.6
2.1	47.3	14.4
2.2	50.2	15.3
2.3	53.2	16.2
2.4	56.4	17.2
2.5	59.5	18.1

Table 14.4 shows what cubic volume will be required in order for a hall of a particular seating capacity to achieve the selected mid-frequency reverberation time. A smaller volume in the final design means a shorter reverberation time. Therefore, any reduction in the height of the ceiling of the room will result in a deleterious effect on the liveness of the hall.

Balconies

A narrow hall is important to acoustical intimacy, and this consideration may dictate several shallow balconies. But if there are several balconies, the number of aisles and access ways has to be increased, and part of this area adds to the total sound-absorbing area of the hall S_T. It is a difficult problem for an architect to accommodate his design to the conflicting requirements of reasonable cubic volume and satisfactory acoustical intimacy.

CLARITY

The clarity of the sound in a hall is determined principally by three factors: the loudness of the direct sound in relation to the loudness of the reverberant sound, the length of the initial-time-delay gap, and the speed with which the music is played. Echoes, of course, also reduce clarity.

LOUDNESS OF DIRECT AND REVERBERANT SOUND

A study of Figure 10.3 reveals that in order for a hall to achieve a reasonably high rating for the loudness of the direct sound, no listener on the main floor should be seated farther from the concertmaster than about 100 feet. In the balcony the distance may be greater, say, as much as 140 feet if the walls and ceiling direct part of the sound into the balcony.

The loudness of the reverberant sound depends on the ratio of the reverberation time at mid-frequencies to the cubic volume of the hall. This ratio, when multiplied by 1,000,000 should lie between 1 and 5 (see Chapter 10).

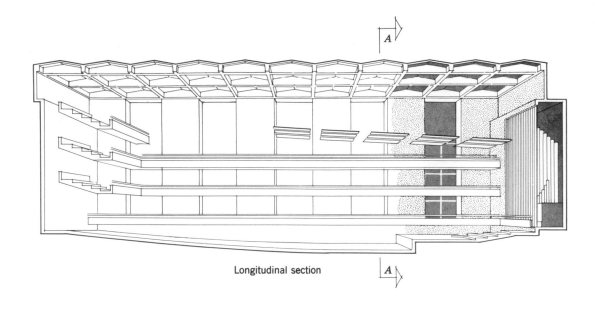

Longitudinal section

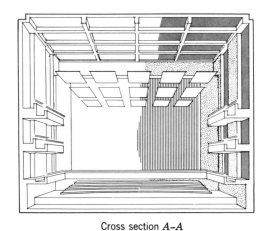

Cross section *A–A*

Figure 14.1. Sketch showing architectural means for achieving a short initial-time-delay gap without sacrificing reverberation time. Features are narrow hall, high ceiling, and shallow balconies.

HALL SHAPE AND INTIMACY (INITIAL-TIME-DELAY GAP)

Any hall whose volume is greater than 600,000 cubic feet is, from an acoustical standpoint, a large hall and poses a considerable problem for the architect if it is to achieve a high intimacy rating (see Chapter 9). A hall that is this large necessarily has either its major ceiling or its side walls located so far away from the listeners that the initial-time-delay gap must be large. That is to say, the surfaces do not provide the necessary short-time-delay reflections. If the volume of a hall is even greater than 600,000 cubic feet, both the side walls and ceiling may be located very far from the audience. This distance may be compensated for by one or another of the four plans shown in Figures 14.1 through 14.4. Two of the

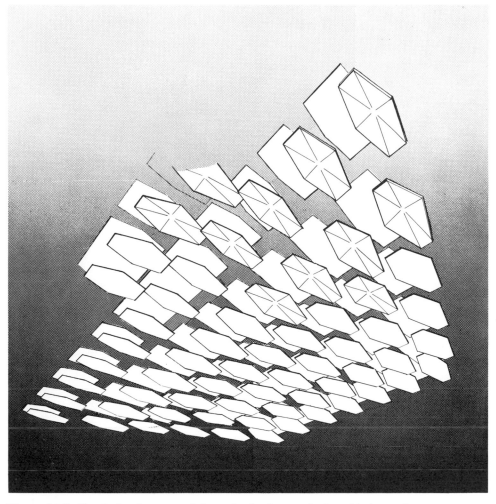

Figure 14.2. Sketch showing suspended sound-reflecting panels for achieving a short initial-time-delay gap without sacrificing reverberation time in Philharmonic Hall, Lincoln Center for the Performing Arts. Features are partly open suspended panels, high sound-reflecting ceiling, and relatively wide hall. *Architect:* Max Abramovitz of the firm Harrison and Abramovitz. *Acoustical consultant:* Bolt Beranek and Newman Inc.

designs shown are plans already carried out in completed halls, and two are early design sketches for contemplated halls.

Figure 14.1 is a sketch of a hall seating about 2000 persons, in which a satisfactorily short initial-time-delay gap—high intimacy rating—is achieved by narrowness.

Figure 14.2 shows part of the acoustical design for Philharmonic Hall, Lincoln Center, New York (see Chapter 15). Discontinuous panels hung at two levels produce an initial-time-delay gap at the center of the main floor of about 20 milliseconds; without the panels the value would be about 40 milliseconds.

Figure 14.3 shows the Music Shed at Tanglewood, a very large fan-shaped hall, virtually without reflections into the audience from its side

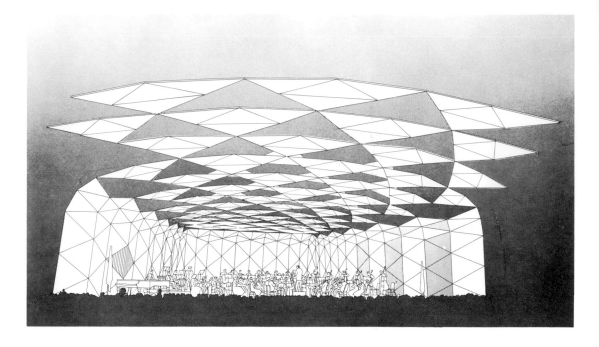

Figure 14.3. Sketch of the sending end of the Tanglewood Music Shed, Lenox, Massachusetts, showing suspended, sound-reflecting panels for achieving a short initial-time-delay gap without sacrificing reverberation time. Features are partly open area in the plane of the panels, very wide fan-shaped hall, and high sound-reflecting ceiling. *Architect:* Eero Saarinen and Associates. *Acoustical consultant:* Bolt Beranek and Newman Inc.

walls. The interposed, suspended ceiling panels provide an initial-time-delay gap at seats in front of the boxes of 19 milliseconds. Prior to the installation of the suspended panels the initial-time-delay gap was about 35 milliseconds (see Chapter 6). Openings between the suspended panels allow circulation for the sound through the spaces above and below them, and for this reason the reverberation time of the hall has not been changed significantly by their installation.

The sketch of Figure 14.4 and the photograph of Figure 14.5 show an early design for an auditorium with a ceiling that has the appearance of being continuous. The initial-time-delay gap of this hall should be close to those achieved with the suspended panels at Tanglewood and Philharmonic Hall. In several other halls currently under design, special constructions at either side and in front of the proscenium opening are being incorporated in order to satisfy the requirements for acoustical intimacy.

Many different ideas might be tried out for the ceilings of large halls. Modern electro-mechanical systems might be employed to raise part of the ceiling to produce a high-ceilinged look when the hall lights are on, but, during the performance, the ceiling could be lowered to provide the proper

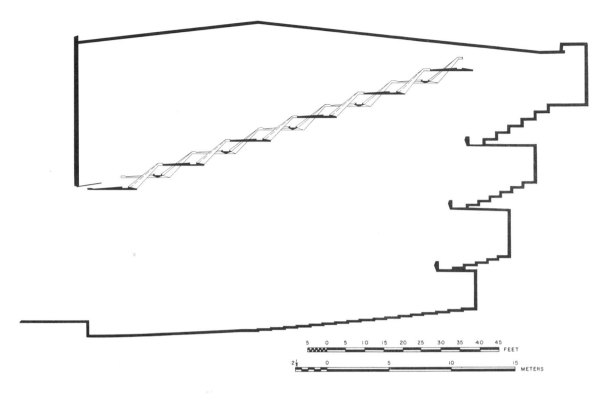

Figure 14.4. Sketch showing architectural means for achieving a short initial-time-delay gap without sacrificing reverberation time. The upper ceiling is acoustically reflective. The lower ceiling looks solid, but is about 40 per cent acoustically transparent.

acoustics. Suspended, partly open side-wall or ceiling panels, either freely exposed or concealed behind acoustically transparent screens, open up the possibility of many interesting designs. In a large hall, these additions may give a space visual intimacy consonant with its acoustical intimacy.

TEXTURE

Texture—the detailed structure of the sound reflection patterns at various locations in a hall—is closely allied with both the initial-time-delay gap and the succession of reflections that follows the first reflection (see Chapter 11). Good texture requires that there be five or more reflections or relatively uniform spacing within the first 70 milliseconds after the arrival of the direct sound, with each successive reflection slightly lower in amplitude than its predecessor. Planning for texture requires careful attention to the detailed shapes of the various wall and ceiling surfaces, the stage enclosure, and the balcony fronts.

When intimacy and texture are satisfactory at all locations, the problem of the uniform distribution of the music from the performing group throughout the hall is largely solved (see Chapter 12).

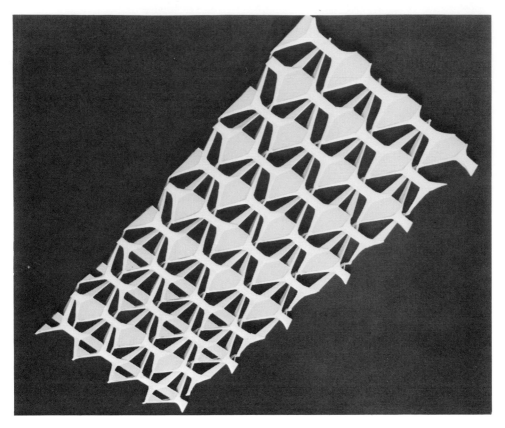

Figure 14.5. Photograph of a model of the suspended ceiling of Figure 14.4. *Architect:* Affleck, Desbarats, Dimakopoulos, Lebensold and Sise. *Acoustical consultant:* Bolt Beranek and Newman Inc.

WARMTH

Warmth is achieved when the ratio of the reverberation time at low frequencies to that at mid-frequencies is satisfactorily large. In design, it is achieved by the choice of appropriate interior finish materials. All thin or light-weight materials should be avoided, particularly plastics and wood less than ¾ inch thick that are not cemented directly to thick plaster or concrete backings. The relative importance of warmth in the total rating of a hall is discussed in Chaper 10. Sound absorption coefficients for various finish materials for halls are given in Table A1.IV of Appendix 1, and in Figure 10.2.

DIFFUSION

Diffusion is produced by relatively large-scale irregularities on the ceiling and side walls of a hall. It serves to reduce tonal harshness. Ceiling and wall coffers and niches, for example, provide effective diffusion in older halls like Boston's Symphony Hall. The contemporary architectural idiom is not without many fine examples of effective acoustical diffusion.

Overlapping concrete plates offer interesting possibilities for the design of both wall and ceiling surfaces. The familiar plaster and lath construction provides a malleable material that is easily formed into shapes that can be visually pleasing as well as acoustically effective. The acoustical attribute of diffusion seems to be of little importance in opera houses but it is essential to an excellent concert hall. If the surfaces of a concert hall are all flat, music played in it sounds harsh (see Chapter 11).

ACOUSTICAL BLEMISHES

The acoustical blemishes—echo, noise, distortion, and non-uniformity —must be avoided by care in the design. These negative attributes are discussed in Chapter 12.

One cannot overemphasize the need for adequate control of all intruding sources of noise—noise from corridors and lobbies, exterior noise from street and aircraft and, most important, the noise of the ventilating system. As a rule, the other three acoustical blemishes are relatively easy to eliminate if the architect is successful in satisfying the positive attributes of acoustical design.

DESIGN OF STAGES FOR CONCERT HALLS AND OPERA HOUSES— BALANCE, BLEND, AND ENSEMBLE

Fewer words have been devoted in the technical literature to the design of stagehouses for concert halls and opera houses than to any other aspect of architectural acoustics. The reason is that there has been little opportunity for systematic research on the subject. An experiment in which changes were made in a stage or its surroundings during or between performances would be difficult and costly. The only simple adjustment that can be tried is the placing or removing of the risers on the stage. To be meaningful an experiment would require both a full orchestra and a full audience, which presents formidable complications. Even with an experimental approach, it is a tedious task to try to compare the multitudinous factors of design and use.

One significant set of experiments was performed recently in New York's new Philharmonic Hall. During the hall's "tuning week" the New

York Philharmonic Orchestra performed selected samples of music a number of times before a jury of well-qualified listeners and an acoustically simulated audience. Adjustments were made in the sizes and arrangement of the risers, in the height and composition of the canopy, and in the reflecting surfaces around the stage. After each change, the listening jury evaluated the effect on the music. The critical importance of every detail at the sending end of a large hall to the achievement of satisfactory balance, blend, and ensemble was striking. The results are summarized in Chapter 15 in the hope that they will serve as a guide to future experimentation.

Concert halls without stagehouses

The simplest type of hall has a permanent stage, designed primarily for concerts and with no special arrangements for the handling of scenery. In most halls of this kind, the stage and the auditorium are essentially one big room with no obvious division or proscenium. Some examples follow of concert halls whose stages are considered satisfactory by the musicians who use them. *Completed before 1901:* Boston, Vienna, Leipzig (destroyed), Glasgow, Amsterdam, Basel, and Zurich; *completed since 1928:* Buffalo, Lenox (Massachusetts), Brussels, Helsinki, Stuttgart, Gothenburg, and Caracas. Eight of these halls have high ceilings over the stage, averaging about 44 feet. Six have low ceilings, averaging about 26 feet. Of the eight halls with high ceilings, all but one were built more than 60 years ago. Of those with low ceilings, all were built within the last 30 years.

Halls with high ceilings

The older halls with high ceilings over the stage are characterized by a relatively shallow stage; the median depth is 28 feet from the front edge, or from the proscenium, to the rear wall. The ceilings of their stages are either horizontal or slope down a few feet toward the rear. The ceiling heights above the stage are about 46 ± 4 feet at the front and about 42 ± 8 feet at the rear, including risers. In these halls a shallow balcony typically extends along the two sides of the stage and some of the musicians sit beneath the small overhang. Shallow balconies along the sides of the stage produce short-time-delay reflections that benefit the performers and contribute to the blending of the sound heard by the audience. The median width of the stage in those of the older halls that have overhanging balconies, measured between the faces of the balconies, is about 45 feet. In a hall with a shallow stage and with sound-reflecting surfaces only a small distance apart at the sides, orchestral ensemble is good. And since the seating space for the orchestra is small, the blend and balance are likely to be good. If the stage is sufficiently narrow there is no need for the ceiling to be low in order to provide proper balance, blend, and ensemble. Thus a high ceiling can be built, which permits a large part of the sound energy to rise freely into the upper reaches of the hall and thus increases the ratio of the loudness of the reverberent sound to the direct sound.

Newer halls

Six of the halls built since 1928 have a low ceiling over the stage. Their stages are considerably deeper, between 35 and 40 feet. The ceiling heights at the front of the stage are about 30 ± 4 feet and at the rear about 21 ± 5 feet, measured above the risers. The width at the front of the stage averages about 80 ± 10 feet, and at the rear about 40 ± 8 feet. The ceilings of some of these halls are quite irregular (e.g., Chapter 6, the Liederhalle in Stuttgart, Germany), with the result that the sounds reflected from them are scattered to all the sections of the orchestra.

Conclusions

From this evidence we conclude that from an acoustical standpoint, if the average width of the stage is greater than about 45 feet, the ceiling should be low and irregular in shape. If the ceiling of the stage averages higher than about 30 feet above the risers, the sound-reflecting walls should be less than 50 feet apart, and the depth of the stage no greater than about 30 feet.

Discussion

Very wide or very deep stages have serious disadvantages. When the stage is wide, a listener seated on either side of the hall hears the instruments near him before he hears the sound from the other side of the stage.

This time difference may be great enough to affect the blend adversely. When the stage is very deep, the sound from the instruments at the back of the stage will arrive at the listener's ears a detectable instant after sound from the front of the stage, with similar adverse effects. In addition, a very wide stage makes it difficult for the conductor to hold the sections of the orchestra in good ensemble. To avoid these troubles, all parts of a stage should fit within a rectangle not exceeding about 60 feet in width and about 40 feet in depth; on the average, musicians like an area of about 20 square feet each.

Wide stages are typically found in halls built since 1930; they constitute one of the principal reasons why today most conductors seat the first and second violins together on the left side of the stage. Seated close to each other, these two sections play in better ensemble. Similarly, many conductors group the cellos and violas together at the right. Twenty-five or more years ago, when most halls had narrow stages, conductors generally seated the first violins on the left, the second violins and violas on the right, and the cellos in the center of the stage.

The stages of some large concert halls are very wide, especially when there is no proscenium arch to separate the stage from the auditorium. In order to obtain good blend there should be a nearby reflecting surface, such as an irregular low ceiling or a suspended canopy over the stage. On the other hand, a satisfactorily long reverberation time requires a large volume of the hall above the stage. We can make this volume of air available for reverberation, and still provide reflecting surfaces less than 30 feet above the front of the stage, by installing a perforated canopy, like the one shown in Figure 14.6. Under such a canopy, the musicians can hear each other well because of the early reflections, while at the same time the open spaces in the canopy permit part of the sound to penetrate it and create general reverberation. If the canopy continues over the front half of the audience, it also contributes to the projection and the uniform distribution of the reflected sound throughout the hall.

An important function of the ceiling over the stage is to maintain balance among the sections of the orchestra. Good balance is achieved by a ceiling of the shape shown in Figure 14.7, provided the sound reflecting

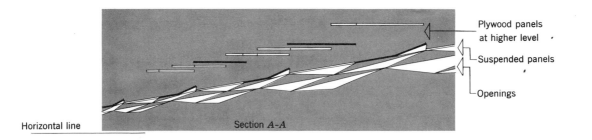

Plywood panels
at higher level

Suspended panels

Openings

Horizontal line

Section *A-A*

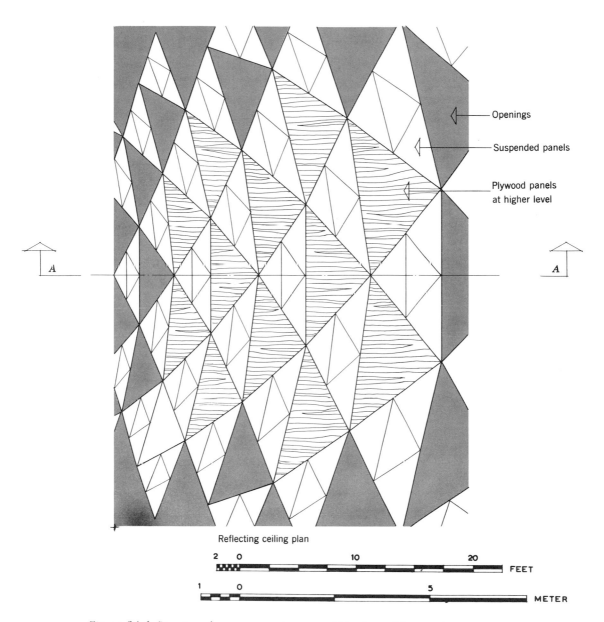

Openings

Suspended panels

Plywood panels
at higher level

A

A

Reflecting ceiling plan

2 0   10   20
FEET

1 0   5
METER

Figure 14.6. Drawing of canopy over the stage of Tanglewood Music Shed, showing extra panels at a second level to improve musician's ability to hear each other. The Tanglewood stage is so wide that the side walls assist the musicians very little in achieving good ensemble.

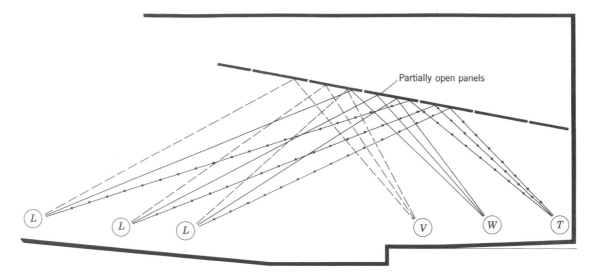

Figure 14.7. Sketch of the sending end of a hall that provides improved orchestral balance on the main floor of the auditorium. The design shown here is intended to be illustrative and is not recommended for adoption without further study. V, violins; W, woodwinds; T, trumpets; L, listeners.

panels continue out over the audience. For each of the instruments V, W, and T, any one of the listeners L receives a strong reflection from the stage ceiling or from one of the reflecting panels. Furthermore, since the distance that each reflection has to travel is nearly the same, good blend is produced. Without the panels over the forward part of the audience, the violins sound weaker than the instruments at the back of the stage and poor string-brass balance results.

An unsatisfactory design for a stage ceiling is shown in Figure 14.8. Here the violins are directed to the forward part, and the brass to the rear of the audience, and the result is a very unsatisfactory string-brass balance in the hall. Also, in the front of the hall, the sound of the woodwinds is lost.

Once a satisfactory type of canopy has been selected, for example, the one shown in Figure 14.7, there is still the important matter of providing good conditions for the orchestra to hear on stage. The undersurface of the canopy should be modulated so that sound is reflected from one side of the orchestra to the other and from back to front. The side and rear walls of the stage should assist in this process and, in addition, should guide the sound of the strings located at the front of the stage to the audience.

For recitals or small performing groups, solid wood panels 10 to 15 feet high should be placed behind the performers grouped at the front of the stage in order to prevent echoes formed at the back of the stage from interfering with the clarity of rapidly moving passages. If the materials are carefully chosen and the panels carefully built, tonal distortion due to selective sound absorption can be avoided.

The best materials to use around the side of a stage are plaster on brick

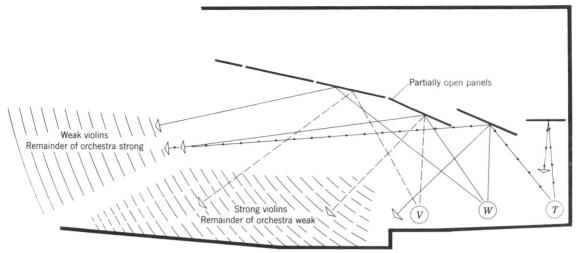

Figure 14.8. Sketch of the sending end of a hall that provides poor orchestral balance on the main floor of the auditorium.

or plaster on masonry block. Ideally the canopy should be of thick plaster, but if excessive weight is a problem, well-framed and randomly braced plywood sheets, approximately ¾ inch thick, should be heavy enough to prevent serious loss of bass. The floor of the stage should be of wood over an air space.

Concert halls with stagehouses

In the United States and Canada, the majority of halls that are used for symphonic music have stagehouses to accommodate theatrical scenery. Often these halls are also used for chamber orchestra concerts, opera, and non-musical events. In many of these halls the reverberation time is under 1.6 seconds. Most of them have prosceniums, between 60 and 120 feet wide, and as many as 3000 to 6000 seats. There is almost universal agreement that an orchestral performance is unsatisfactory to both performer and listener when the orchestra is located behind the proscenium under a high stagehouse without a sound-reflective enclosure.

Many kinds of demountable enclosures or "shells" have been tried, with varying success. But the enclosure must not be considered alone—it is actually a vital element in the acoustics of the hall. Although the designs of enclosures are sometimes limited by the way in which they are to be demounted and stored, the same principles of acoustical design should be applied to a stagehouse as those that govern the stage end of a hall without stagehouse.

The weak points of many demountable stage enclosures are the loss of the low frequencies and the excessive loudness of instruments at the back of the stage compared to those at the front. Loss of bass may be prevented by choosing relatively heavy materials for the enclosure that do not absorb much low-frequency sound, and by avoiding cracks or openings into the stagehouse. The loudness balance between instruments at the back and the front of the stage can be controlled by the orientation of the ceiling panels, by the extension of suspended panels out into the hall proper, and by selective sound absorption.

One reason why instruments at the back of an orchestra enclosure often overpower the strings at the front is the lack of reflecting surfaces in the forward part of the hall to reinforce the sound of the forward instruments properly. In the Academy of Music in Philadelphia, balcony faces starting at the edges of the proscenium reflect the energy from the violins into the front part of the audience. In the design of Figure 14.7 the sound from V (violins) must reflect from hanging panels and from the side walls in front of the stage in order to reach the listener L, because the stage enclosure itself does not help. In other words, the stage enclosure and the front part of the auditorium must be planned together.

The balance between the brass and percussion and the string sections may be controlled by the limited use of sound-absorbing materials in the enclosure adjacent to the brass and percussion instruments. In the Academy of Music, light canvas sections are provided in place of the hard walls of the shell behind these instruments. The amount, type, and location of such sound-absorbing materials must be coordinated with the arrangement of the instruments on the stages and must complement other sound-reflecting surfaces in the hall.

Since labor costs and the time required to mount and demount the stage enclosure are significant factors in a multi-purpose hall, there is an increasing interest in mechanization. A completely mechanized demountable stage enclosure has been installed in the Northrup Auditorium at the University of Minnesota and is shown in Figure 14.9. The panels are made of damped steel, and there are changeable sections at the back of the stage for the control of the brass and percussion sounds.

Opera-house stages

Not only does an opera singer have to compete with a large orchestra, but usually the orchestra is in the hall proper, with the audience, whereas

Figure 14.9. Photograph of an all-steel (vibration-damped), automatically demountable orchestra enclosure in the Cyrus Northrup Memorial Hall, Minneapolis, Minnesota. Shown are the sound-diffusing side walls (the ceiling is similarly constructed) and removable sections near the floor for control of balance among the sections of the orchestra. *Structural and mechanical design:* George C. Izenour. *Acoustical design:* Bolt Beranek and Newman Inc.

the singer is in the stagehouse behind the proscenium opening—which is almost a separate room. Huge modern opera houses favor the singer even less than do the older conventional smaller houses in Europe. There are several reasons for this. The large clusters of stage lights force the singer to perform far behind the proscenium, so that much of his voice is lost in the stagehouse. The area of stage between the singer and the orchestra pit, including the forestage, which could provide effective reinforcement of a singer's voice, is often smaller than in the older opera houses. The new halls are wider, with the result that there are no reflecting surfaces near the edges of the proscenium to direct the voice into the center of the house. And finally, a large seating capacity demands many deep balconies, which raise the auditorium ceiling so high that it no longer reinforces the singers' voices, except in the uppermost balcony.

The effect that a singer's position behind the proscenium exerts on the projection of his voice is shown in Figure 14.10. From the forward position the proscenium opening limits the projection of the singer's voice to an angle of about 80 degrees. If he moves farther back, the angle is decreased to 50 degrees. Practically all the vocal power that strikes outside this angle is trapped inside the stagehouse. In the example of Figure 14.10 only 40 per cent as much of the power of the singer's voice projects through the proscenium when he sings from the back as from the front position. This loss in vocal power is especially serious to the career of a singer, since the

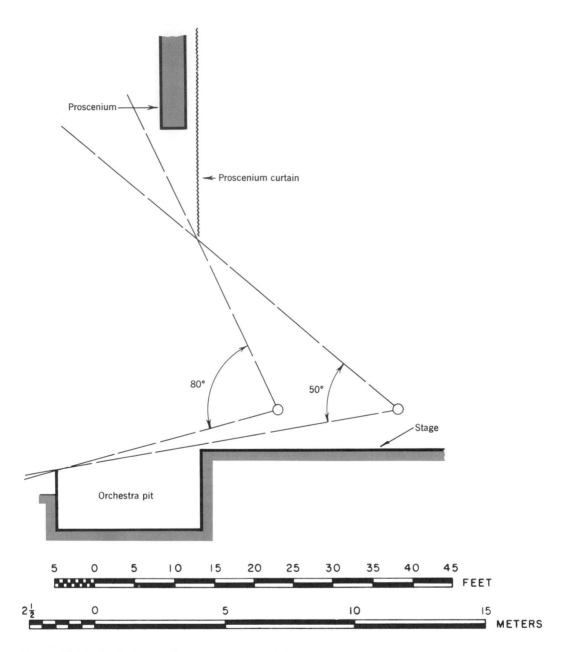

Figure 14.10. Sketch showing the projection of sound through a proscenium opening as related to the position of a singer on stage. Only 40 per cent as much sound projects through the proscenium from the rear as from the front position.

strength of his voice is judged by his ability to override the loudness of the pit orchestra, whose angle of projection to the house is seldom restricted at all.

Following are some steps that can be taken in the stagehouse to increase the projection of the singers' voices from positions deep in the stage.

1. The stage can be so designed that, except while scenery is being changed, it can be made very small by closing off the two side stages and

the rear stage by means of heavy steel doors (see the stage of the Vienna Staatsoper in Chapter 6). Hard reflecting surfaces are thus provided at the sides and back of the performing stage, which preserve the strength and warmth of the voice.

2. The cyclorama should be of heavy material, painted canvas, aluminum, or plaster, in order to be massive enough to reflect the singers' voices.

3. In order to ensure live acoustics on stage, scenery should not be stored on the stage or overhead in the stagehouse. Teasers should be kept to a minimum to reduce sound absorption.

4. Wooden stage sets should be used in place of canvas to avoid absorption of sound (see, for example, the Vienna Staatsoper in Chapter 6).

The rating chart presented in Figure 13.2 shows the relation between the initial-time-delay gap in milliseconds and the rating scale for acoustical intimacy. In order for an opera house to have excellent acoustics it must have an initial-time-delay gap shorter than 25 milliseconds, at least at the center of the main floor, and preferably in much of the audience area. In the fine, small opera houses of Europe, the sound reflections responsible for the short initial-time-delay gaps are produced either from balcony faces that are no more than 75 feet apart or from large surfaces, properly oriented in the hall, that are installed above and at the sides of the proscenium.

Can suitable initial-time-delay gaps be provided in wide opera houses or in halls where there are no large reflecting surfaces near the stage? The best way to create the important short-time-delay reflections seems to be to provide intermediate sound-reflecting surfaces below the main ceiling, directly in front of the proscenium and extending over at least the front half of the main floor. Hanging panels or a suspended false ceiling sufficiently open to afford access of the sound into the space above will preserve a long reverberation time.

Architects of large auditoriums can rarely plan a sufficiently narrow hall and still maintain the required seating arrangements; and sometimes there are objections to suspending an intermediate ceiling or to hanging panels. But there seems to be little choice. The architectural problems that this important requirement entails must be faced. No amount of wishful thinking will produce an initial-time-delay gap shorter than 25 milliseconds; it takes solid and usually visible surfaces. If economic or other factors demand a large hall that does not provide the required reflections naturally from the main ceiling or side-wall surfaces, additional reflecting surfaces must be added and integrated with the hall design. They are part of the price of a large hall.

DESIGN OF ORCHESTRA PITS

For non-Wagnerian opera, the acoustical requirements of an orchestra pit are for clear, undistorted projection of the music into the hall, in good balance and blend, without tonal distortion. In order to sing in good ensemble with the orchestra, the singers must be able to hear a clear and balanced orchestral sound, so that they can adjust their voice levels properly. The musicians in the pit should be able to hear other sections of the orchestra without the undesirably long time-delays that result from too long a pit. And the musicians also need to hear the singers in order to maintain good ensemble. As for visual requirements, it is desirable for all the singers and players to be able to see the conductor easily.

For Wagnerian opera, on the other hand, the creation of a "mystical" sound by an "invisible" orchestra seems to have been an important element in the composer's dramatic conception, at least for his late works. This requirement led Wagner to develop the sunken, covered pit whose acoustical behavior is quite different from the open pit. Some pits combine features of both of these plans, but generally with only moderate success.

For discussion, then, let us classify orchestra pits into three types:
1. Open pit (e.g., the Vienna Staatsoper).
2. Sunken pit, covered (e.g., the Bayreuth Festspielhaus).
3. Sunken pit, open (e.g., the Eastman Theatre in Rochester).

Open pit

The first objection to an entirely open pit is the disturbing visual effect on the audience of the lights from the conductor's and orchestra's music stands. A second objection is that, in order to accommodate a large orchestra, a fully open pit must be about 22 feet wide, measured from the stage to the

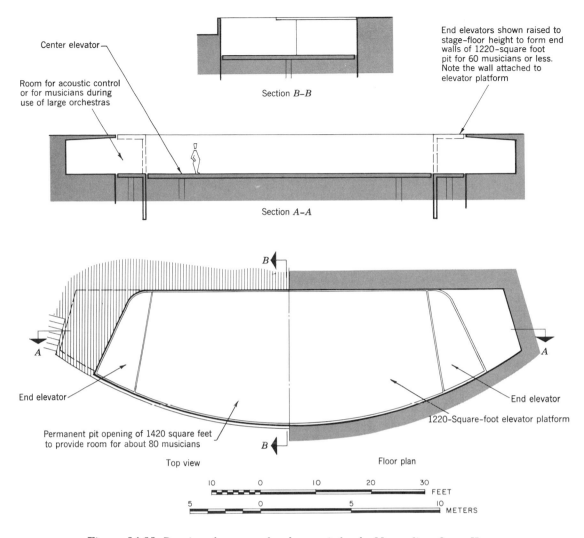

Figure 14.11. Drawing of a proposed orchestra pit for the Metropolitan Opera House, Lincoln Center for the Performing Arts. Drawing prepared for the architect, Wallace K. Harrison of the firm Harrison and Abramovitz, by Bolt Beranek and Newman Inc.

railing on the audience side, at the centerline, and a sizable gulf is thereby created between the singers and the audience. Some conductors prefer an open pit so that they can be seen easily by the audience.

A slight overhang of the pit by the forestage is not objectionable acoustically and has the advantage of increasing the reflecting area of the stage between the singers and the audience. An overhang of about 3 feet is found in the present Metropolitan Opera House, as well as in the opera houses recently built in Hamburg, Mannheim, Cologne, Gelsenkirchen, and East Berlin. La Scala in Milan has a sliding forestage with a minimum overhang of about 3.5 feet and a maximum overhang of about 12 feet. Several of the conductors who were interviewed expressed themselves strongly against adjusting the overhang at La Scala to more than 3.5 feet.

An open pit has been designed by Bolt Beranek and Newman Inc. as part of a study for the proposed Metropolitan Opera House in New York (shown in Figure 14.11). Its average width is 21.5 feet. There is no overhang on the stage side. The floor is made up of three elevators whose heights can be adjusted individually.

The open area of the pit, with the three elevators at the lower level, is 1420 square feet. (The open area of the pit in the existing Metropolitan Opera House is 1000 square feet and that of the Vienna Staatsoper is 1150 square feet.) If there are 80 musicians in the pit, each one will have an average of 17.7 square feet of floor area. The elevators at the two ends can be raised to form end walls, thereby reducing the pit area to 1220 square feet.

A special feature of the pit in Figure 14.11 is the overhangs at each end, which form small rooms. These rooms are planned to lie behind the French horns at one end and the percussion instruments at the other. Sound-absorbing materials can be included on some of the surfaces of these small rooms to prevent them from ringing like empty barrels when the pit is not occupied by an orchestra. For a large orchestra—for Wagner, say, or Berg— these spaces can serve some of the musicians. If desired, solid panels can cover the sound-absorbing materials when a full orchestra performs.

The wall at the stage edge of the pit is vertical and hard so as not to absorb sound. It is intended that the double basses be placed against this wall to provide strong bass tone.

Sunken pit, covered

The antithesis of the open pit is the covered pit designed by Wagner for the Festspielhaus in Bayreuth, Germany. It is partly buried beneath the stage and the remaining portion is nearly completely covered by an overhang. The Bayreuth pit is used with a very large orchestra in a house that has a relatively long reverberation time. Comments about the pit from Herbert von Karajan, Bruno Walter, Joseph Wechsberg, Wieland Wagner, Irving Kolodin, and Dimitri Mitropoulos are contained in the discussion of the Festspielhaus in Chapter 6.

Except for Wagner's music, the Bayreuth pit is not considered satisfactory. The string tone is muffled and the orchestra takes on an eerie sound.

S. Hughes, writing in *Great Opera Houses* [Wiedenfeld and Nicholson, London (1956)], comments on the limited influence of Wagner's pit:

It is interesting, in passing, to note how remarkably little influence all Wagner's high-flown ideas about theatrical architecture and its contribution to the Music of the Future have had on posterity. Wherever, since the construction of the Bayreuth Theatre, a new opera house has been built in Europe, it has been on the familiar 18th century Italian model [except for the Prinzregententheater in Munich]. We have heard strangely little about the virtues of the "mystic gulf" of the sunken orchestra pit.

Sunken pit, open

There are two types of open sunken pit: one is a duplicate of the Bayreuth pit, but with the cover removed, and one is simply an extension of a standard pit under the stage. The acoustics of the two are much the same: some of the instruments are exposed and the rest are in a "box." To the best of my knowledge, no existing pit that is in large part buried under a platform gives the orchestra the natural kind of sound heard in the opera houses of Vienna, Milan, Paris, or London.

It seems clear that if a new opera house is designed in which primarily Italian opera is to be performed, the pit should be like that of Figure 14.11. For opera in the Wagnerian style, a Bayreuth pit is perhaps the best choice.

15
Philharmonic Hall,
The Lincoln Center for the Performing Arts

At 10:00 o'clock Monday morning, May 28, 1962, Seiji Ozawa, a gifted young assistant conductor of the New York Philharmonic Orchestra for the 1961–1962 season, raised his baton before the 106 men and women of the Orchestra and the brass and woodwinds proclaimed the eloquent opening chords of the *Third Symphony* of Brahms. Philharmonic Hall—whose stage until moments before had been a swarm of workmen installing temporary doors, wall paneling, stage platforms, chairs, and music racks—suddenly resounded to its first symphonic music! As the strings entered and the magnificent leaping theme developed in tutti, it was apparent that the hall would fulfill its designers' great expectations and that the new home for the Philharmonic would be an acoustical success.

Much still remained to be done; tuning week had been scheduled far enough in advance of the actual completion of construction to permit the critical adjustment of details that can make a good hall into a great one. The reflecting panels behind the gold mesh screen surrounding the stage were not yet installed; the optimum height for the stage canopy had not been determined; the best arrangement of orchestra risers had still to be decided; and there was still the necessity to discover and correct any slight echoes or other anomalies before the public came to the hall. In short, the hall was to undergo a "shakedown cruise" well in advance of its christening, at the first formal concert on September 23, 1962. This was the very purpose of the nine "rehearsals" of the orchestra and the flurry of activity that constituted tuning week. But before we go further let us become acquainted with the hall and its goals.

Philharmonic Hall is the first building to be completed in New York's new Lincoln Center for the Performing Arts, the most ambitious and exciting civic-cultural development in the history of our country. Comprising a concert hall, an opera house, two theaters, a school for the performing arts, a library, and a host of ancillary facilities, Lincoln Center is scheduled for completion before the end of the 1960's. It should play a leading role in advancing the performing arts in a setting that promises to be nothing short of ideal.

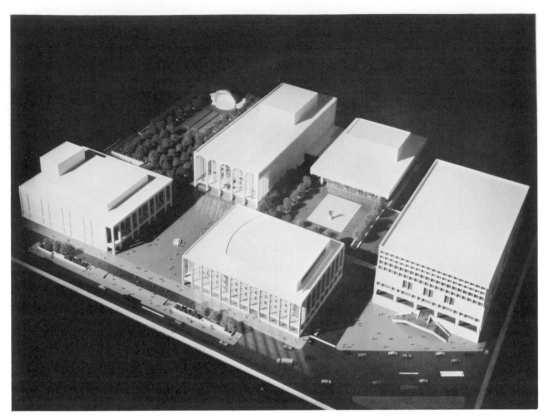

Figure 15.1. Architectural model as of April 1962 of Lincoln Center for the Performing Arts as seen from the east. Clockwise from the left are the New York State Theater, Damrosch Park and Bandshell, Metropolitan Opera House, Vivian Beaumont Theater and Library-Museum of the Performing Arts, Juilliard School, and Philharmonic Hall.

Preliminary architectural planning for Philharmonic Hall and the Metropolitan Opera House began in 1956, when Wallace K. Harrison of the architectural firm of Harrison and Abramovitz arranged a conference in New York City between the Lincoln Center Board of Directors and a group of architects and consultants, to discuss the programs for these two buildings and to exchange ideas on the tasks that lay ahead. Max Abramovitz was designated architect for the concert hall. Bolt Beranek and Newman Inc. was named acoustical consultant to work with the architect. Hope Bagenal of Leaside, England, was engaged as advisory acoustical consultant. I determined to accelerate the study described in Chapter 1, and to expand it to include many halls throughout the world, so that the most complete and up-to-date knowledge would be brought into the acoustical design of Philharmonic Hall.

At the outset of the planning for Philharmonic Hall, our staff had to depend largely upon the acoustical literature as the guidebook, since no hall intended primarily for concerts had been constructed in the United States since before World War II. By 1957, however, the first results of the present study of 54 concert and opera halls became available, and their implications could be translated into specific recommendations to the architect. By the fall of 1958 the acoustical consultant was in a position to make confident recommendations about the cubic volume, the basic shape and dimensions, the size of the audience area, and the stage design for Philharmonic Hall. The preliminary plans of the architect were approved by the Building Committee in July 1959 and the major features of the design have remained fixed since that date.

GOALS

It is vital that the goals for any important concert hall be clearly stated before serious planning is undertaken. Lincoln Center, the architect, and the acoustical consultant agreed from the start that the goals were three.

First, Philharmonic Hall was to accommodate principally the regular repertoires of the New York Philharmonic Orchestra, the Boston Symphony Orchestra, and the Philadelphia Orchestra. Although other uses were contemplated, it was not to be an "all-purpose hall." A large pipe organ and a sound-amplification system for speech were planned, but the acoustics of the hall for symphonic concerts were not to be comprised in favor of either organ or speech.

Second, the seating capacity of the hall was to be no greater than is consistent with good acoustics.

Third, no effort was to be spared that would help Philharmonic Hall to assume a place among the best halls in the world—halls like those in Boston, Vienna, Amsterdam, and Basel.

The views of the New York Philharmonic Society were presented in a letter addressed by the late George Judd, Jr., to the architect on April 20, 1959.

Dear Mr. Abramovitz:

I should like to confirm by this letter the Society's position relative to the acoustics of the new Philharmonic Hall.

Not being technicians in the field, we shall not state our desires in figures or formulas but shall relate them to acoustics of halls in existence including those at Boston, Symphony Hall; London, Royal Festival Hall;

Amsterdam, Concertgebouw; Vienna, Grosser Musikvereinssaal; Caracas, Aula Magna; and Buffalo, Kleinhans Hall. Our choice is based upon the experience in these halls of conducting or listening on the part of our Music Director, Mr. Leonard Bernstein, as well as the consensus obtained from numerous visiting conductors. In addition, performances have been heard by the management of the Society and by members of our Board, including the writer, in these halls.

Based upon the above, in the Society's judgment, the acoustics of the Hall should approximate as closely as possible those of the Boston Symphony Hall, when filled, but in no event should the reverberation time be shorter. We feel the reverberation time of London Festival Hall too short, while that of the Vienna Grosser Musikvereinssaal and Amsterdam Concertgebouw may be slightly longer than is necessary. We understand, however, that it is much more feasible to adjust from a longer reverberation to a shorten than vice-versa. If this is true, special care should be taken not to run any danger of too short a time. . . .

As stated before, our views are based upon experience in existing halls. We must look to yourself as the architect and Messrs. Bolt Beranek and Newman as the acousticians to translate these desires into the technical formulas necessary to produce the corresponding best results in the new hall.

George Judd, Jr., Manager

SOME OF THE DESIGN CONSIDERATIONS

Chapter 14 discussed in detail the major steps in the design of a concert hall or opera house. These steps were followed throughout the planning of Philharmonic Hall. Listed below are some of the important design considerations which were established early and which formed the basis for specific detailed recommendations as the project progressed.

Cubic volume

Investigation of some halls that are successful homes for major symphony orchestras revealed that their cubic volumes are relatively low. Philharmonic Hall, therefore, could not be too large if the third goal named above was to be achieved. Table 15.1 gives cubic volumes of four excellent halls that were suggested as appropriate models for Philharmonic Hall. The median of their volume is 600,000 cubic feet.

At the time the plans were being considered, no hall whose cubic volume was greater than 850,000 cubic feet—which is Carnegie's size—had impressed any of the conductors or music critics as a satisfactory acoustical model. The musicians spoke of the sound in large halls as "muddy" or "barn-like." There was no question that a cubic volume as small as 600,000 cubic feet would accommodate far too few seats for a city the size of New York. An absolute limit of 850,000 cubic feet was recommended for the size of the hall, a limit that exceeds by about 40 per cent the median of the four excellent halls in Table 15.1. The compromise on cubic volume was accepted in the expectation that the application of new principles and techniques could bring about the intimacy heretofore so closely dependent on small size.

Table 15.1   Cubic volumes and mid-frequency reverberation times
of four excellent concert halls

Name	Volume cubic feet	T_{mid} seconds
Basel, Stadt-Casino	370,000	1.7
Vienna, Grosser Musikvereinssaal	530,000	2.05
Boston, Symphony Hall	662,000	1.8
Amsterdam, Concertgebouw	663,000	2.0
MEDIAN	600,000	1.9

Liveness

On the basis of the information on liveness given in Chapter 9, and in accordance with the request contained in the Philharmonic Society's letter of April 20, 1959, it was recommended that the reverberation time of the hall with full audience at mid-frequencies be between 1.85 and 1.95 seconds.

The mid-frequency reverberation times of the four comparison halls, with full audience, are also given in Table 15.1.

Warmth

The interviews with musicians had established that the best-liked halls are relatively rich in bass. It was recommended that the bass ratio (see Chapter 10) be 1.2, or even slightly higher. In order to achieve this ratio, virtually no thin wood could be used in the hall unless it was cemented securely to a solid backing, with the exception of some wood strips around the stage.

Audience area

If we assume a cubic volume of 850,000 cubic feet, a reverberation time of 1.9 seconds at mid-frequencies with full audience, carpet covering part of the aisles, some wood strips around the stage, and seating area for the orchestra of about 2000 square feet, we can calculate from Table 14.4 that the audience area, S_A, must not exceed about 18,000 square feet.

No specification was made for the number of seats to be contained in the hall; however, once the allowable total seating area is established within the framework of a given acoustical design, considerations of safety and comfort determine the actual number of seats. Table 15.2 shows the numbers of seats that would fill an audience area of 18,000 square feet according to the area per seat allowed in eight comparison halls. If the seating could be as crowded and the aisles as narrow as nineteenth century standards permitted, then as many as 3000 seats might have been squeezed into Philharmonic Hall. However, an area per person of about 6.6 square feet (including aisles) was considered necessary by the architect and owner for the comfort and safety of New York audiences. As finally designed, Philharmonic Hall seats 2644 persons with the normal 40-foot-deep stage, and somewhat fewer when the stage is extended into the audience area.

Table 15.2   Relation between area per seat and the number of seats that can occupy 18,000 square feet

*Area per seat** square feet*	*Number of seats possible in Philharmonic Hall*
5.7 (Boston)	3160
6.3 (Vienna)	2860
6.5 (San Francisco)	2770
7.0 (Stuttgart)	2570
7.1 (London, Royal Festival)	2540
7.4 (Buffalo)	2430
7.6 (Caracas)	2370
8.5 (Bonn)	2120

* Includes allowance for aisles up to 3.5 feet (see Appendix 3).

Intimacy

Because the most important attribute of the acoustics in a concert hall is intimacy, it was recommended that sound-reflecting panels be hung over the stage and the front half of the auditorium at such a height that the initial-time-delay gap for sound from the concertmaster's position would not exceed 23 milliseconds at the center of the main floor. Reflecting panels of this kind should cover more than 50 per cent of the projected area in which they hang and should approach as near the side walls as the architect feels is aesthetically acceptable. It was also recommended that the hall be as nearly rectangular in cross sections and as narrow as possible. The incorporation of these features in the design would ensure that the sequence of sound reflections—or acoustical texture—would be conducive to clarity, good attack, brilliant sound, and adequate fullness of tone.

Balconies

It was recommended that the balconies extend forward on the side walls in order to reduce both the depth of the balcony overhang at the back and the effective acoustical width of the hall. The balcony overhangs were to conform as closely as possible to the recommendations of Chapter 12, especially Figure 12.8(a).

Stage dimensions

In order to assure ample space for chorus and orchestra without sacrificing good ensemble, balance, and blend, it was recommended that the stage be no wider than 55 feet at the front and no less than 48 feet deep at the centerline; it should be extendable to accommodate a large chorus in addition to the orchestra. The stage dimensions finally chosen are somewhat wider and shallower, almost identical to those of Carnegie Hall—in deference to the request of the New York Philharmonic Society.

Stage canopy and side-wall design

To assure good ensemble it was recommended that a large reflecting canopy be erected over the orchestra at a height above the front of the stage no greater than 27 feet. It was anticipated that slight changes in the stage acoustics would be necessary during the tuning period and also, perhaps, from time to time throughout the life of the hall. For this purpose, it was recommended that the height of the canopy and the angles of the individual panels in it be adjustable. It was also recommended that an acoustically transparent but visually opaque screen be constructed 4 feet inside the structural wall surrounding the stage. Splayed sound-reflecting panels were to be installed behind the screen where they would not be seen, so as to reflect sound across the stage and to project it into the auditorium.

Additional sound-absorbing materials

No special sound-absorbing materials were to be used in the hall. However, in order to eliminate as far as possible undesirable changes in reverberation time resulting from partial occupancy, fully upholstered seats and carpeting under the seats were recommended. The acoustical recommendation called for no carpets in the aisles. In order to permit a reduction of the reverberation time for those occasions in which clarity of speech or musical drama was essential, it was recommended that draw curtains be provided for the upper spaces at the sides of the stage. For adjustment of balance and blend, a small amount of sound-absorbing material might be added in back of the visual screen behind certain sections of the orchestra. Draw curtains were recommended for this space also. The need for such materials was to be determined during the tuning period.

Ventilation noise

It was recommended that the steady noise from ventilation not exceed the lower curve of Figure 12.2 at any seat in the hall. Care was needed in the design of the mechanical system to ensure that the air supply and return ducts that serve the main hall would not transmit either noise from the air-conditioning equipment or any other noise to the hall and that the air-conditioning outlets would not generate an appreciable amount of noise.

Noise from exterior sources

Intermittent noises in the hall from sources outside the hall should not exceed the upper curve of Figure 12.2 in the lowest two octave bands, and

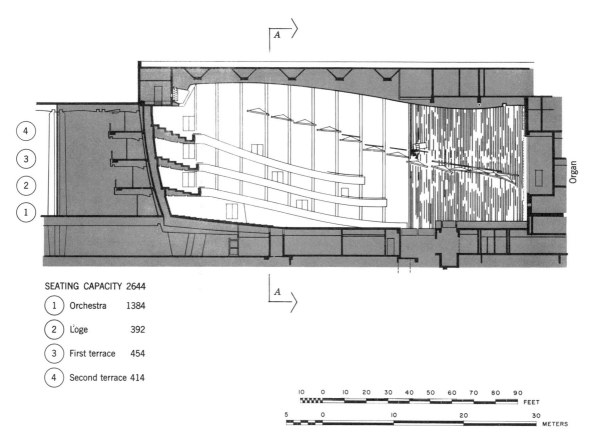

Figure 15.2. Longitudinal section of Philharmonic Hall along the centerline.

SEATING CAPACITY 2644

1 Orchestra 1384

2 Loge 392

3 First terrace 454

4 Second terrace 414

the lower curve in the other bands. Three important sources of external noise that required careful consideration were street noise, the nearby subway, and jet aircraft.

Sound system

A sound system of quality adequate for radio broadcasting was required for the amplification of speech and solo singing voice, and for cinema. No provision was made for amplification of orchestral music or for drama.

THE FINAL DESIGN

The final architectural design of Philharmonic Hall, drawn to emphasize the acoustical features, is shown in Figures 15.2 through 15.12. Figure 15.3 shows a photograph of the unpainted, unfinished hall taken during tuning week. The dominant architectural features of the completed hall are the glittering gold leaf of the canopy overhead, the gilded faces of the loge and the two terraces above it, sweeping like great arms downward toward the stage, and the gold screen around the stage. The side walls and ceiling are

Figure 15.3. Photograph of Philharmonic Hall, taken during tuning week from the rear corner of the loge.

deep blue, and the seats are upholstered in four shades of gold. Sight lines and thus "hearing lines" are excellent.

Organ

The organ in Philharmonic Hall is to be used in ensemble as well as for recitals. It will accompany a chorus on the stage of the auditorium, perform in concerts with a symphony orchestra, and join with orchestra and chorus in large choral works. To be effective for such uses, it must be so located that sufficient sound from it reaches the conductor, the members of the orchestra, and the singers in the chorus. It must be near enough to the chorus and orchestra for all three to be heard in good ensemble by both the conductor and the audience.

Careful analysis showed that to achieve these goals and ensure balance with the ensemble, placing the organ in the rear wall of the stage was more satisfactory than either splitting it into two parts and placing one part on either side of the stage or locating it in the ceiling above the front of the stage. The stage canopy can be raised above the position shown in Figure 15.2, nearly to the stage ceiling, to expose all the pipes during organ recitals. However, when the stage canopy is in its normal position, the open spaces in it permit the sound to penetrate satisfactorily for organ used as an accompaniment to chorus or orchestra.

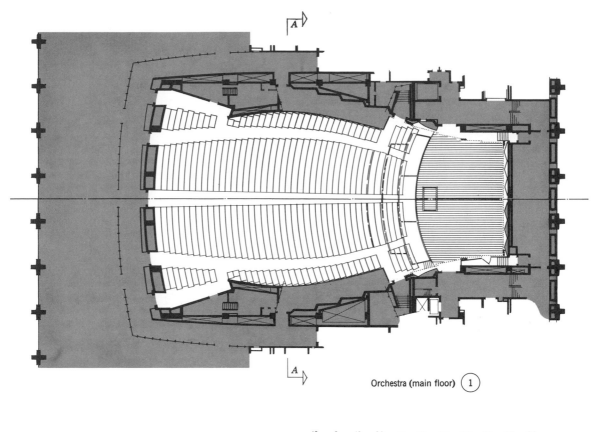

A

A

Orchestra (main floor) (1)

Figure 15.4. Plan of the main floor (known in the United States as the "orchestra"). The first balcony, called the loge, descends to floor level at the front of the main floor. By removal of several rows of seats the depth of the stage can be increased from its basic depth of 40 feet at the centerline to either 48 or 56.5 feet. The elevators can be dropped to form an orchestra pit up to 16 feet deep. The small elevator at the front center of the stage may be used for bringing the piano, organ console, and orchestra chairs up from the storage space to the stage.

Noise

The measures taken to control earth-borne and structure-borne subway noise and vibration include lead-asbestos vibration-isolation pads under all columns of the building, a vibration-isolation joint in many of the exterior and interior walls and partitions at or near the basement level, and a somewhat resilient lining (glass-fiber pads plus gravel) around all underground exterior walls where the subway is close to the building.

Measurements made in 1961 indicated that vibrations would not be felt, and that passing subway trains would probably not be heard inside the hall—even during very quiet intervals when no music is being played. The listeners confirmed these predictions during tuning week.

In order to exclude aircraft and street noise, the ceiling of the hall is sus-

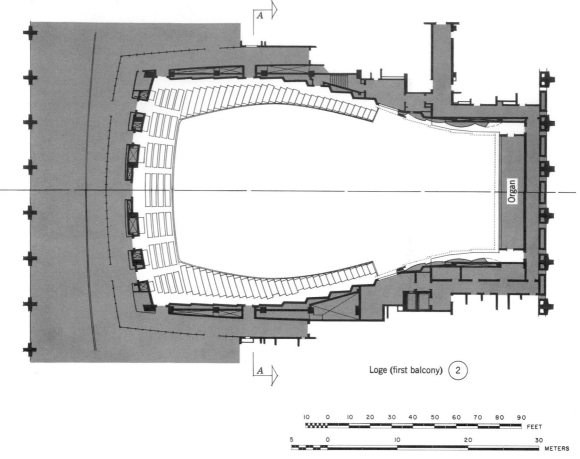

Loge (first balcony) ②

10	0	10	20	30	40	50	60	70	80	90	

FEET

5	0		10		20		30	

METERS

Figure 15.5. Plan of the first balcony (loge). Television, radio, and observers' booths are located at both sides of the hall behind windows, and about 50 feet from the rear wall of the stage.

pended from elastic hangers, resonant at a very low frequency, and the side walls and entrance doors are separated from the street by two layers of glass.

The ventilation system is quieted by a combination of packaged sound-attenuating units at the outlets of the fans, linings on all ducts, and adequate closures between the fan rooms and the auditorium. Acoustical measurements, performed on the manufacturer's premises, assured freedom from noise at the grilles of the auditorium diffusers.

The walls of the auditorium are 8-inch concrete block. Surrounding the hall at each level, a glass-walled corridor excludes noise originating in the lobbies. The sounds of the tuning of instruments are excluded from the hall by inner floating walls and floors in the tuning rooms behind the stage.

Acoustical flexibility

Consideration was given in the design of the hall to the probability that musical tastes and preferences will continue to evolve with the passage

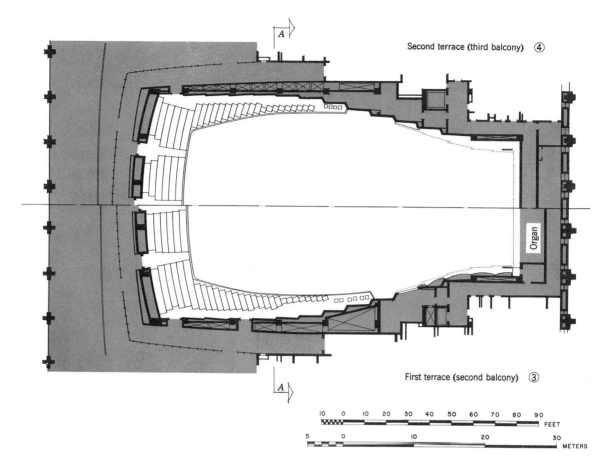

Figure 15.6. Half-plans of the second and third balconies (first and second terraces).
Each balcony overhang covers four or five rows of seats underneath.

of time. The reverberation time of the hall can be shortened by the addition of sound-absorbing materials above the hanging panels, either over the stage or over the audience, or lengthened by the removal of carpets from the aisles; for this purpose, the floor beneath the carpet is rubber tile. The stage can be enlarged by means of the lifts to accommodate larger groups of performers. Hearing conditions on the stage can be changed by adjustments in the height and details of the canopy and by modifications of the sound-reflecting surfaces behind the visually opaque but acoustically open screen at the sides and back of the stage. Philharmonic Hall is probably the first hall to be designed as a living hall—a hall whose acoustics can be changed as tastes change, without gross or visible changes in the structure.

Physical properties of the hall

Length of hall, projected horizontally from the front of the
        40-ft-deep stage to the most distant listener   130 ft
Width of the upper hall at the transverse section *A-A*
        (Figure 15.6) measured between the walls   106 ft

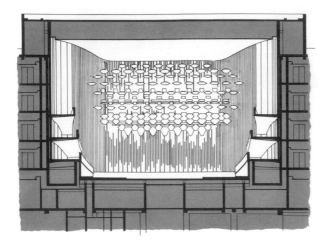

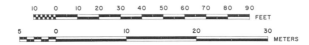

Figure 15.7. Transverse section *A-A* (see Figure 15.2) showing the cross sections of the three balconies and the rectangular cross section of the hall.

Distance between faces of loge at transverse section *A-A* (Figure 15.5)	80 ft
Height of the ceiling at transverse section *A-A* (Figure 15.7)	66 ft
Area of the audience seating, without aisles (40-ft-deep stage assumed)	13,500 sq ft
Area of audience seating, with aisles up to 3.5 ft in width (40-ft-deep stage assumed) (S_A)	17,150 sq ft
Total area of floor, including all aisle areas but not the 40-ft-deep stage area	19,280 sq ft
Width of organ-chamber opening	50 ft
Height of organ-chamber opening	26 ft
Height of organ chamber, inside	27 ft
Depth of organ chamber	11 ft
Height of lower edge of organ opening above flat stage	12 ft
Width of stage at rear, inside acoustic screen	52 ft
Width of stage 20 ft from rear, inside acoustic screen	56 ft
Width of stage 40 ft from rear, inside acoustic screen	61 ft
Area of 40-ft-deep stage (S_O)	2,050 sq ft
Area of 48-ft-deep stage	2,600 sq ft
Area of 56.5-ft deep stage	3,100 sq ft
Sum of S_A and S_O (above): ($S_T = S_A + S_O$)	19,200 sq ft
Volume (V)	865,000 cu ft
V/S_T	45 ft
Number of seats with 40-ft-deep stage (N_A)	2,644
S_A/N_A (area per seat, including 3.5 ft of aisles)	6.5 sq ft

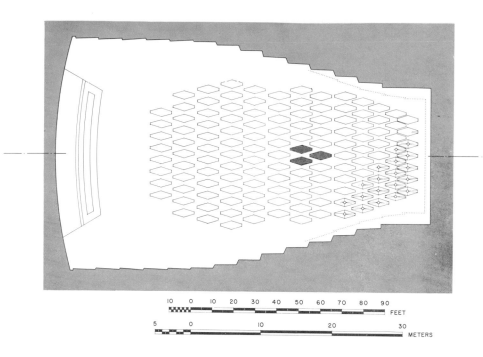

Figure 15.8. Plan of the ceiling viewed from below, showing only the gilded sound-reflecting panels. Note that three hanging panels in the center are rendered acoustically transparent for the sound-reinforcement loudspeakers.

Row-to-row seat spacing:

Main floor, center	33.5 in.
Loge, center	38 in.
Terraces 1 and 2, center	36 in.

Seat-arm to seat-arm spacing:

Main floor, center	21–23 in.
Loge, center	25 in.
Terraces 1 and 2, center	20–23 in.

Ceiling	1½-in. plaster on metal lath suspended from rubber mounts
Hanging panels	1½ to 2-in. plaster on metal lath
Side walls	plaster on solid cement block
Floors	rubber tile
Carpets	on all aisles of the main floor and loge; none under the seating
Stage floor	2-in. wood over wooden joists over 3-ft air space
Stage height	42 in.
Seating	top of seat bottom and backrest upholstered in porous mohair cloth, over thick, porous polyurethane pads, over springs; underseat is metal, perforated with six 2-in. holes and covered with porous mohair. Rear of backrest solid, covered with mohair.

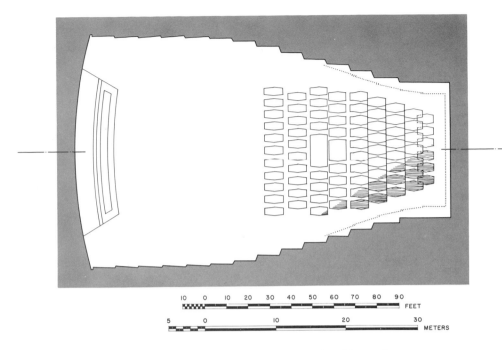

Figure 15.9. Plan of the second level of sound-reflecting panels, painted deep blue, and located about 2 feet above the gilded panels, where they will blend in with the blue of the ceiling.

Credits

Architect	Max Abramovitz of the firm Harrison and Abramovitz
Acoustical consultant	Bolt Beranek and Newman Inc.*
Advisory acoustical consultant	Hope Bagenal
Architectural seating consultant	Ben Schlanger
Theater seat design consultant	Donald Wallance
Lighting consultant	Richard Kelly and Associates
Interior design consultant	Donald Oenslager
Mechanical and electrical engineers	Syska and Hennessy, Inc.
Structural engineers	Ammann and Whitney
General contractor	Fuller, Turner, Walsh and Slattery

THE TUNING PERIOD

From the inception of the project, it was anticipated that certain features of this vast undertaking would benefit from an opportunity for fine-scale adjustment or revisions prior to the finishing. In the present state of the acoustical craft, it is possible to predict accurately the required cubic volume, the area to be allowed for the seating, the general shape and basic proportions of the hall, the dimensions of the stage, the allowable amounts of carpet and other absorptive materials, and the basic acoustical design for a reflecting canopy above the stage and front part of the hall.

* Leo L. Beranek, principal in charge, F. Russell Johnson, project manager. Other senior staff members who participated were David L. Klepper, Laymon N. Miller and Ronald L. McKay.

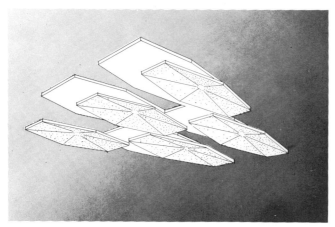

Figure 15.10. Perspective view of a typical section of suspended panels, looking upward.

Acoustics has not yet developed a way to determine, accurately and in advance, the specifications for the fine details—the orientation of the reflecting panels around the stage, the exact height and proportion of open area of the canopy, the angles of the individual panels in the canopy or around the stage.

Consequently, in 1957, a tuning week was planned, to be conducted at an appropriate time near the completion of the hall, with the New York Philharmonic Orchestra to perform and with their music director, Leonard Bernstein, in attendance. During this week, refinements of the acoustics were to be made, to suit the tastes of the musicians whose home the hall would be.

Tuning week

Tuning week started on Monday, May 28, 1962. The adjustments of the acoustics were made with the help of the Philharmonic Orchestra and a group of highly qualified listeners, working together with the acoustical consultant, the architect, and the building contractor. So far as I know, in no major American Hall, from the Academy of Music in Philadelphia, opened in 1857, to the Ford Auditorium in Detroit, opened in 1956, have the acoustics been adjusted experimentally prior to its opening. Indeed, it was not until about 1935 that satisfactory electronic measuring equipment existed at all, and not until 1950 did the modern magnetic tape recorder become a practical adjunct to acoustical testing.

The Philharmonic Orchestra was engaged for one week to play nine rehearsals. The repertoire included selections from all the principal musical periods, and called for various sizes and combinations of instrumental and vocal groups. The principal test pieces, some of which were repeated several times during the week, were: Brahms, *Variations on a Theme by Haydn;* Ravel, *Daphnis and Chlöe;* Lalo, *Symphonie Espagnole;* Gabrieli, *Canzoni*

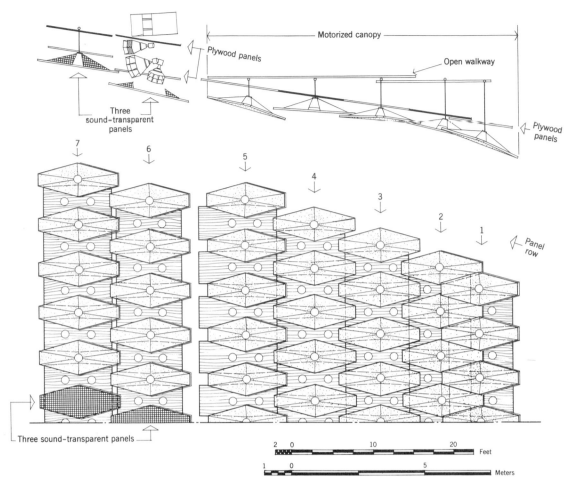

Figure 15.11. Details of the motorized canopy over the 40-foot stage and the fixed panels over the first seven rows of seats. *Above:* section showing the individual panel slopes and the loudspeakers. *Below:* reflected ceiling plan.

for Brass Choirs; Bach, *Brandenburg Concerto No. 5;* Haydn, *Symphony No. 83;* Mozart, *Symphony No. 41;* and Moussorgsky-Ravel, *Pictures at an Exhibition.* Some contemporary works performed were: Stravinsky, *Petrouchka* and *Capriccio for Piano and Orchestra;* Webern, *Six Pieces for Orchestra;* Piston, *Symphony No. 3;* Bloch, *Schelomo;* and Britten, *Young Person's Guide to the Orchestra.* In all, compositions of 30 different composers were played.

Since our acoustical adjustments would have significance only for the occupied hall, one of the important problems of tuning week was how to provide an "audience" of 2600 people. The corridors, stairways and approaches to the building were not yet completed—construction went on, only occasionally interrupted, during tuning week—and entry by a large number of people was deemed unsafe. Even if a live audience could have been arranged, there would have been the difficulties of carrying on experiments in a "goldfish bowl" and of keeping a succession of audiences quiet

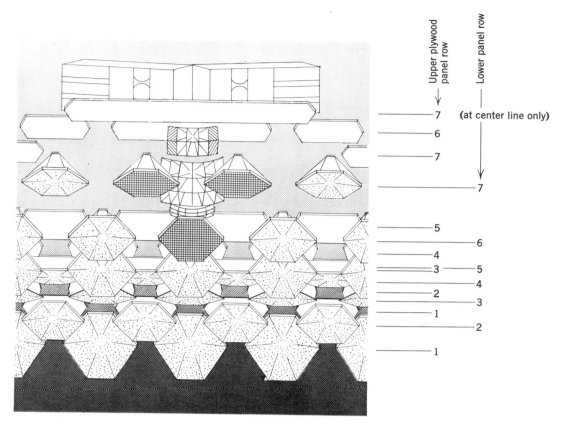

Upper plywood panel row

Lower panel row

7 (at center line only)

6

7

7

5

6

4

5

3

4

2

3

1

2

1

Figure 15.12. Front view of the loudspeaker cluster shown in relation to panel rows 6 and 7, and the three acoustically transparent panels.

and entertained for a total of 22 hours during the week. It was of no little significance, moreover, that the ventilation and air-conditioning equipment were not yet in operation and the hall would have been virtually uninhabitable for an audience on some of the 90-degree days of tuning week. Consequently, a synthetic audience, real only in the acoustical sense, was provided. Each seat could be "occupied" by a flexible, glass-fiber mat, 30 by 40 inches and 1 inch thick (shown in Figure 15.13), which was calculated to absorb approximately the same amount of sound as a seated person, at least at frequencies above 400 cycles per second. Of course these "instant people" could not applaud—but neither could they cough or interrupt the proceedings!

The chief advantage of the simulated audience was that the audience occupancy could be held constant throughout the week, and consequently all evaluations of acoustical changes could be made under similar conditions. These glass-fiber batts could be easily and quickly installed or removed, and a crew of carpenters and workmen was available throughout tuning week to effect the required changes at a moment's notice.

Acoustical measurements were made at nearly every rehearsal during

Figure 15.13. Each seat could be occupied by a flexible glass-fiber mat measuring 30 by 40 inches and 1 inch thick. These "instant people" simulated the acoustical absorption of a real audience.

the week, using as sound sources impulse noises produced by a pistol and a small yachting cannon; continuous and interrupted "white noises" in octave frequency bands; warbled tones; pulses of sine waves; and the sound of the orchestra itself, as described below. Measurements were made of the reverberation time at 25 frequencies between 40 and 10,000 cycles per second for the hall empty and with simulated audience, of the initial-time-delay gaps at seats on the main floor and in the first terrace, and of the ratios of direct-to-reverberant sound intensities at several locations in the hall.

Acoustical measurements made with electronic instruments alone do not demonstrate all the important acoustical characteristics of a hall. Tests must also be made with the orchestra as the source of sound. In order to include in proper balance all the frequencies that can be produced by the full orchestra, special orchestral sounds were needed. T. J. Schultz of Bolt Beranek and Newman prepared and orchestrated a set of chords for performance both by full orchestra and by sections of the orchestra—utilizing the entire frequency range of the orchestra and with the frequencies of the

Figure 15.14. Photograph of part of the original score for Daniel Pinkham's *Catacoustical Measures.*

individual instruments distributed very evenly throughout the musical scale.

The thought occurred that if this test were ever to be repeated in a hall with a real audience, these discords would be better received if they were made part of a composition that would in itself have musical interest. Bolt Beranek and Newman, therefore, commissioned composer Daniel Pinkham to incorporate Dr. Schultz's chords into a special musical composition, about four minutes in length, to be used as an acoustical test in both empty and occupied halls. Delivered a few days before tuning week, Pinkham's *Catacoustical Measures,** has proved to be a lively diversion as well as a valuable tool in the testing of concert-hall acoustics. A few bars of Pinkham's manuscript are shown in Figure 15.14. The Pinkham *Measures* and the Brahms *Variations* became the standard pieces for acoustical tests during tuning week, and they were repeated after any significant acoustical change was made in the hall.

---

* Webster's defines *catacoustics* as "the science of reflected sounds or echoes." [*Webster's New International Dictionary*, Second Edition.]

After each acoustic change these two pieces were recorded on two 2-channel magnetic-tape recorders, connected to the electrical output of two binaural "dummy" heads. The dummy heads were specially designed to approximate the acoustical properties of the human head, and each of them was equipped with two miniature condenser microphones for ears. The binaural heads were mounted on small boxes placed on two seats, one on the main floor, and one in the first terrace. With these tape recordings it is possible to recreate the conditions of listening at two locations in the hall and to hear again the music as it sounded during a particular phase of the experiments.

The special listening panel who judged the quality of the acoustics at each phase of the tuning consisted of Leonard Bernstein, Music Director of the Orchestra, Seiji Ozawa, John Canarina, and Maurice Peress, Assistant Conductors of the Orchestra in the 1961–1962 season, Carlos Moseley, Manager of the Orchestra, Stefan Bauer-Mengelberg, Henry Friend of the Juilliard School of Music, John McClure of Columbia Records, Vincent Rousseau of the Architect's office, and five members of Bolt Beranek and Newman Inc. Acting as chairman of the group was Reginald Allen, Executive Director of Lincoln Center for the Performing Arts.

From time to time, this panel was joined by Erich Leinsdorf, Leopold Stokowski, Andre Kostelanetz, Bruno Zirato, and by several of New York's music critics.

It was the pleasure of everyone in the listening panel to discover that there was very good agreement about what was heard and what was inaudible at any given time. The various changes were evaluated by the group in conference after each hour of performance. There was no doubt in the mind of any of the listeners that the results achieved on the final day proved the value of tuning week. And all agreed on the effects of even subtle changes in the acoustics of the hall. The notion that acoustics is a personal matter and that it cannot be properly evaluated even by qualified listeners was thoroughly exploded. The divergences in the musicians' and music critics' judgment on the acoustical quality of some of the halls in Chapter 6 undoubtedly stems from the fact that the listeners were comparing different performances, generally by different orchestras under different conductors, from different positions in the hall. When well-qualified listeners have the opportunity to listen to the same music under identical conditions their judgments are in remarkably close agreement. The comments of this special listening panel were recorded and used as the basis for the improvements made in the hall during and following tuning week.

In addition to the special panel, the members of the orchestra were invited to submit criticism. Three times during the week, the players filled out "comment cards" and returned them for tabulation and study. Their remarks were entered on a master diagram of the stage, from which it was possible to learn which sections of the orchestra had difficulty hearing either themselves or other sections of the orchestra. Their comments led to changes in the height of the canopy, in the orientation and number of the individual panels in the canopy, and in the number and splay of the reflecting panels in the side walls of the stage.

Detailed changes made during tuning week

The rehearsal on the first morning was played without audience, real or simulated. The appearance of the hall at that time can be seen in Figure 15.3. The principal impression at this session was of the long reverberation time—nearly 2.8 seconds at mid-frequencies. The orchestra members made their first reports about the sound on the stage, and as a result the stage canopy was lowered. In the audience, the percussion and brass were too loud. To remedy this imbalance, the stepped risers provided beneath the percussion section were removed, and some sound-absorbing materials were placed behind the visual screen near the brasses to reduce their loudness relative to that of the woodwinds.

During most of tuning week, the acoustic absorption of the pipe organ, which had not yet been installed, was simulated by placing inside the organ chamber 400 square feet of 1-inch glass-fiber blanket and 800 square feet of ¼-inch plywood with air space behind it. This simulation was intended to anticipate the absorbing effect of the organ, but it was found in the course of tuning week to be excessive at low frequencies.

On Monday afternoon, the synthetic audience was installed. The music that night was played in an environment of reduced reverberation—2.2 sec-

Figure 15.15. Members of the special listening panel and visitors judging the sound in the loge of Philharmonic Hall during tuning week. *Left to right—front:* Leonard Bernstein, John McClure, and Leo L. Beranek; *rear:* Bruno Zirato and Walfredo Toscanini.

onds at mid-frequencies. The first adjustment of the canopy over the stage was promising, but the results fell short of the desired goal—the musicians still complained of being unable to hear each other and some string-brass imbalance was still noted. Also, some deficiency in the bass was noted and a slight echo was observed in several parts of the hall.

A dramatic moment occurred when Leopold Stokowski, who was present during this session, asked if he might conduct the orchestra. Playing only the two opening chords of Beethoven's *Eroica Symphony*, he listened attentively to the response of the hall. He had these two chords repeated by each section of the orchestra alone. As we all listened again to the sound dying away in the hall, one hundred and thirty people became absolutely quiet, expectant. Stokowski finally reported that he found the sound "splendid," apart from the slight echo we had all noticed, which appeared to come from high up in the back of the hall. He too found the bass weak relative to the brass and percussion, a problem that remained with us until Saturday.

After the Monday night session, in order to enhance the bass frequen-

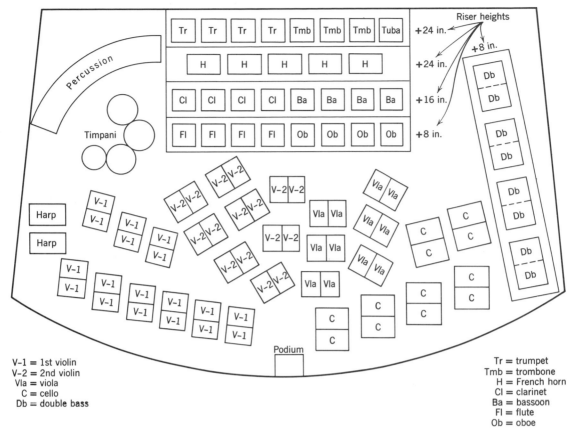

Figure 15.16. Arrangement of the New York Philharmonic Orchestra on the stage of Philharmonic Hall with riser heights and positions indicated for the Saturday afternoon rehearsal, June 2, 1962.

cies, a solid wall was constructed behind the double basses in the right rear corner of the stage, and 8-inch risers were provided for the double-bass section.

The Tuesday morning rehearsal was spent in determining the best adjustment of the sound-reflecting panels around the stage for hearing conditions among the members of the orchestra on the stage.

A photograph of a few members of the listening group, which was taken at the beginning of the Tuesday morning rehearsal, is shown in Figure 15.15. The arrangement of the orchestra on the stage is shown in Figure 15.16.

After listening for a while from a seat in the loge, Leonard Bernstein offered to conduct the closing number, Ravel's *Daphnis and Chlöe*. Partly because the orchestra was becoming accustomed to the hall, partly because the workmen in the rest of the building had gone to lunch (thereby reducing the extraneous noise to a very low level), but mainly because of Bernstein's skillful and exciting direction, this performance was memorable! All who were present agreed that when the minor imperfections were corrected, the hall would meet the most demanding standards.

On Tuesday afternoon, observations were made throughout the hall and on stage, and it was decided that the addition of more sound-reflecting panels, about 2 feet above the canopy over the front part of the main floor, would further increase the ratio of direct to reflected sound on the main floor of the hall and, hence, the loudness, clarity, and brilliance of the violin tone. The annoying echo, moreover, was traced to a complex sound path involving two balcony railings, the upper rear wall, and portions of the motion-picture projection booth.

Wednesday, May 30, was a holiday, and since the orchestra did not perform, the opportunity was provided to install the additional sound-reflecting panels that were needed above the main floor. Further adjustments were made in the orientation of the individual panels of the stage canopy, and in the splays of the panels in the side walls, using a highly directive electrostatic loudspeaker as a sound source to determine the optimum angle of orientation for each reflecting surface. To improve the loudness of the lower registers of the cellos, their position was interchanged with the violas, and 8-inch risers were placed beneath them.

The Thursday morning rehearsal revealed some improvement in the loudness of the bass and a great improvement in the clarity, loudness, and brilliance of the violin tone on the main floor. The orchestral tone was nearly perfect in the upper terraces.

On Thursday evening, Margaret Harshaw and Albert da Costa of the Metropolitan Opera, accompanied by the Philharmonic Orchestra under the baton of George Schick, sang excerpts from operas of Wagner and Puccini. Later, a group of young singers from the Metropolitan Opera Studio sang selections from Mozart's *Cosi Fan Tutti*. Various positions of the singers on stage were tried. It was apparent that the sound-reflecting surfaces at both sides of the front of the stage and some of the panels of the canopy needed to be adjusted to direct more of the singers' voices onto the main floor.

Friday night and early Saturday morning, the workmen covered the front of the projection booth with a canvas in a temporary effort to remove the echo. The thin plywood in the organ chamber was removed, on the organ builder's assurance that the instrument would absorb far less low-frequency sound than had been assumed. It had been observed also that, with a small orchestra on stage for the Mozart opera, the increased reverberation time was too high for the English libretto to be understood. This test illustrated clearly the need for providing adjustable sound-absorbing curtains in the side areas of the stage to reduce the reverberation time for this type of performance. Music of the Baroque period was also found to benefit from adjustable canvas curtains, which were tried Friday afternoon.

On Saturday morning, with most of the required adjustments implemented at least in temporary form, the music in the hall sounded far better than on Monday. The removal of the thin plywood from the organ chamber restored full bass to the hall, and the cellos and double basses sounded out with warm, rich tones. Now the cellos and violas could be restored to their original positions, as Bernstein wanted them. The canvas over the front of the projection booth had eliminated the echo. The added panels in the audience canopy made the music clear and distinct in all parts of the hall— yet with complete fullness of tone. On stage, owing to the added panels at the sides and in the stage canopy, the orchestra members could hear each other well.

John Canarina wrote on his comment card of Saturday, June 2, "There is no comparison between today and the rest of the week. The sound today is bright, alive, warm, and properly balanced. It is like a completely different hall."

One third of the orchestra members filled out cards after the last rehearsal. Typical comments were: "75 per cent better," "The over-all characteristics are excellent," "I believe you are on the right track to design the proper acoustics," "The sound is very even all around the hall," "Whatever you did between Friday and Saturday made a great improvement," "The feeling on stage is much more unified and the sound more compact." "Listening in audience more gratifying," "100 per cent improvement," "There is more definition in the sound and, more important, more depth in the bass sound," "Vast improvement."

We were constantly reminded throughout tuning week of five basic tenets of acoustical design emphasized by my study: (a) the ratio of cubic volume to total sound-absorbing area, V/S_T, must be at least 43 feet if a reverberation time of 1.9 seconds or longer is to be achieved; (*b*) preservation of the bass requires that there be virtually no thin wood in the hall— even 800 square feet of ¼-inch plywood can almost completely remove the bass; (*c*) relatively intense, short-time-delay reflections from some surfaces —like Philharmonic Hall's suspended, double layer of clouds—are essential; (*d*) a stage canopy and side walls or a stage enclosure is absolutely necessary for the orchestra members to hear each other and for the sounds of the various instruments to blend properly and project well into the auditorium; and (*e*) even the slightest echo is disastrous.

Tuning week ended optimistically with a feeling of accomplishment and with the conviction that when all the temporary adjustments were permanently installed during the ensuing three months, and after the hall had undergone whatever further tuning was suggested by its initial year, Philharmonic Hall would indeed satisfy the high goals its planners had set for it.

REVERBERATION TIMES

The reverberation times calculated before construction of Philharmonic Hall are given in Table 15.3. During tuning week, some of the carpets and nearly all of the wood-slat screen around the stage were missing. Several rows of seats at the front of the hall were not yet installed. With these

Table 15.3 Reverberation times for Philharmonic Hall, fully occupied. Estimated before construction.

Frequency cycles per second	Reverberation time seconds	Estimated accuracy of prediction seconds
67	2.7	±0.4
125	2.4	±0.3
250	2.2	±0.2
500	2.0	±0.1
1000	1.8	±0.05
2000	1.6	±0.05
4000	1.3	±0.1
6000	1.1	±0.1

omissions, the reverberation times were measured for two conditions: (1) the orchestra on stage, auditorium seats empty; and (2) the orchestra on stage, synthetic audience in the hall. The results are given in Table 15.4. It is estimated that when the hall is completed, the reverberation times will fall within the range of values given in Table 15.3.

FINAL ADJUSTMENTS

Figures 15.2 through 15.12 show the final design for the hall. Some surfaces around the motion-picture booth have been treated with sound-absorbing material to control the echo. The augmented upper layer of panels above the visible gilded clouds in the audience canopy is shown in Figure 15.9. Specially shaped sound-reflecting panels have been installed behind the visually opaque screen around the stage to project the sound of the strings and of the soloists across the stage and onto the main floor (see Figures 15.4 to 15.6). In addition, the panels in the canopy over the stage and the forward part of the audience have been slanted to project the sound from the strings and soloists into the hall (see Figures 15.2 and 15.12). In order to be able to reduce the reverberation for special concerts where music for small orchestra is to be played—say Baroque or chamber music—or where opera theater is to be performed, manually operated draw draperies have been installed in the spaces above the canopy on either side of the

Table 15.4 Reverberation times measured during tuning week

Frequency cycles per second	Reverberation time with orchestra without audience seconds	Reverberation time with orchestra with simulated audience seconds
67	3.3	3.3
125	3.1	3.0
250	3.1	2.6
500	2.9	2.2
1000	2.6	2.2
2000	2.4	2.1
4000	1.8	1.6
6000	1.3	1.2

stage. Draperies provided in the wall beneath the organ and on the rear left wall of the stage can be used to control the loudness of the brass and percussion, if desired. A solid wall has been constructed along the lower right edge of the stage to strengthen the double basses. And, finally, in order to ensure the richest possible bass, instructions were issued that no thin plywood was to be used in any part of the final construction!

Thus Saturday, June 2, 1962, ended a unique chapter in the annals of acoustical design—five years of sympathetic cooperation between artists and scientists. Whether history will award Philharmonic Hall a position among the world's finest environments for concert music is still too early for us to judge. But the understanding already engendered among musicians, architects, and acousticians should enrich the acoustical designs of the future and avoid many pitfalls of the past.

Audience and Seat Absorption in Large Halls

Until now, it has not been possible to predict from existing formulas with reasonable accuracy the most common acoustical characteristic of a hall, namely, the reverberation time, even when full architectural information was available. This fact is attested to in technical papers on London's Royal Festival Hall,[1] Edmonton and Calgary's Alberta Jubilee Auditoriums,[2] Tel Aviv's F. Mann Auditorium,[3] and Bonn's Beethoven Hall.[4] It is also true for other halls on which details have not been published. In each of these cases the design calculations with full audience have been 0.3 to 0.5 sec higher than the measured results.

Admittedly, the situation has improved since Wallace C. Sabine, an assistant professor, 27 years of age, was approached in 1895 by President Eliot of Harvard to improve the acoustics of the Fogg Art Museum (now called Hunt Hall) in Cambridge, Massachusetts. His colleagues looked upon his new assignment as a grim joke, and his senior professor warned him that he was "undertaking a problem that fairly bristles with difficulties, the extreme complexity of which seems to indicate that a complete solution is hopeless."[5]

After five years of research, Sabine gave acoustics the classical reverberation equation. He spent considerable effort in making careful measurements of the coefficients of sound absorption of the principal materials associated with concert halls. These he tabulated for 512 cps in his first lengthy paper on the subject, "Reverberation,"[6] as shown in Table A1.I. These numbers are very close to those published in texts and handbooks today. Sabine intended that they be used in this equation:

$$T = \frac{0.049\,V}{S\bar{\alpha}_{Sab} + 4mV} \tag{1}$$

Table A1.I   Coefficients of sound absorption at 512 cps*

Plaster on lath	0.033
Plaster on tile	0.025
Glass	0.027
Wood, solid, hard	0.061
Drapery: Shelia	0.23
Cretonne	0.15
Audience, per person (ft²)	4.75
Orchestra, per man (ft²)	5.15

* See footnote 6.

Reprinted with changes from *The Journal of the Acoustical Society of America*, Vol. 32, No. 6, pp. 661–670, June, 1960.

[1] P. H. Parkin, W. A. Allen, H. J. Purkis, and W. E. Scholes, *Acustica*, **3**, 1–21 (1953).

[2] T. D. Northwood and E. J. Stevens, *J. Acoust. Soc. Am.*, **30**, 507–516 (1958).

[3] L. L. Beranek, *J. Acoust. Soc. Am.*, **31**, 882–892 (1959).

[4] E. Meyer and H. Kuttruff, *Acustica*, **9**, 465–468 (1959).

[5] William Dana Orcutt, *Wallace Clement Sabine, A Study in Achievement*, privately printed in 1933. The Fogg quotation is from p. 104. The Krehbiel quotation (on a later page) is from p. 145. A few copies of this book are still available. (Send inquiries to Leo L. Beranek.)

[6] W. C. Sabine, *Collected Papers on Acoustics*, Harvard University Press, Cambridge, Massachusetts, 1927. The paper entitled "Reverberation" was first published in the *American Architect* in 1900.

Table A1.II Value of the air absorption coefficient m in units of inverse feet. Room temperature is assumed

Relative Humidity	Absorption coefficient m (ft^{-1})			
	2000 cps	4000 cps	6000 cps	8000 cps
30%	0.0010	0.0034	0.0057	0.0091
50%	0.0008	0.0023	0.0046	0.0067
70%	0.0006	0.0020	0.0039	0.0057

The $4mV$ term was introduced by Knudsen much later.[7]

In this equation, V is the volume in ft^3, S is the total area of the floor, ceiling, and walls in ft^2, and $\overline{\alpha}_{Sab}$ is the average absorption coefficient in the room defined as follows:

$$\overline{\alpha}_{Sab} = \frac{S_1\alpha_1 + S_2\alpha_2 + S_3\alpha_3 + \cdots + N_1a_1 + N_2a_2}{S} \quad (2)$$

where

$$S = S_1 + S_2 + S_3 + \cdots \text{ ft}^2 \quad (3)$$

and α_1, α_2, α_3, etc. are the absorption coefficients of particular surfaces in the room with areas, respectively, of S_1, S_2, S_3, etc. (ft^2); N_1 is the number of occupied seats with a total absorption each of a_1 (ft^2) and N_2 is the number of empty seats with a total absorption each of a_2 (ft^2). The quantity m is the coefficient of molecular absorption in the room in ft^{-1}, given approximately by Table A1.II. It may be neglected below 1500 cps.

Sabine in one of his papers (see footnote 6) tabulates audience absorption as measured in the Jefferson Physical Laboratory

Lecture Hall at Harvard both on a "per person" and on a "unit area" basis. However, both he and subsequent writers used the "per person" concept [using N_1a_1 in Eq. (2)] in their published calculations.

A thing to observe is that when Sabine applied his own formula, using "per person" audience absorption values and absorption coefficients determined in certain Harvard lecture rooms, to the estimation of the reverberation time with full audience in two concert halls, his estimates were far from the reverberation times actually measured (see Table A1.III). Not only are Sabine's calculated results inaccurate, but the percentage differences for the two halls are quite unlike. Furthermore variation in the percentage differences cannot be attributed to differences in the shape of the halls because the shapes are quite similar. Nor can errors in Sabine's calculations be held responsible, because his computations are published in detail for all to check (see footnote 6).

Sabine never published data taken after completion of Boston Symphony Hall, for which he was the consultant. When pressed for the data by Henry E. Krehbiel of the New York *Tribune*, Sabine wrote that the only real test of his work must come with the actual use of the hall for the exact purpose of its erection (see footnote 5).

We hasten to add that the actual reverberation time in Boston's Symphony Hall is probably near optimum for a hall of this type, and that the hall might not have been as well accepted by audiences if the reverberation time had come out as high as predicted. The discussion here is not intended to remove any of the luster from this famous hall, which is rated among the top two or three in the world by nearly every conductor interviewed by the author.

The purpose of this appendix is to clarify

[7] V. O. Knudsen, *J. Acoust. Soc. Am.*, **3**, 126–138 (1931).

Table A1.III   Comparison of reverberation times at 500 cps for fully occupied halls as calculated by Sabine in 1900 and as measured with modern equipment

Hall	Measured by	Measured	Calculated	Per cent difference
Leipzig, Gewandhaus (now destroyed)	Meyer and Cremer (1933) and by Kuhl (1960)	1.55* sec	2.30 sec	44%
Boston, Symphony Hall	Bolt Beranek and Newman (1957)	1.8	2.31	28%

*Based on recent data of Dr. Kuhl taken from phonograph records, this number is about 10% higher than that reported in the literature by Meyer and Cremer.

the principal reason for the serious differences between calculations and measured results, which occurred in Sabine's time and still occur today. It will be shown that the absorption values for audience used in Eq. (2) are at fault and not Eq. (1).

CLASSICAL VERSUS AUTHOR'S POSTULATE

In most halls for music, the sound absorbed by an audience accounts for a large percentage of the total absorption. A survey of the literature reveals a range of values for the absorbing power of a seated person at 500 cps from 3.1 to as high as 6.5 sabins (ft²).[8-12] Because a very small change in reverberation time, for example, from 1.5 to 1.6 sec (7%) is detectable by an experienced listener, the error (nearly 2:1) that can occur in calculations from the uncertainty in seat absorption is intolerably large.

The reverberation-time data of Appendix 2 are used here to derive a more meaningful measure of audience absorption. The halls selected for this part of the study have nearly the same average absorption coefficient.

Hence, it is convenient to use the simple Sabine reverberation equation in the calculations.

Because the Sabine equation treats the sound field on a statistical basis, it only takes the shape of a hall into account insofar as the ratio of V/S is concerned. Most of the halls studied here have volumes in the range from 250,000 to 1,000,000 ft³. The median value of V/S for these halls is about 10 ft. Except for a very few cases, V/S lies between 9 and 11 ft.

For full audiences and for halls with no added sound-absorbing materials, and at frequencies below 1500 cps, Eq. (1) reduces approximately to $T \doteq 0.049 \times (V/N_1)(1/a_1)$. The *classical postulate* is that a_1 is a constant. In other words, audience absorption is taken to be proportional to the number of people in the audience. Hence, approximately, the reverberation time should be proportional to "volume per seat." Therefore, the ratio V/N_1 has been spoken of by writers (e.g., see footnote 12) as an important criterion for determining the maximum

[8] P. H. Parkin, W. A. Allen, H. J. Purkis, and W. E. Scholes, *Acustica*, **3**, 1–21 (1953).

[9] L. L. Beranek, *Acoustics*, McGraw-Hill Book Company, New York, 1954, pp. 300–301.

[10] H. J. Sabine, *Handbook of Noise Control*, edited by C. M. Harris, McGraw-Hill Book Company, New York, 1957, Chap. 18, p. 18-3.

[11] V. O. Knudsen and C. M. Harris, *Acoustical Designing in Architecture*, John Wiley and Sons, New York, 1950.

[12] W. Furrer, *Raum- und Bauakustik für Architekten*, Birkhäuser Verlag, Basel and Stuttgart, 1956.

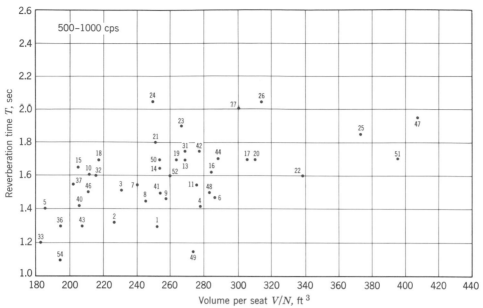

Figure A1.1. Plot of reverberation times at mid-frequencies (500–1000 cps) in halls with 100% audience versus volume per seat. Some of the halls have small amounts of porous sound-absorbing material, but the shift in reverberation time due to that material is not over 0.1 sec. For computational accuracy, however, those halls are not included in Figure A1.2.

expected reverberation time. It is a simple enough matter to check the concept of "volume per seat" by plotting measured reverberation times for a number of halls versus volume per seat. The result is shown in Figure A1.1. The correlation is very poor. For example, contrary to Eqs. (1) to (3), the same reverberation time of 1.6 sec was obtained in halls with volumes per seat ranging between 200 and 340 ft³ per seat or of 1.9 sec with volumes between 270 and 410 ft³ per seat.

Because of the scatter of the data, as shown in Figure A1.1, many observers have speculated that the reverberation time in a hall depends in a major way on the shape of the hall, or on differences from one hall to another in the acoustical behavior of the same finish materials or both. If the shape of the hall changed the reverberation time as much as is indicated by Figure A1.1, this would be in direct opposition to Eqs. (1) to (3), and the Sabine approach would have to be abandoned or modified in a major way.

Believing that Eqs. (1) to (3) are fundamentally sound and that the acoustical absorption of the materials does not depend in a major way on the shape of the hall or on dif-

ferences in materials from one municipality to another, the author proposes the postulate that: *The absorbing power of a seated audience, chorus, or orchestra in a large music hall increases in proportion to the floor area they occupy, nearly independently of the number of seated persons in that area (uniform distribution of persons assumed).*

Since the time that this paper was first presented, it has come to the author's attention that Meyer and Jordan[13] had shown that the reverberation time in the pre-World War II Berlin Philharmonie Saal was nearly unchanged whether the attendance at a concert was 50 or 100%, even though the seats were not highly absorbent. Their result yields independent support to the postulate given above.

The author wishes to emphasize, however, that the data in the present paper are for near-100% occupancy with seating densities (including aisles) between 4.5 and 8.5 ft² per person. No study was made of partial occupancy. Orchestra densities varied between 12 and 20 ft² per musician, including their instruments and music racks.

13 E. Meyer and V. Jordan, *Elek. Nachr.-Tech.*, **12**, 219 (1935).

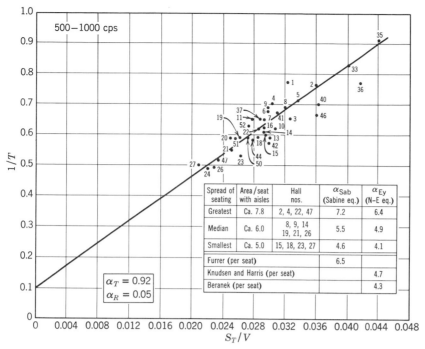

Figure A1.2. Plot of the reciprocal of the reverberation time (measured) versus the ratio of the total occupied areas (audience area plus 3.5-ft aisles plus chorus area, if occupied, plus orchestra area) to the volume, for halls with neglible amounts of sound-absorbing materials (draperies, etc.). The values for a [see Eq. (2)] in the upper three lines of the inserted table are for $\alpha_T = 0.92$ (Sabine equation) or for this coefficient reduced by 12% (Norris-Eyring equation). The three lower numbers are taken from books by Furrer (footnote 12), Beranek (footnote 9), and Knudsen and Harris (footnote 11).

The chart shows $1/T$ on the vertical axis (from 0 to 1.0) and S_T/V on the horizontal axis (from 0 to 0.048). Label "500–1000 cps" appears at top left. Boxes show $\alpha_T = 0.92$ and $\alpha_R = 0.05$.

Spread of seating	Area/seat with aisles	Hall nos.	α_{Sab} (Sabine eq.)	α_{Ey} (N–E eq.)
Greatest	Ca. 7.8	2, 4, 22, 47	7.2	6.4
Median	Ca. 6.0	8, 9, 14 19, 21, 26	5.5	4.9
Smallest	Ca. 5.0	15, 18, 23, 27	4.6	4.1
Furrer (per seat)			6.5	
Knudsen and Harris (per seat)				4.7
Beranek (per seat)				4.3

TEST OF NEW POSTULATE

To test the new postulate let us arbitrarily separate the absorption in a concert hall into two categories: (1) the audience, chorus, and orchestra absorption; and (2) the remaining absorption. If we now limit our studies to halls without any significant area of added porous sound-absorbing materials, then, at least for frequencies of 500 cps and above, we should have a homogeneous set for study. A few of the halls so selected had some of their surfaces made of acoustically flexible materials such as thin wood paneling, which are effective in absorbing sound at the lower frequencies. By assigning suitable absorption coefficients to those surfaces, these few halls could also be included as part of the group used for validating the new postulate.

To conform to the preceding stipulation, Eqs. (1) and (2) are rewritten:

$$\bar{\alpha}_{Sab} = 0.049 \frac{V}{S} \frac{1}{T} - 4m\frac{V}{S} \tag{4}$$

$$\bar{\alpha}_{Sab} = \frac{S_T \alpha_T + S_R \alpha_R}{S} \tag{5}$$

where S_T = the floor area (including aisle areas up to 3.5 ft in width[14]) occupied by the audience, chorus, and the orchestra; S_R = remaining surface areas of the room, *including the undersides of the balconies*; $S = S_R + S_T$; α_T = absorption coefficient for audience, orchestra, and chorus for the floor area S_T occupied by them; α_R = aver-

[14] In computing aisle areas, widths up to 3.5 ft (1m) of aisles lying within audience areas are included. Also, a strip of aisle, 3.5 ft wide, around the edge of an audience area is included. No such allowance is made at the front edge of a balcony where the audience is seated against the balcony rail. If the aisles are wider than 3.5 ft the excess width is not included as part of the audience area. The reason for including the 3.5-ft width is diffraction of sound around the edges of the audience. One expects that a smaller width than this should be used for unoccupied seats —perhaps only about one-half as much.

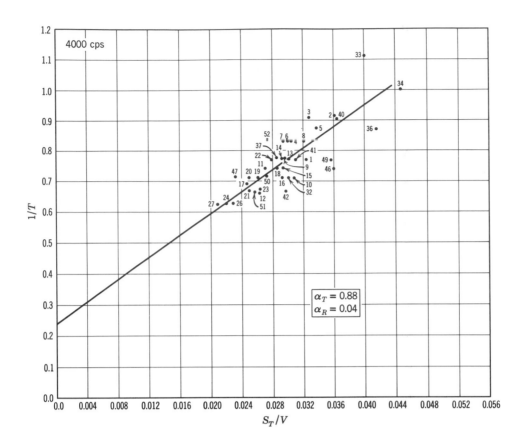

Figure A1.3. Plot of measured $1/T$ versus S_T/V for 4000 cps. For those halls (about one-half of the total) in which the humidity was checked with audience present, the relative humidity was found to be about 60%. Some of the scatter of the points may be due to humidities differing from 60%. The values for α_T and α_R in Figures A1.2 to A1.6 may not be exactly the same as those listed in Table A1.IV, because Table A1.IV was developed from smoothed curves passing through the values given in Figures A1.2 to A1.6.

age absorption coefficient for *all* other surfaces of the room, including in that average the absorbing power of walls, ceiling, doors, ventilating grilles, glass areas, organ openings, statues, chandeliers, underbalconies, etc.

Equating the right-hand sides of Eqs. (4) and (5), remembering that $S = S_T + S_R$ and assuming $V/S \doteq 10$, yields:[15]

$$20.4\frac{S_T}{V}\left(\alpha_T - \alpha_R\right) + 2.04\alpha_R + 81.6m$$

$$= \frac{1}{T} \quad (6)$$

When $1/T$ of Eq. (6) is plotted versus S_T/V, the result is a straight line, with a slope of 20.4 $(\alpha_T - \alpha_R)$ and an intercept at $S_T/V = 0$ of $1/T = (2.04\alpha_R + 81.6m)$. Consequently, α_T and α_R can be determined.

Typical plots for 125, 250, 500–1000, 2000, and 4000 cps are shown in Figures A1.2 to A1.6. Similar plots were made for halls with unoccupied upholstered seating of two types. The results of the entire study, yielding absorption coefficients for use in the Sabine equation, Eq. (1), are given in Table A1.IV.

If the old postulate that V/N_1 is roughly proportional to reverberation time were correct, then, of course, the points for the vari-

---

[15] The assumption of $V/S = 10$ does not limit the validity of the results, because it is only an intermediate step in arriving at an answer. The validity of

the answer is checked for each hall individually, using, in each case, the actual value of V/S.

ous halls would not fall on a straight line in Figures A1.2 to A1.6 because the area per seat (with aisles) varies between 4.6 and 8.0 ft². In that case either the shape of the hall or gross variability of sound absorption coefficients from hall to hall, or both, would have had to be introduced into the calculations. However, the points do determine straight lines and the intercepts are reasonable. It is true that because of the long extrapolation, any one intercept on Figures A1.2 to A1.6 may be subject to some error. However, when graphs of α_T and α_R are plotted versus frequency with the ranges of uncertainty indicated at each frequency, lines can be drawn within the range bars that vary

Table A1.IV Absorption coefficients of (1) occupied audience, orchestra, and chorus areas; (2) unoccupied "average" well-upholstered seating areas; (3) unoccupied leather-covered thinly upholstered seating areas; (4) thin wood paneling areas with air-space behind; and (5) 1.0-in. damped plaster walls and ceiling or 1.5-in. wood walls. The numbers below are for use in the Sabine equation:

$$T = \frac{0.049V}{S\overline{\alpha}_{Sab} + 4mV}$$

Description*,†	\multicolumn{8}{c}{Absorption coefficients, $\overline{\alpha}_{Sab}$ Frequency, cps}
	67	125	250	500	1000	2000	4000	6000
(1) Occupied audience, orchestra, and chorus areas, S_T	0.34	0.52	0.68	0.85	0.97	0.93	0.85	0.80
(2) Unoccupied "average" cloth-covered, well-upholstered seating areas (seats with perforated bottoms)	0.28	0.44	0.60	0.77	0.89	0.82	0.70	0.64
(3) Unoccupied leather-covered upholstered seating areas	—	0.40	0.50	0.58	0.61	0.58	0.50	0.46
(4) Thin (0.2 to 0.4-in.) wood paneling areas with air space behind	—	0.42	0.21	0.06	0.05	0.04	0.04	0.04
(5) 1.0-in. damped plaster or thick (more than 1.5-in. thick) well-fitted wood walls (these absorption coefficients have averaged in them the absorption of usual doors, ventilating grilles, etc. in the room), S_R	0.19	0.14	0.10	0.06	0.45	0.04	0.04	0.04

*The occupied areas include aisle widths up to, but not exceeding, 3.5 ft.
Orchestra areas include men, instruments, and music racks.

†The values in rows (1) to (3) include the absorption of a reflective floor beneath the seats. Carpet under the seats will not affect the values in row (1). The increase in absorption for row (2) will be significant.

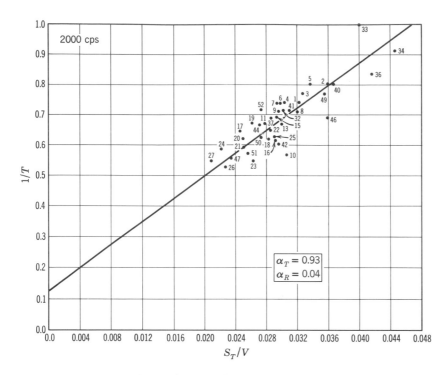

Figure A1.4. Same as Figure A1.3, but for 2000 cps.

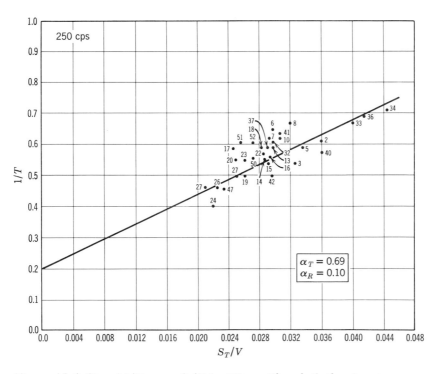

Figure A1.5. Plot of $1/T$ versus S_T/V for 250 cps. Those halls that do not appear on this graph were left off because they contain thin wood paneling or large amounts of other sound-absorbing material.

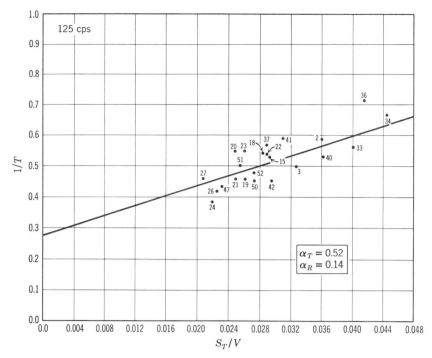

Figure A1.6. Same as Figure A1.5, except for 125 cps.

smoothly with frequency and in a manner consistent with other observations in the literature. These smoothed lines for α_T and α_R interact so that the results given in Table A1.IV are more accurate as a whole than one would judge from any one plot.

It is interesting to compare the results obtained from this study with those given in several books in the literature. The table in the lower right-hand corner of Figure A1.2 shows that for the three groups of fourteen halls enumerated there, the group median area per seat ranges between about 5.0 and 7.8 ft² per seat (with aisles). Multiplication of these areas by $\alpha_T = 0.92$ yields sound absorption a in sabins ranging between 4.6 and 7.2.

Knudsen and Harris (footnote 11) and Beranek (footnote 9) gave coefficients (for use in the Norris-Eyring equation; see original paper in *J. Acoust. Soc. Am.*, **32**, 661–670 [June 1960]), applicable to relatively crowded seating, of 5.2 to 5.7 ft² per person. Furrer's number of 6.5 (for use in Sabine's equation) is applicable to quite comfortable seating of 7 ft² per person. Note that if the calculated reverberation time of the hall is

1.8 sec, using the Sabine formula and an audience absorption of 5 sabins per person, and if the actual area per seat is 7 ft², the achieved reverberation time will be about 1.5 sec, or 0.3 sec too low, as stated in the introduction to this appendix.

APPLICATION OF THE RESULTS TO CALCULATION OF REVERBERATION TIME IN TYPICAL HALLS

The absorption coefficients of Table A1.IV were derived from the average of the measured results in the halls studied. These halls contained little or no added sound-absorbing materials (draperies, acoustical tiles, etc.). To test the results for the individual halls, the absorption coefficients from Table A1.IV and the *exact* areas and volumes were substituted in Eq. (1) and the reverberation times calculated. Then, at 125, 500–1000, and 2000 cps the differences between the calculated and measured reverberation times were found. The average difference is nearly zero, and the average deviation about 0.05 sec. The reliability of the prediction method seems established for the individual cases as well as for the graphical average.

549

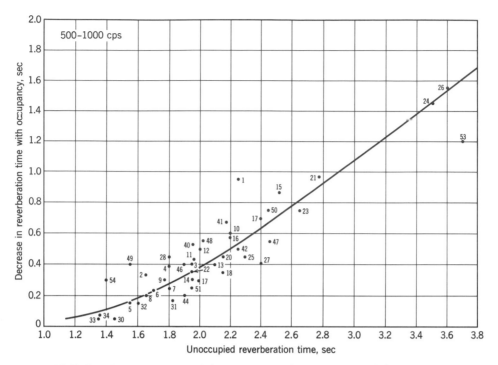

Figure A1.7. Plot for 500-1000 cps of decrease in reverberation time with full occupancy as a function of unoccupied reverberation time. All types of seats ranging from folding steel chairs (No. 24) to exceptionally heavily upholstered seats (Nos. 3 and 16) and all shapes and volumes of halls are included. Halls No. 13, 19, 21, 23, 25, 26, and 27 are rectangular and very similar in shape and construction.

UNOCCUPIED VERSUS OCCUPIED REVERBERATION TIMES

Very frequently it is relatively easy to measure the reverberation times for a hall empty but it is difficult to obtain the occupied reverberation times. It is helpful, therefore, to have an approximate relation at each frequency between the reverberation times for empty and full halls. These relations are also useful in seeking artifacts in measured data or in spotting unusual acoustical behavior in particular halls.

For those of the halls for which data are available, both empty and full, the differences between the (measured) occupied and unoccupied reverberation times are shown in Figures A1.7 to A1.9 for frequencies of 125, 500–1000, and 2000 cps. As shown by the curves, the incremental differences are about the same between 250 and 2000 cps. At higher frequencies, where air absorption becomes more important, the differences should be less.

SEAT DESIGN

An interesting discovery was made during the studies of unoccupied halls. It was found that in eight of the halls an unexpected absorption "peak" occurred in the vicinity of 250 cps. The reverberation times for these empty halls are shown in Figure A1.10. A study of each of these halls reveals that the principal reason for this unexpected absorption peak is the seats. It is found that the seat bottoms are not perforated and the cloth covering (upholstery material) is nearly impervious to air flow, causing a sort of "bubble resonance."

An attempt was made to correlate the scatter of points on the graphs leading to row 2 of Table A1.IV with the detailed construction of the well-upholstered seats. There was no correlation even though the seats have a large range in exposed area of upholstery material. One explanation for this result is that the larger upholstered seats are generally spaced more widely apart so that fewer

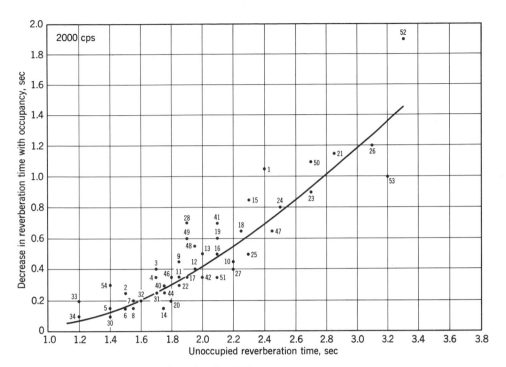

Figure A1.8. Same as Figure A1.7, but for 2000 cps.

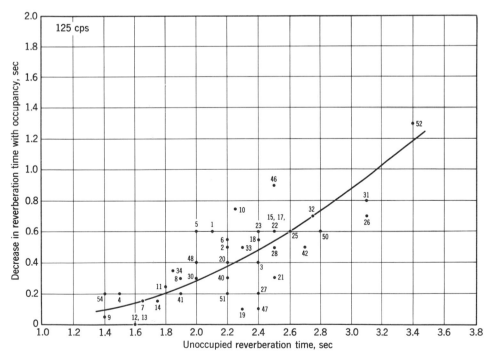

Figure A1.9. Same as Figure A1.7, but for 125 cps.

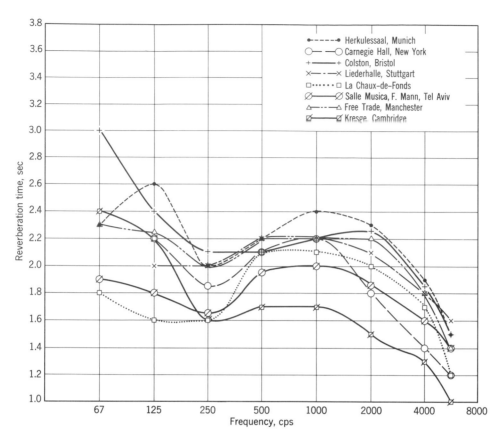

Figure A1.10. Reverberation time (unoccupied halls) versus frequency for halls in which a peak in seating absorption occurred at about 250 cps.

of them are required to produce the "area" absorption coefficients of Table A1.IV. This study also indicated that, except for eliminating the peak in absorption shown in Figure A1.10, perforated bottoms had little effect on the absorbing efficiency of well-upholstered seats.

The author does not mean to say that a careful study made in one hall would not show differences in the area absorption coefficients due to differences in details of seat construction, but the differences certainly are not outstanding enough to show up in comparisons made among seating areas in the different halls studied here.

REVERBERATION TIME VERSUS FREQUENCY CHARACTERISTIC

It is interesting to construct from the lines on Figures A1.2 to A1.6, plots of reverberation time versus frequency, normalized to the mid-frequency value of reverberation

time. This was done for $T_{500-1000} = 1.35$ sec and $T_{500-1000} = 1.8$ sec, and the results are given in Figure A1.11. The two curves shown are not expected to be alike, because the walls have a greater part in the total absorption in the room for the 1.8-sec case than for the 1.35-sec case. We see that the reverberation time for these fully occupied halls, on the average, decreases about 0.07 sec for each octave increase in frequency between 125 and 4000 cps.

COMMENT

One naturally asks whether it is reasonable that the absorption coefficient α_R should be as low as 4 to 5% at 500 to 2000 cps. A 5% value for α_R means that if the seats were removed from these halls the reverberation times would be about 10 sec at those frequencies. In one lecture room in Boston, with a volume of 65,000 ft³, and wooden schoolroom chairs, a reverberation time of

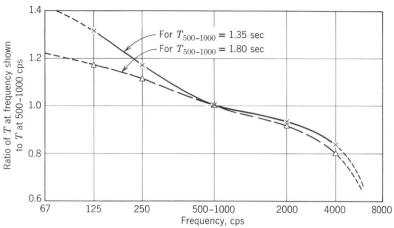

Figure A1.11. Graphs of reverberation times relative to reverberation time at 500–1000 cps versus frequency. The two curves are for reverberation times at 500—1000 cps of 1.35 sec and 1.8 sec. The data are taken from the lines drawn in Figures A1.2 to A1.6. These curves are valid only for halls without added porous sound-absorbing material or thin-wood paneling. They apply to halls with damped-plaster or thick-wood interiors and for full occupancy.

5.6 sec at 500 cps has been measured. In still another, with a volume of 58,000 ft³ and wooden benches, a reverberation time of 4.0 sec at 500 cps has been measured. Because the ratio of volume to total surface area (V/S) increases about as $V^{1/3}$, a room with 10 times the volume should have a reverberation time about twice those times just quoted, if the rooms are constructed of the same materials. Hence, 10 sec at 500 cps for an "unseated" hall of 600,000 ft³ volume does not seem unreasonable.

If the unseated reverberation time were found to be lower than 10 sec, one possible explanation is shown by some measurements of Balachandran.[16] He found that the absorption coefficient of an area in a room is a function of the state of diffusion of the sound field in that room. For example, he showed that at 2000 cps in his reverberation chamber the absorption coefficient of an area was diminished as absorbing materials were introduced on adjoining areas. A similar change in the state of sound diffusion must occur in a concert hall after the chairs are installed.

It is apparent, therefore, that the results of this appendix may not be applicable to small

lecture rooms, classrooms, reverberation chambers, and other rooms whose volumes, shapes, and materials are significantly different from those of the large concert halls and opera houses included in the present study. Furthermore, common sense tells us that if the area per person increases much above 10 ft², the area absorption coefficients of Table A1.IV must decrease. An interesting confirmation of this statement has been reported to the author by Lyle F. Yerges, formerly of the U. S. Gypsum Company. That company found, using 7.5 sabin functional (hanging) absorbers, uniformly spaced, that there was no further reduction in reverberation time when the number of units was increased beyond one unit per 10 ft² of ceiling area.

Prior to its submission for publication, the author sent this study to a number of acousticians for comment. Two of them commented that the 125 cps absorption for the seated audience, α_T, seems too high. Meyer and Kuttruff suggest in *Acustica* (footnote 4) that α_T at 125 cps should be as low as 0.25 instead of 0.52. One reviewer commented that a value for α_R (the absorption for the remaining areas) of 0.14 at 125 cps is too high. Inspection of Figure A1.6 and Eq. (6) shows that if either α_R or α_T is

[16] C. G. Balachandran, *J. Acoust. Soc. Am.*, **31**, 1319–1321 (1959).

made smaller, the other must be increased. If α_T is as low as 0.25 at 125 cps then we find from Figure A1.6 and Eq. (6) that α_R must also equal 0.25. Obviously, the walls and ceiling are not as absorbent as the audience, so α_T cannot be as low as 0.25. W. C. Sabine, in his careful pioneering measurements (footnote 6) performed in a lecture room (volume 60,000 ft^3) at Harvard with and without audience, found $\alpha_T = 0.72$ at 125 cps.

The author believes that in some halls, where the plaster is on solid backing (brick, concrete block, or poured concrete), α_R may be less than 0.14, say, 0.10 at 125 cps. None of the 11 halls shown in Figure A1.6 were of this type. Most had plaster walls that were "damped," i.e., did not ring when tapped with the knuckles.

Collected Tables of Acoustical and Dimensional Data

Table A2.Ia   Concert halls: dimensional and acoustical characteristics and year of dedication

Name	V Volume ft³ (m³)	S_A Audience Area ft² (m²)	S_O Orchestra Area ft² (m²)	S_T Total Area ft² (m²)	V/S_T ft (m)	N_A Seats	V/N_A ft³ (m³)	S_A/N_A ft² (m²)
AMERICA								
Baltimore, Lyric Theatre	744,000 (21,000)	16,700 (1550)	1690 (157)	18,400 (1710)	40.4 (12.2)	2616	284 (8.0)	6.4 (0.59)
Bloomington, Indiana University Auditorium	950,000 (26,880)	26,240 (2440)	2000 (186)	28,240 (2625)	33.6 (10.2)	3788	251 (7.1)	7.0 (0.65)
Boston, Symphony Hall	662,000 (18,740)	15,000 (1390)	1600 (149)	16,600 (1550)	39.9 (12.1)	2631	252 (7.1)	5.7 (0.53)
Buffalo, Kleinhans Music Hall	644,000 (18,220)	21,000 (1950)	2200 (204)	23,200 (2160)	27.8 (8.42)	2839	227 (6.4)	7.4 (0.69)
Cambridge, Kresge Auditorium	354,000 (10,020)	9280 (860)	1270 (118)	10,550 (980)	33.6 (10.2)	1238	286 (8.1)	7.5 (0.70)
Chicago, Arie Crown Theatre– McCormick Place	1,291,000 (36,500)	33,100 (3080)	2000 (186)	35,100 (3265)	36.8 (11.2)	5081	254 (7.2)	6.5 (0.60)
Chicago, Orchestra Hall	536,000 (15,170)	18,000 (1670)	2000 (186)	20,000 (1855)	26.8 (8.12)	2582	208 (5.9)	7.0 (0.65)
Cleveland, Severance Hall	554,000 (15,700)	13,000 (1210)	2000 (186)	15,000 (1395)	36.9 (11.2)	1890	289 (8.2)	6.9 (0.64)
Detroit, Henry and Edsel Ford Auditorium	676,000 (19,130)	19,900 (1850)	2200 (204)	22,100 (2055)	30.6 (9.27)	2926	231 (6.5)	6.8 (0.63)
Lafayette, Indiana, Purdue University Hall of Music	1,320,000 (37,350)	37,200 (3460)	2300 (214)	39,500 (3675)	33.4 (10.1)	6107	216 (6.1)	6.1 (0.57)
Lenox, Massachusetts, Tanglewood Music Shed	1,500,000 (42,450)	30,800 (2860)	2200 (204)	33,000 (3065)	45.5 (13.8)	6000	250 (7.1)	5.1 (0.47)
New York, Carnegie Hall	857,000 (24,250)	19,160 (1780)	2200 (204)	21,360 (1985)	40.1 (12.2)	2760	311 (8.8)	6.9 (0.64)
New York, Grace Rainey Rogers Auditorium	193,600 (5480)	5300 (490)	1600 (149)	6900 (640)	28.1 (8.51)	708	273 (7.7)	7.5 (0.70)
Philadelphia, Academy of Music	555,000 (15,700)	16,700 (1550)	2000 (186)	18,700 (1735)	29.7 (9.0)	2984	186 (5.3)	5.6 (0.52)
Rochester, New York, Eastman Theatre	900,000 (25,470)	20,530 (1910)	2200 (204)	22,730 (2115)	39.6 (12.0)	3347	269 (7.6)	6.1 (0.57)
San Francisco, War Memorial Opera House	771,000 (21,800)	21,240 (1970)	2100 (195)	23,340 (2165)	33.0 (10.0)	3252	237 (6.7)	6.5 (0.60)
ARGENTINA								
Buenos Aires, Teatro Colón	737,400 (20,870)	19,000 (1765)	2200 (204)	21,200 (1970)	34.8 (10.6)	2487	296 (8.4)	7.6 (0.71)
AUSTRIA								
Salzburg, Neues Festspielhaus	547,500 (15,500)	14,800 (1375)	2100 (195)	16,900 (1570)	32.4 (9.82)	2158	254 (7.2)	6.9 (0.64)
Vienna, Grosser Musikvereinssaal	530,000 (15,000)	10,600 (985)	1400 (130)	12,000 (1115)	44.2 (13.4)	1680	315 (8.9)	6.3 (0.59)
BELGIUM								
Brussels, Palais des Beaux-Arts	442,000 (12,500)	14,000 (1300)	2000 (186)	16,000 (1485)	27.6 (8.36)	2150	206 (5.8)	6.5 (0.60)
CANADA								
Edmonton and Calgary, Alberta Jubilee Auditoriums	759,000 (21,480)	21,000 (1950)	2000 (186)	23,000 (2135)	33.0 (10.0)	2731	278 (7.9)	7.7 (0.72)
Vancouver, Queen Elizabeth Theatre	592,000 (16,750)	19,300 (1790)	2000 (186)	21,300 (1975)	27.8 (8.42)	2800	211 (5.6)	6.9 (0.64)
DENMARK								
Copenhagen, Radiohuset, Studio 1	420,000 (11,890)	8700 (810)	2300 (214)	11,000 (1015)	38.2 (11.6)	1093	384 (10.9)	8.0 (0.74)

$T_{500-1000}$ (Occup.) Reverberation Time T_{mid} sec	t_I Initial-Time-Delay Gap msec	Average Bass Ratio	Year Dedicated	SEAT SPACING				Stage Height in. (cm)
				Main Floor Row-to-Row in. (cm)	Main Floor Seat-to-Seat in. (cm)	Balcony Row-to-Row in. (cm)	Balcony Seat-to-Seat in. (cm)	
1.5	21; 11	1.05	1894	31 (79)	19.5 (50)	31–33 (79–84)	20 (51)	51.5 (131)
1.5	40; 10	1.14	1941	34 (86.5)	20.5 (52)	34 (86.5)	22 (56)	35.5 (90)
1.8	15; 7	1.17	1900	30–33 (76–84)	21 (53)	29–33 (74–84)	21 (53)	54 (137)
1.32	32; 12	1.27	1940	38 (96)	22–26 (56–66)	40 (102)	21–26 (53–66)	42 (107)
1.47	15; 10	1.08	1955	34–36 (86–91)	22 (56)	—	—	32 (81)
1.7*	36; 14	ca. 1.18	1961	38–40 (96–102)	22 (56)	38–40 (96–102)	22 (56)	30 (76)
1.3*	40; 24	ca. 1.18	1905	34 (86.4)	19 (48)	34 (86.4)	21 (53)	43 (109)
1.7	20; 13	ca. 1.18	1930	38 (97)	22 (56)	30 (76)	20 (51)	32 (81)
1.55	28; 6	1.27	1956	36 (91)	20–21.5 (51–55)	36 (91)	20–21.5 (51–55)	42 (107)
1.6	45; 6	1.28	1940	33 (84)	25 (64)	32 (81)	21.5 (55)	42 (107)
2.05	19; 12	1.24	1938	33 (84)	17–20 (43–51)	—	—	30 (76)
1.7	23; 16	1.06	1891	33–35 (84–89)	22–23 (56–58)	32–35 (81–89)	20–22 (51–56)	48 (122)
1.15	15; 13	1.22	1954	36 (91)	22 (56)	36–40.5 (91–103)	22 (56)	30 (76)
1.4	19; 10	1.11	1857	30–33 (76–84)	20–21.5 (51–55)	30–32 (76–81)	18–21 (46–53)	52 (132)
1.75	55; 31	1.26	1923	32.5 (83)	20 (51)	31 (79)	20–21 (51–53)	36 (91)
1.7*	51; 30	ca. 1.20	1932	31 (79)	21 (53)	36 (91)	21 (53)	39 (100)
1.8*	19; 13	ca. 1.20	1908	39 (99)	23.5 (60)	27.5–31.5 (70–80)	19.5 (50)	43.5 (110)
1.5	23; 14	1.08	1960	29.5–31.5 (75–80)	17–20 (43–51)	29.5 (75)	17–20 (43–51)	35.5 (90)
2.05	12; 9	1.12	1870	31 (79)	21 (53)	36 (91)	21 (53)	39 (99)
1.42	23; 4	1.34	1929	33 (84)	22 (56)	35–36 (89–91)	22 (56)	46.5 (118)
1.42	31; 8	0.95	1957	33 (84)	20–22 (51–56)	36–37 (91–94)	24–27.5 (61–70)	42 (107)
1.5	24; 6	1.25	1959	33–34 (84–86)	19.5–21 (50–53)	34 (86)	19.5–21 (50–53)	41 (104)
1.5	29; 27	1.07	1945	32–34 (81–86)	21–22 (53–56)	32–34 (81–86)	21–22 (53–56)	27.5 (70)

*Estimate

Name	V Volume ft³ (m³)	S_A Audience Area ft² (m²)	S_O Orchestra Area ft² (m²)	S_T Total Area ft² (m²)	V/S_T ft (m)	N_A Seats	V/N_A ft³ (m³)	S_A/N_A ft² (m²)
Copenhagen, Tivoli Koncertsal	450,000 (12,740)	12,240 (1136)	2100 (195)	14,340 (1330)	31.0 (9.39)	1789	252 (7.1)	6.8 (0.63)
FINLAND								
Helsinki, Kulttuuritalo	354,000 (10,000)	10,180 (945)	1790 (166)	11,970 (1110)	29.6 (8.97)	1500	236 (6.7)	6.8 (0.63)
Turku, Konserttisali	340,000 (9600)	8000 (745)	1750 (163)	9750 (910)	34.9 (10.6)	1002	339 (9.6)	8.0 (0.74)
GERMANY								
Berlin, Benjamin Franklin Kongresshalle	457,500 (12,950)	10,300 (960)	1000 (93)	11,300 (1055)	40.5 (12.3)	1220	375 (10.6)	8.4 (0.78)
Berlin, Musikhochschule Konzertsaal	340,000 (9600)	8000 (740)	1830 (170)	9830 (910)	34.6 (10.5)	1340	254 (7.2)	6.0 (0.56)
Berlin, Sender Freies Berlin, Grosser Sendesaal	455,700 (12,900)	8600 (800)	2000* (186)*	10,600 (985)	43.0 (13.0)	1120	407 (11.5)	7.7 (0.72)
Bonn, Beethovenhalle	555,340 (15,700)	12,000 (1115)	2200 (204)	14,200 (1320)	39.1 (11.8)	1407	395 (11.2)	8.5 (0.79)
Leipzig, Neues Gewandhaus	375,000 (10,600)	9750 (905)	1250 (116)	11,000 (1020)	34.0 (10.3)	1560	240 (6.8)	6.3 (0.59)
Munich, Herkulessaal	480,000 (13,600)	7250 (675)	1810 (168)	9060 (845)	53.0 (16.1)	1287	373 (10.6)	5.6 (0.52)
Stuttgart, Liederhalle, Grosser Saal	565,000 (16,000)	14,000 (1300)	1900* (177)*	16,500 (1535)	34.2 (10.4)	2000	283 (8.1)	7.0 (0.65)
GREAT BRITAIN								
Bristol, Colston Hall	475,000 (13,450)	12,310 (1145)	1150 (107)	13,460 (1250)	35.3 (10.7)	2180	218 (6.2)	5.6 (0.52)
Edinburgh, Usher Hall	565,000 (16,000)	15,300 (1420)	1200 (111)	16,500 (1530)	34.2 (10.4)	2760	205 (5.8)	5.5 (0.51)
Glasgow, St. Andrew's Hall	569,000 (16,100)	13,500 (1255)	1400 (130)	14,900 (1385)	38.2 (11.6)	2133	267 (7.6)	6.3 (0.59)
Liverpool, Philharmonic Hall	479,000 (13,500)	13,900 (1290)	1400 (130)	15,300 (1420)	31.3 (9.48)	1955	245 (6.9)	7.1 (0.66)
London, Royal Albert Hall	3,060,000 (86,600)	37,800 (3510)	2200 (204)	40,000 (3715)	76.5 (23.2)	6080	503 (14.2)	6.2 (0.58)
London, Royal Festival Hall	775,000 (22,000)	21,230 (1970)	1860 (173)	23,090 (2145)	33.6 (10.2)	3000	258 (7.3)	7.1 (0.66)
Manchester, Free Trade Hall	545,000 (15,400)	14,800 (1375)	1940 (180)	16,740 (1555)	32.6 (9.88)	2569	212 (6.0)	5.8 (0.54)
ISRAEL								
Jerusalem, Binyanei Ha'Oomah	873,000 (24,700)	23,000 (2140)	2800 (260)	25,800 (2400)	33.8 (10.2)	3142	278 (7.9)	7.3 (0.68)
Tel Aviv, Fredric R. Mann Auditorium	750,000 (21,200)	18,300 (1700)	2100† (195)†	20,800 (1930)	36.0 (10.9)	2715	276 (7.8)	6.7 (0.62)
NETHERLANDS								
Amsterdam, Concertgebouw	663,000 (18,700)	12,200 (1135)	1600 (149)	13,800 (1285)	48.0 (14.5)	2206	301 (8.5)	5.5 (0.51)
SWEDEN								
Gothenburg, Konserthus	420,000 (11,900)	8900 (830)	1450 (135)	10,350 (965)	40.6 (12.3)	1371	306 (8.7)	6.5 (0.60)
SWITZERLAND								
Basel, Stadt-Casino	370,000 (10,500)	8000 (740)	1650 (153)	9650 (895)	38.3 (11.6)	1400	264 (7.5)	5.7 (0.53)
La Chaux-de-Fonds, Salle Musica	278,000 (7870)	7000 (650)	1350 (125)	8350 (775)	33.3 (10.1)	1032	269 (7.6)	6.8 (0.63)
Zurich, Grosser Tonhallesaal	402,500 (11,400)	9440 (875)	1560 (145)	11,000 (1020)	36.6 (11.1)	1546	260 (7.4)	6.1 (0.57)
VENEZUELA								
Caracas, Aula Magna	880,000 (24,900)	20,300 (1885)	2200 (204)	22,500 (2090)	39.0 (11.8)	2660	331 (9.4)	7.6 (0.71)

*Plus 600 ft² (55.7 m²) of chorus area.   †Plus 400 ft² (37.2 m²) of chorus area.

$T_{500-1000}$ (Occup.) Reverberation Time T_{mid} sec	t_I Initial-Time-Delay Gap msec	Average Bass Ratio	Year Dedicated	SEAT SPACING				Stage Height in. (cm)
				Main Floor Row-to-Row in. (cm)	Seat-to-Seat in. (cm)	Balcony Row-to-Row in. (cm)	Seat-to-Seat in. (cm)	
1.3	16; 14	1.10	1956	31–32 (79–81)	23–25 (58–64)	31–32 (79–81)	23–25 (58–64)	32 (81)
1.05	26; 17	1.17	1957	36 (91)	21 (53)	—	—	34.5 (88)
1.6	37; 24	1.14	1953	45 (114)	25–26 (64–66)	—	—	35 (89)
1.2	25; 19	ca. 1.30	1957	39 (99)	25.5 (65)	—	—	26.7 (68)
1.65	18; 4	1.06	1954	33 (83)	20.5 (52)	33 (84)	20.5 (52)	30 (76)
1.95	21; 13	1.15	1959	35.5 (90)	21.5 (55)	—	—	29.5 (75)
1.7	27; 14	1.12	1959	39.5 (100)	25 (64)	25 (64)	39.5 (100)	43.5 (110)
1.55	8; 6	1.00	1886	29–30 (73–76)	21.5–22.5 (55–57)	31.5 (80)	20 (51)	36 (91)
1.85	24; 10	1.01	1953	31 (78)	20 (51)	33 (84)	19–20 (48–51)	37 (94)
1.62	29; 12	1.06	1956	39–40 (99–102)	23.5 (60)	39 (99)	20 (51)	49 (125)
1.7	14; 6	1.04	1951	29.5–30.5 (75–78)	20 (51)	32 (81)	20 (51)	43 (109)
1.65	33; 11	1.15	1914	28–33.5 (71–85)	19.5–21.5 (50–55)	28 (71)	19–20 (48–51)	53 (135)
1.9	20; 8	0.95	1877	31.5 (80)	20 (51)	29 (74)	20 (51)	56.5 (144)
1.5	25; 18	1.00	1939	34 (86)	20 (51)	33–36.5 (84–93)	20–20.5 (51–52)	35.5 (90)
2.5	65(35); 70	1.29	1871	33–37 (84–94)	23.5 (60)	32 (81)	18.5 (47)	40 (102)
1.47	34; 14	0.88	1951	31 (79)	21.5 (55)	34 (86)	20 (51)	30 (76)
1.6	25; 7	0.97	1951	31 (79)	18 (46)	31–32 (79–81)	18 (46)	60.5 (154)
1.75	26; 13	1.20	1960	35.5 (90)	19.5–27 (50–69)	35.5 (90)	20 (51)	44.5 (113)
1.55	30; 7	0.98	1957	30–33 (76–84)	20 (51)	35 (89)	19 (48)	30 (76)
2.0	21; 9	1.10	1887	28.5 (72)	20.5 (52)	30–33 (76–84)	20–22 (51–56)	58.5 (149)
1.7	33; 22	1.06	1935	35.5 (90)	21.5 (55)	35.5 (90)	21.5 (55)	47 (119)
1.7	16; 6	1.24	1876	32 (81)	20 (51)	32 (81)	18 (46)	36 (91)
1.7	14; 6	1.03	1955	29.5 (75)	20.5 (52)	35.5 (90)	20.5 (52)	47 (119)
1.6	14; 6	1.22	1895	29 (74)	20.5 (52)	30 (76)	20.5 (52)	48 (122)
1.35	30; 10	1.44	1954	36 (91)	20.5–22 (52–56)	35 (89)	20.5–22 (52–56)	39.5 (100)

Table A2.Ib   Opera houses: dimensional and acoustical characteristics and year of dedication

Name	V Volume ft³ (m³)	S_A Audience Area with Standees ft² (m²)	S_O Pit Area (Open) ft² (m²)	S_{OF} Pit Area (Floor) ft² (m²)	S_P Proscenium Area ft² (m²)	S_T Total Area ft² (m²)	V/S_T ft (m)
AMERICA							
Baltimore, Lyric Theatre	720,000 (20,380)	15,714 (1460)	1024 (95)	1088 (101)	2612 (243)	19,350 (1800)	37.2 (11.3)
Bloomington, Indiana University Auditorium	902,000 (25,500)	25,740 (2390)	878 (81.5)	878 (81.5)	1652 (153)	28,270 (2625)	31.9 (9.67)
Chicago, Arie Crown Theatre– McCormick Place	1,283,800 (36,300)	33,100 (3075)	970 (90)	1130 (105)	3520 (327)	37,590 (3490)	34.2 (10.4)
Detroit, Henry and Edsel Ford Auditorium	630,000 (17,800)	19,900 (1850)	970 (90)	1050 (97.5)	1300 (121)	22,170 (2060)	28.4 (8.61)
Lafayette, Indiana, Purdue University Hall of Music	1,270,000 (35,900)	37,210 (3460)	840 (78)	840 (78)	3626 (337)	41,680 (3875)	30.5 (9.24)
New York, Metropolitan Opera House	690,000 (19,500)	24,050 (2235)	980 (91)	1130 (105)	2700 (251)	27,730 (2575)	24.9 (7.54)
Philadelphia, Academy of Music	533,000 (15,080)	15,700 (1460)	640 (59.5)	690 (64)	2401 (223)	18,740 (1740)	28.4 (8.61)
Rochester, New York, Eastman Theatre	846,500 (23,950)	20,530 (1905)	770 (71.5)	1750 (163)	2752 (256)	24,050 (2230)	35.2 (10.7)
San Francisco, War Memorial Opera House	738,600 (20,900)	22,240 (2065)	760 (71)	1075 (99.9)	2430 (226)	25,430 (2360)	29.0 (8.8)
ARGENTINA							
Buenos Aires, Teatro Colón	726,300 (20,550)	19,000 (1765)	675 (62.7)	2050 (190)	3402 (316)	23,080 (2145)	31.5 (9.54)
AUSTRIA							
Salzburg, Neues Festspielhaus	495,000 (14,000)	14,100 (1310)	800 (74.3)	950 (88)	2100 (195)	17,000 (1580)	29.1 (8.82)
Vienna, Staatsoper	376,600 (10,660)	12,850 (1195)	1150 (107)	1150 (107)	1720 (160)	15,720 (1460)	24.0 (7.27)
CANADA							
Edmonton and Calgary, Alberta Jubilee Auditoriums	723,000 (20,460)	21,000 (1950)	950 (88)	1250 (116)	2625 (244)	24,575 (2280)	29.4 (8.91)
Vancouver, Queen Elizabeth Theatre	525,500 (14,870)	19,300 (1800)	585 (54.3)	785 (73)	2215 (206)	22,100 (2060)	23.8 (7.21)
FRANCE							
Paris, Théatre National de l'Opéra	352,000 (9960)	12,120 (1130)	840 (78)	—	2538 (236)	15,500 (1445)	22.7 (6.88)
GERMANY							
Bayreuth, Festspielhaus	364,000 (10,300)	8500 (790)	371 (34)	1485 (138)	1638 (152)	10,510 (975)	34.6 (10.5)
GREAT BRITAIN							
London, Royal Opera House	432,500 (12,240)	14,630 (1360)	670 (62.2)	670 (62.2)	1700 (158)	17,000 (1580)	25.4 (7.70)
ITALY							
Milan, Teatro alla Scala	397,000 (11,245) [318,200]† [9000]†	14,000 (1301) [7700]‡ [(715)]‡	1200 (111)	1350 (125)	2400 (223)	17,600 (1635) [11,300]‡ [(1050)]‡	22.5 (6.82) [28.2] [(8.54)]

†Volume in well only.   ‡Main floor seating area only.

N_A Seats	N_{ST} Standees	N_T Effective Seats	V/N_T ft³ (m³)	S_A/N_T ft² (m²)	$T_{500-1000}$ (Occup.) Reverberation Time T_{mid} sec	t_I Initial-Time-Delay Gap sec	Year Dedicated	SEAT SPACING Main Floor Row-to-Row in. (cm)	Seat-to-Seat in. (cm)	Balcony Row-to-Row in. (cm)	Seat-to-Seat in. (cm)
2456	—	2456	294 (8.3)	6.4 (0.59)	1.4	21; 11	1894	31 (79)	19.5 (50)	31–33 (79–84)	20 (51)
3718	—	3718	242 (6.8)	6.9 (0.64)	1.4	40; 10	1941	34 (86)	20.5 (52)	34 (86)	22 (56)
5081	—	5081	253 (7.2)	6.5 (0.60)	1.5*	36; 14	1961	38–40 (96–102)	22 (56)	38–40 (96–102)	22 (56)
2926	—	2926	215 (6.1)	6.8 (0.63)	1.45	28;6	1956	36 (91)	20–21.5 (51–55)	36 (91)	20–21.5 (51–55)
6107	—	6107	208 (5.9)	6.1 (0.57)	1.45	45; 6	1940	33 (84)	25 (64)	32 (81)	21.5 (55)
3639	280	3779	183 (5.2)	6.4 (0.59)	1.2	22; 18	1883	33–35 (84–89)	22–23 (56–58)	32–35 (81–89)	20–22 (51–56)
2836	—	2836	188 (5.3)	5.5 (0.51)	1.35	19; 10	1857	30–33 (76–84)	20–21.5 (51–55)	30–32 (76–81)	18–21 (46–53)
3347	—	3347	253 (7.2)	6.1 (0.57)	1.65	55; 31	1923	32.5 (83)	20 (51)	31 (79)	20–21 (51–53)
3252	300	3402	217 (6.1)	6.5 (0.60)	1.6*	51; 30	1932	31 (79)	21 (53)	36 (91)	21 (53)
2487	600	2787	261 (7.4)	6.8 (0.63)	1.7*	19; 13	1908	39 (99)	23.5 (60)	27.5–31.5 (70–80)	19.5 (50)
2158	—	2158	229 (6.5)	6.5 (0.60)	1.45	23; 14	1960	29.5–31.5 (75 80)	17–20 (43 51)	29.5 (75)	17–20 (43–51)
1658	560	1938	195 (5.5)	6.6 (0.61)	1.3	15; 6	(1869) 1955	32–33 (81–84)	22–23.5 (56–60)	36 (91)	21 (53)
2731	—	2731	265 (7.5)	7.7 (0.715)	1.35	31; 8	1957	33 (84)	20–22 (51–56)	36–37 (91–94)	24–27.5 (61–70)
2800	—	2800	188 (5.3)	6.9 (0.64)	1.35	24; 6	1959	33–34 (84–86)	19.5–21 (50–53)	34 (86.4)	19.5–21 (50–53)
2131	200	2231	158 (4.5)	5.4 (0.50)	1.1*	17; 15	1875	38 (96)	22–22.5 (56–57)	26 (66)	20.5 (52)
1800	—	1800	202 (5.7)	4.7 (0.44)	1.55	14; 4	1876	28 (71)	21.5 (55)	24–32 (61–81)	18–21 (46–53)
2180	58	2209	196 (5.6)	6.6 (0.61)	1.1	19; 13	1858	33 (84)	24 (61)	Varies	
2289	400	2489	160 (4.53)	5.6 (0.52)	1.2	15; 12	1778 (1946)	29 (74)	18.5 (47)	30 (76)	16 (41)

*Estimate.

Table A2.IIa   Occupied concert halls: Measured reverberation times of halls for orchestra with audience
(All times are in seconds)

Name	Acoustical Measurements by	Average at 500–1000 cps	Frequency in cps								V/S_T ft
			67	125	250	500	1000	2000	4000	6000	
AMERICA											
Baltimore, Lyric Theatre	BBN,* 1960	1.47	—	1.6	1.55	1.5	1.45	1.4	1.25	1.0	40.4
Boston, Symphony Hall	BBN, 1957	1.8	2.3	2.2	2.0	1.8	1.8	1.7	1.5	1.35	39.9
Buffalo, Kleinhans Music Hall	BBN, 1959	1.32	1.85	1.7	1.65	1.35	1.3	1.25	1.1	1.0	27.8
Cambridge, Kresge Auditorium	MIT, 1955 BBN, 1958	1.47	2.1	1.65	1.55	1.5	1.45	1.35	1.25	1.2	33.6
Chicago, Arie Crown Theatre–McCormick Place	Calculated	1.7	2.9	2.2	1.8	1.75	1.65	1.6	1.4	1.1	36.8
Cleveland, Severance Hall	Ormestad et al., 1959	1.7	—	—	—	1.75	1.65	1.5	1.35	1.0	36.9
Detroit, Henry and Edsel Ford Auditorium	BBN, 1959	1.55	2.2	2.0	1.85	1.6	1.5	1.3	1.1	1.0	30.6
Lenox, Massachusetts, Tanglewood Music Shed	BBN, 1959	2.05	—	2.6	2.5	2.25	1.85	1.7	1.6	1.4	45.5
New York, Carnegie Hall	BBN, 1958	1.7	2.3	1.8	1.8	1.8	1.6	1.6	1.4	1.3	40.1
New York, Grace Rainey Rogers Auditorium	BBN, 1960	1.15	—	1.6	1.2	1.1	1.2	1.3	1.3	1.0	28.1
Philadelphia, Academy of Music	BBN, 1958	1.4	—	1.4	1.7	1.45	1.35	1.25	1.15	1.0	29.7
AUSTRIA											
Salzburg, Neues Festspielhaus	BBN, 1959 Schwaiger, 1960	1.5	1.7	1.7	1.6	1.5	1.5	1.4	1.3	1.1	32.4
Vienna, Grosser Musikvereinssaal	See Notes†	2.05	2.4	2.4	2.2	2.1	2.0	1.9	1.6	1.3	44.2
BELGIUM											
Brussels, Palais des Beaux-Arts	Raes and BBN, 1961	1.42	—	1.9	1.75	1.5	1.35	1.25	1.1	1.0	27.6
CANADA											
Edmonton and Calgary, Alberta Jubilee Auditoriums	Northwood, 1957	1.42	—	1.3	1.45	1.45	1.4	1.35	1.2	—	33.0
Vancouver, Queen Elizabeth Theatre	BBN, 1960	1.5	2.7	1.6	1.25	1.5	1.5	1.45	1.35	1.25	27.8
DENMARK											
Copenhagen, Radiohuset, Studio 1	Jordan, 1945	1.5	1.6	1.6	1.6	1.5	1.5	1.5	1.2	—	38.2
Copenhagen, Tivoli Koncertsal	Jordan, 1956	1.3	—	1.5	1.35	1.3	1.3	1.35	1.3	1.1	31.0
FINLAND											
Helsinki, Kulttuuritalo	Arni, 1960	1.05	1.0	1.2	1.25	1.1	1.0	0.9	0.9	0.7	29.6
Turku, Konserttisali	Arni, 1958	1.6	2.5	1.9	1.75	1.6	1.6	1.55	1.3	1.0	34.9

*Bolt Beranek and Newman Inc.   †Notes refer to tables on pages 568 and 569.

Name	Acoustical Measurements by	Average at 500–1000 cps	Frequency in cps								V/S_T ft
			67	125	250	500	1000	2000	4000	6000	
GERMANY											
Berlin, Musikhochschule Konzertsaal	ITA, 1958	1.65	—	1.6	1.8	1.7	1.6	1.6	1.3	1.1	34.6
Berlin, Sender Freies Berlin, Grosser Sendesaal	ITA, 1959	1.95	—	2.3	2.2	2.0	1.9	1.8	1.4	1.25	43.0
Bonn, Beethovenhalle	Meyer and Kuttruff, 1959	1.7	—	2.0	1.65	1.7	1.7	1.75	1.65	1.3	39.1
Leipzig, Neues Gewandhaus	Est. from Kuhl, 1959, and Meyer and Cremer, 1933	1.55	—	1.5	1.6	1.55	1.55	1.35	1.2	1.0	34.0
Munich, Herkulessaal	Mueller, 1958 BBN, 1960	1.85	1.8	2.0	1.75	1.85	1.85	1.8	1.65	1.3	53.0
Stuttgart, Liederhalle, Grosser Saal	ITA, 1960 Cremer, 1956	1.62*	—	—	1.8	1.6	1.65	1.6	1.4	1.3	34.2
GREAT BRITAIN											
Bristol, Colston Hall	Parkin, 1951	1.7	2.2	1.85	1.7	1.7	1.7	1.6	1.35	1.2	35.3
Edinburgh, Usher Hall	See Notes	1.65	1.8	1.9	1.85	1.7	1.6	1.45	1.35	1.2	34.2
Glasgow, St. Andrew's Hall	See Notes	1.9	1.6	1.8	1.8	1.9	1.9	1.8	1.5	1.4	38.2
Liverpool, Philharmonic Hall	Parkin, 1949 BBN, 1950	1.5	1.6	1.5	1.5	1.5	1.5	1.4	1.25	1.2	31.3
London, Royal Albert Hall	See Notes	2.5	3.4	3.4	2.9	2.6	2.4	2.2	2.0	1.6	76.5
London, Royal Festival Hall	See Notes	1.47	—	1.35	1.35	1.45	1.5	1.4	1.3	1.1	33.6
Manchester, Free Trade Hall	Somerville, 1951	1.6	1.6	1.5	1.6	1.6	1.6	1.75	1.4	1.2	32.6
ISRAEL											
Jerusalem, Binyanei Ha'Oomah	BBN, 1960	1.75	2.4	2.2	2.0	1.75	1.75	1.65	1.5	1.35	33.8
Tel Aviv, Fredric R. Mann Auditorium	BBN, 1957	1.55	1.5	1.55	1.5	1.55	1.55	1.5	1.3	1.2	36.0
NETHERLANDS											
Amsterdam, Concertgebouw	See Notes	2.0	—	2.2	2.2	2.1	1.9	1.8	1.6	1.3	48.0
SWEDEN											
Gothenburg, Konserthus	See Notes	1.7	—	1.9	1.7	1.7	1.7	1.55	1.45	1.1	40.6
SWITZERLAND											
Basel, Stadt-Casino	Furrer, 1936	1.7	2.2	2.2	2.0	1.8	1.6	1.5	1.4	1.2	38.3
La Chaux-de-Fonds, Salle Musica	Furrer, 1956	1.7	1.7	1.6	1.7	1.8	1.6	1.5	1.3	1.0	33.3
Zurich, Grosser Tonhallesaal	Furrer, 1936	1.6	2.3	2.1	1.8	1.65	1.55	1.4	1.2	1.0	36.6
VENEZUELA											
Caracas, Aula Magna	BBN, 1954	1.35	1.9	2.0	1.9	1.4	1.3	1.2	1.0	0.9	39.0

*With large chorus behind orchestra.

Table A2.IIb Occupied opera houses: Measured reverberation times of opera houses with audience (All times are in seconds)

Name	Acoustical Measurements by	Average at 500–1000 cps	Frequency in cps								V/S_T ft
			67	125	250	500	1000	2000	4000	6000	
AMERICA											
Bloomington, Indiana University Auditorium	BBN, 1959	1.4	1.9	1.7	1.5	1.45	1.35	1.3	1.3	1.25	31.9
Lafayette, Indiana, Purdue University Hall of Music	BBN, 1959	1.45	2.2	2.05	1.65	1.5	1.4	1.4	1.4	1.35	30.5
New York, Metropolitan Opera House	BBN, 1959	1.2	2.0	1.8	1.5	1.3	1.1	1.0	0.9	0.8	24.9
Rochester, New York, Eastman Theatre	BBN, 1959	1.65	2.8	2.3	1.85	1.75	1.55	1.45	1.3	1.1	35.2
AUSTRIA											
Vienna, Staatsoper	Winckel, 1959 BBN, 1959 Capek, Schwaiger, 1960	1.3	1.55	1.4	1.45	1.4	1.2	1.2	1.15	1.0	24.0
GERMANY											
Bayreuth, Festspielhaus	Reichardt, 1951 BBN, 1959 Bruckmeyer, 1960 Winckel, 1960	1.55	—	1.75	1.7	1.6	1.5	1.4	1.3	—	34.6
Berlin, Benjamin Franklin Kongresshalle	Estimated from "empty" data	1.2	1.9	1.6	1.6	1.25	1.15	1.15	1.1	1.0	40.5
GREAT BRITAIN											
London, Royal Opera House	Parkin et al., 1950	1.1	—	1.2	1.15	1.1	1.1	1.1	1.1	—	25.4
ITALY											
Milan, Teatro alla Scala	See Notes	1.2	—	1.5	1.4	1.25	1.15	1.1	1.0	—	22.5 (28.2)

Table A2.IIIa   Unoccupied concert halls: Measured reverberation times of halls for orchestra without audience (All times are in seconds)

Name	Acoustical Measurements by	Average at 500–1000 cps	Frequency in cps							
			67	125	250	500	1000	2000	4000	6000
AMERICA										
Baltimore, Lyric Theatre	BBN, 1960	2.02	—	2.0	2.05	2.05	2.0	1.95	1.6	1.1
Boston, Symphony Hall	BBN, 1958	2.77	—	2.5	2.8	2.7	2.85	2.85	2.1	1.6
Buffalo, Kleinhans Music Hall	See Notes	1.65	2.4	2.2	1.9	1.7	1.6	1.5	1.4	1.2
Cambridge, Kresge Auditorium	BBN, 1958	1.7	2.4	2.2	1.6	1.7	1.7	1.5	1.3	1.0
Chicago, Arie Crown Theatre–McCormick Place	BBN, 1961	2.45	4.0	2.8	2.2	2.3	2.6	2.7	2.1	1.5
Cleveland, Severance Hall	Ormestad et al., 1959	1.9	3.2	2.7	2.1	1.9	1.9	1.75	1.5	1.1
Detroit, Henry and Edsel Ford Auditorium	BBN, 1959	1.95	2.8	2.4	2.1	2.1	1.8	1.7	1.3	1.1
Lenox, Massachusetts, Tanglewood Music Shed	BBN, 1958	3.5	—	4.7	4.5	4.0	3.0	2.5	2.4	—
New York, Carnegie Hall	BBN, 1958	2.15	—	2.2	1.85	2.1	2.2	1.8	1.4	1.2
New York, Grace Rainey Rogers Auditorium	BBN, 1960	1.55	—	—	1.5	1.4	1.7	1.9	1.6	1.3
Philadelphia, Academy of Music	See Notes	1.55	—	2.0	1.8	1.6	1.5	1.4	1.3	1.0
AUSTRIA										
Salzburg, Neues Festspielhaus	Schwaiger	2.17	1.9	1.9	2.3	2.25	2.1	2.1	1.8	1.5
Vienna, Grosser Musikvereinssaal	See Notes	3.6	3.5	3.1	3.3	3.7	3.5	3.1	2.2	1.7
BELGIUM										
Brussels, Palais des Beaux-Arts	See Notes	1.95	—	2.2	2.4	2.0	1.9	1.75	1.6	1.35
CANADA										
Edmonton and Calgary, Alberta Jubilee Auditoriums	Northwood, 1957	1.8	—	1.5	1.7	1.8	1.8	1.7	1.5	—
Vancouver, Queen Elizabeth Theatre	BBN, 1960	1.9	3.7	2.5	1.9	1.9	1.9	1.8	1.55	1.4
DENMARK										
Copenhagen, Radiohuset, Studio 1	Jordan, 1945	2.0	1.6	1.6	1.7	2.0	2.0	1.9	1.2	1.0
Copenhagen, Tivoli Koncertsal	Jordan, 1956	2.25	1.6	2.1	2.1	2.2	2.3	2.4	2.1	1.8
FINLAND										
Turku, Konserttisali	See Notes	1.95	—	2.5	2.1	2.0	1.9	1.85	1.6	1.2
GERMANY										
Berlin, Musikhochschule Konzertsaal	ITA, 1958 Meyer, 1956	1.95	—	1.75	2.1	2.1	1.8	1.75	1.5	1.2

Table A2.IIIa   Unoccupied concert halls: Measured reverberation times of halls for orchestra without audience (All times are in seconds) (*continued*)

Name	Acoustical Measurements by	Average at 500–1000 cps	Frequency in cps							
			67	125	250	500	1000	2000	4000	6000
GERMANY (*continued*)										
Berlin, Sender Freies Berlin, Grosser Sendesaal	ITA, 1959	2.45	—	2.4	2.45	2.4	2.5	2.45	2.0	1.7
Bonn, Beethovenhalle	Meyer and Kuttruff, 1959	1.95	—	2.2	2.1	2.0	1.9	2.1	1.8	1.4
Leipzig, Neues Gewandhaus	Kuhl (recordings), 1959, with orchestra	1.8	—	1.55	1.9	1.9	1.7	1.5	1.3	1.2
Munich, Herkulessaal	See Notes	2.3	2.3	2.6	2.0	2.2	2.4	2.3	1.9	1.5
Stuttgart, Liederhalle, Grosser Saal	ITA, 1956	2.2	—	2.0	2.0	2.2	2.2	2.1	1.8	1.6
GREAT BRITAIN										
Bristol, Colston Hall	Somerville, 1953	2.15	3.0	2.4	2.1	2.1	2.2	2.25	1.85	1.5
Edinburgh, Usher Hall	See Notes	2.52	2.4	2.5	2.55	2.6	2.45	2.3	1.9	1.3
Glasgow, St. Andrew's Hall	See Notes	2.65	2.5	2.4	2.4	2.6	2.7	2.7	2.2	1.5
Liverpool, Philharmonic Hall	Somerville, 1953 Parkin, 1949	1.65	2.3	1.9	1.8	1.7	1.6	1.55	1.45	1.2
London, Royal Albert Hall	See Notes	3.7	5.1	5.0	4.3	3.9	3.5	3.2	2.6	2.3
London, Royal Festival Hall	See Notes	1.77	—	1.4	1.5	1.7	1.85	1.85	1.55	1.25
Manchester, Free Trade Hall	Somerville, 1952	2.2	2.3	2.25	2.0	2.2	2.2	2.2	1.8	1.4
ISRAEL										
Jerusalem, Binyanei Ha'Oomah	BBN, 1960	2.25	2.9	2.7	2.4	2.3	2.2	2.0	1.8	1.5
Tel Aviv, Fredric R. Mann Auditorium	BBN, 1957	1.97	1.9	1.8	1.65	1.95	2.0	1.85	1.6	1.4
NETHERLANDS										
Amsterdam, Concertgebouw	See Notes	2.4	2.5	2.4	2.4	2.4	2.4	2.2	1.8	1.5
SWEDEN										
Gothenburg, Konserthus	See Notes	2.0	2.0	2.5	2.0	1.9	2.1	1.9	1.6	1.15
SWITZERLAND										
Basel, Stadt-Casino	Jordan and Brandt, 1958 Furrer, 1957	2.4	—	2.3	2.65	2.5	2.3	2.1	1.7	1.45
La Chaux-de-Fonds, Salle Musica	Furrer, 1956 Jordan and Brandt, 1958	2.1	1.8	1.6	1.6	2.1	2.1	2.0	1.7	1.2
Zurich, Grosser Tonhallesaal	Furrer, 1936	3.85	3.0	3.4	3.8	3.9	3.8	3.3	2.5	2.0
VENEZUELA										
Caracas, Aula Magna	BBN, 1954	1.8	2.4	2.5	2.25	1.85	1.75	1.9	1.7	1.25

Table A2.IIIb   Unoccupied opera houses: Measured reverberation times of opera houses without audience
(All times are in seconds)

Name	Acoustical Measurements by	Average at 500–1000 cps	Frequency in cps							
			67	125	250	500	1000	2000	4000	6000
AMERICA										
Bloomington, Indiana University Auditorium	BBN, 1959	1.45	—	2.0	1.55	1.5	1.4	1.4	1.4	—
Lafayette, Indiana, Purdue University Hall of Music	BBN, 1959	1.6	3.4	2.75	2.0	1.7	1.5	1.6	1.55	1.4
New York, Metropolitan Opera House	BBN, 1959	1.35	2.7	2.3	1.7	1.5	1.2	1.2	1.0	0.9
Rochester, New York, Eastman Theatre	BBN, 1959	1.82	3.5	3.1	2.5	1.9	1.75	1.7	1.55	1.3
AUSTRIA										
Vienna, Staatsoper	Bruckmeyer	1.8	—	2.0	1.9	1.8	1.8	1.7	1.5	—
GERMANY										
Berlin, Benjamin Franklin Kongresshalle	Cremer, 1957	1.3	2.3	1.9	1.85	1.4	1.2	1.2	1.15	1.05
GREAT BRITAIN										
London, Royal Opera House	Parkin, 1952	1.4	—	1.4	1.4	1.4	1.4	1.4	1.4	—
ITALY										
Milan, Teatro alla Scala	Paolini, 1947	1.35	—	1.85	1.5	1.35	1.35	1.2	1.15	—

NOTES TO TABLES A2.II AND A2.III

Where several differing sets of reverberation data basic to the averages given in the tables of this appendix exist, they are presented below. The author's choices in the tables were usually based on discussions with the engineers who made the measurements or on consistency between unoccupied and occupied data. In some cases, the data differ from those published in the literature because later data were supplied by the engineers involved or they acknowledged errors. These notes and the final tabulations were checked with sources to assure accuracy.

| Engineer | Date | Occupancy and Signal | Frequency in cps | | | | | | | | Measured for |
			67	125	250	500	1000	2000	4000	6000	
BUFFALO, *Kleinhans Hall*											
Potwin	1941	Unoccup., Warble Tone	—	2.0	1.65	1.55	1.45	1.4	1.3	—	Concert
Bolt and Kessler	1950	Unoccup., Random Noise	—	2.2	1.8	1.6	1.5	1.5	1.5	1.25	Concert
BBN	1959	Unoccup., Impulse	2.5	2.3	2.0	1.8	1.6	1.5	1.35	1.15	Concert
PHILADELPHIA, *Academy of Music*											
Potwin	1941	Unoccup., Warble Tone	—	1.9	1.7	1.55	1.5	1.4	1.3	—	Concert
BBN	1958	Unoccup., Impulse	—	2.0	1.9	1.6	1.5	1.4	1.3	1.0	Concert
VIENNA, *Grosser Musikvereinssaal*											
BBN	1959	Unoccup., Chords	3.5	3.0	3.2	3.7	3.5	3.0	2.2	1.6	Concert
Brandt and Jordan	1958	Unoccup., Noise	—	3.2	3.2	3.6	3.4	3.2	2.3	1.7	Concert
ABC and Skalar	1956	Unoccup., Impulse	3.6	3.2	3.5	3.9	3.8	3.1	2.2	1.7	Concert
BBN	1959	Occup., Chords	2.4	2.3	2.2	2.1	2.0	1.9	1.6	1.3	Concert
ABC and Skalar	1956	Occup., Chords	2.5	2.4	2.4	2.1	2.1	2.1	1.7	1.3	Concert
BRUSSELS, *Palais des Beaux-Arts*											
Raes	1961	Unoccup., White Noise	1.8	1.8	2.3	2.0	1.9	1.8	1.6	1.3	Concert
RTB	1961	Unoccup., White Noise	—	2.2	2.5	2.05	1.85	1.7	1.55	1.45	Concert
TURKU, *Konserttisali*											
Arni	1958	Unoccup., Impulse	3.2	2.5	2.0	2.0	1.7	1.8	1.5	1.1	Concert
Brandt and Jordan	1953	Unoccup., Noise	—	2.8	2.4	2.1	2.0	1.9	1.8	1.6	Concert
Meyer	1956	Unoccup., Warble Tone	—	2.3	2.0	2.0	2.0	1.9	1.6	1.2	Concert
MUNICH, *Herkulessaal*											
Cremer	1953	Unoccup., Impulse	—	2.55	2.35	2.3	2.4	2.4	2.1	1.6	Concert
Kuhl	1954	Unoccup., Warble Tone	2.5	2.9	1.75	2.2	2.5	2.3	1.9	1.5	Concert
Meyer	1956	Unoccup., Warble Tone	—	2.7	1.95	2.2	2.5	2.3	1.9	1.5	Concert
Mueller	1960	Unoccup., Impulse	2.2	2.15	2.1	2.1	2.25	2.2	1.8	1.4	Concert
EDINBURGH, *Usher Hall*											
Brandt and Jordan	1958	Unoccup., Noise	—	2.5	2.6	2.6	2.5	2.2	1.9	1.2	Concert
Somerville	1950	Unoccup., Warble Tone	2.4	2.4	2.45	2.5	2.4	2.25	1.85	1.4	Concert
Parkin	1949	Unoccup., Impulse	—	2.6	—	2.7	—	2.5	2.2	—	Concert
Somerville	1950	Occup., Chords	1.8	1.95	1.85	1.65	1.5	1.3	1.2	1.1	Concert
Parkin	1949	Occup., Chords	—	1.9	—	1.8	—	1.6	1.5	—	Concert

Engineer	Date	Occupancy and Signal	Frequency in cps								Measured for
			67	125	250	500	1000	2000	4000	6000	
GLASGOW, *St. Andrew's Hall*											
Brandt and Jordan	1958	Unoccup., Noise	—	2.3	2.3	2.6	2.8	2.8	1.9	1.4	Concert
Parkin	1949	Unoccup., Impulse	—	2.6	—	3.3	—	3.4	2.9	—	Concert
Somerville	1956	Unoccup., Warble-Impulse	2.5	2.4	2.45	2.6	2.7	2.65	2.3	1.6	Concert
Parkin	1949	Occup., Chords	—	2.1	—	2.2	—	2.1	2.0	—	Concert
Somerville	1950	Occup., Chords	1.6	1.6	2.0	1.8	1.7	1.7	1.5	1.4	Concert
LONDON, *Royal Albert Hall*											
Parkin	1947	Unoccup., Impulse	5.4	5.5	4.6	4.2	3.8	3.3	2.8	2.6	Concert
Somerville	1949	Unoccup., Warble Tone	4.3	3.0	3.3	3.3	2.9	2.7	2.1	1.5	Concert
N.W.D.R.	—	Occup., Chords	3.4	3.5	2.9	2.6	2.4	2.2	2.0	1.6	Concert
Parkin	1947	Occup., Chords	3.6	3.4	3.0	2.75	2.4	2.3	1.95	1.7	Concert
LONDON, *Royal Festival Hall*											
Brandt and Jordan	1958	Unoccup., Noise	—	1.4	1.5	1.7	1.8	1.9	1.5	1.2	Concert
Somerville	1951	Unoccup., Warble Tone		1.9	1.85	1.85	2.0	2.0	1.65	1.3	Concert
Thiele	1956	Unoccup., Warble	—	1.25	1.55	1.7	1.85	1.8	1.5	1.1	Concert
Parkin	1959	Unoccup., Impulse	1.65	1.45	1.45	1.6	1.75	1.85	1.75	1.35	Concert
Somerville	1951	Occup., Chords	—	1.8	1.6	1.55	1.6	1.2	1.1	1.05	Concert
Parkin	1959	Occup., Impulse	—	1.35	1.35	1.35	1.4	1.45	1.35	1.1	Concert
MILAN, *Teatro alla Scala*											
BBN	1959	Occup., Chords	—	1.55	1.4	1.3	1.3	1.15	1.1	—	Opera
Furrer	—	Occup., Chords	—	1.2	1.1	0.9	0.9	0.8	0.8	—	Opera
Reichardt	—	Occup., Chords	—	1.5	1.5	1.25	1.0	0.8	0.6	—	Opera
AMSTERDAM, *Concertgebouw*											
Brandt and Jordan	1958	Unoccup., Noise	—	1.8	2.3	2.3	2.3	2.2	1.8	1.4	Concert
BBN and Geluk	1958	Unoccup., White Noise, Impulse	—	2.6	2.55	2.4	2.4	2.2	1.8	1.6	Concert
BBN	1958	Occup., Chords	—	2.2	2.2	2.1	1.9	1.8	1.6	1.3	Concert
Geluk	1958	Partly Occup., Chords	—	2.25	2.25	2.2	2.2	1.9	1.7	—	Concert
GOTHENBURG, *Konserthus*											
Winckel	1959	Unoccup., Impulse	—	2.1	1.7	1.8	2.2	2.25	1.8	—	Concert
Brandt and Jordan	1958	Unoccup., Noise	—	2.5	2.0	1.9	2.1	1.9	1.6	1.2	Concert
Ingemansson	1960	Unoccup., Impulse	2.0	2.6	2.1	2.1	2.0	1.6	1.5	1.1	Concert
Kuhl	1959	Occup., Chords	—	1.75	1.6	1.7	1.8	1.6	1.45	1.1	Concert
Ingemansson	1960	Occup., Impulse	—	2.0	1.8	1.6	1.6	1.5	1.4	1.1	Concert

Terminology and Conversion Factors

TERMINOLOGY

The following is a glossary of the symbols used in the presentation of technical data in Chapter 6, and in the later technical chapters.

V = Volume of the hall in cubic feet. In *concert halls* it includes the volume of air in the main hall and in the orchestra enclosure or shell. If there is a stagehouse, it does not include that volume of the stagehouse that lies outside the orchestra enclosure. Excluded also is the volume occupied by the solid balcony structure.

In *opera houses*, V includes the volume of air contained in the house forward to the main curtain. It does not include the volume of air in the stagehouse or the volume occupied by the solid balcony structures.

S — Area, defined specifically as below, in square feet.

S_T = Total surface area occupied by the audience, the orchestra, and the chorus, if any, in square feet. It includes also the area of aisles up to a width of 3.5 feet. (For further details, see S_A.) In *concert halls* the total area $S_T = S_A + S_O + S_C$; in *opera houses*, the total area $S_T = S_A + S_O + S_P$ (see definitions below).

S_A = Audience seating area in square feet. It includes the sum of: (*a*) the area of floor covered by the audience; (*b*) the area of aisles for widths up to 3.5 feet if they lie within the audience area or around the edge ᶜ an audience area (no aisle allowance is

made at the front edge of a balcony where the audience is seated against a balcony rail; if the aisles are wider than 3.5 feet, the excess is not included as part of the audience area); and (*c*) the area used as standing room.

S_O = Area of the orchestra or open area of the orchestra pit in square feet. It includes the area occupied by the orchestra, plus a strip 3.5 feet wide around the periphery, unless the players are seated against a wall.

S_C = Chorus area, if occupied. In most of the halls in this study the chorus area is included as part of the audience area or as part of the orchestra area.

S_P = Area of the velour curtain exposed at the proscenium (i.e., area of the proscenium opening) in square feet. It is assumed that the asbestos or steel curtain is pulled up.

N_A = Number of seats in the hall.

N_S = Number of persons permitted to stand in the hall (standees).

$N_T = N_A + (N_S/2)$ = Number of seats plus half the number of standees. This number is used in comparisons among opera houses where there is often considerable standing room.

$\overline{\alpha}_{Sab}$ = Average sound absorption coefficient defined in Eq. (2) of Appendix 1 for use in the Sabine reverberation equation, Eq. (1) of Appendix 1.

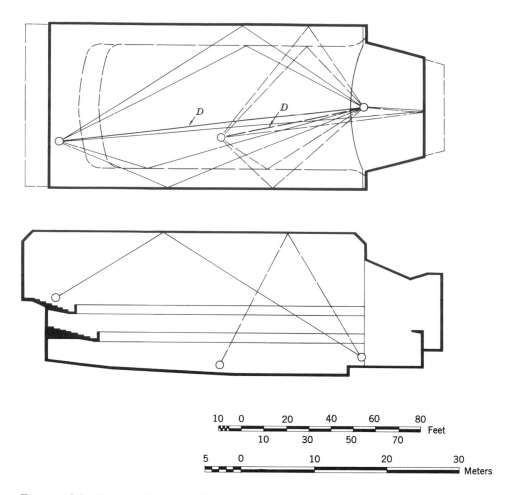

Figure A3.1. Sketch of Symphony Hall, Boston, showing direct and some reflected sound paths at mid-main-floor and mid-balcony positions. *D* indicates the path of the direct sound to either position.

α_T = Sound absorption coefficient for audience, orchestra, and chorus for the floor area S_T.

α_R = Average sound absorption coefficient for all surfaces of the room other than S_T, including in the average the absorption of walls, ceiling, doors, ventilating grilles, glass areas, organ openings, statues, chandeliers, underbalconies, etc.

m = Air absorption coefficient in units of inverse feet (see Table A1.II of Apendix 1).

T = Reverberation time in seconds. It is the time required for the sound in a room to decay by 60 decibels after its source is cut off. Because the reverberation time is differ-ent at different frequencies and for various degrees of occupancy of a hall, it must be specified for each condition and degree of occupancy under consideration. Detailed tables for the 54 halls, measured with and without audience, are given in Appendix 2, Tables A2.II and III.

$T_{500-1000}$ (Occup.) = The mid-frequency reverberation time defined as the average of the reverberation times at 500 and 1000 cycles per second (cps) (approximately the C's that lie one and two octaves above middle C) for the fully occupied hall. In acoustical literature, reverberation time is usually given for a frequency of 500 cps, which is generally longer than $T_{500-1000}$. $T_{500-1000}$ is believed to provide a more meaningful meas-

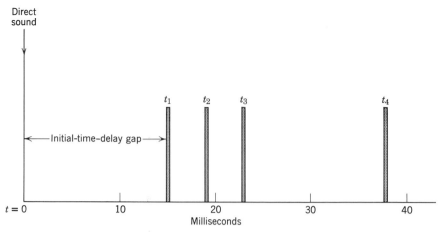

Figure A3.2. Reflection pattern for mid-main-floor seat. The direct sound arrives at $t = 0$. The first four reflections arrive 15, 19, 23, and 38 msec later.

ure, because the center of the hearing range for music lies within this frequency range.

t_I = Initial-time-delay gap in milliseconds. It is equal to the length of time it takes for the first reflection from the walls, ceiling, or balcony fronts to reach a listener's ear *after* the direct sound from the performer has reached him. The value of t_I varies throughout the hall. In those cases where the time delay between the first and second reflections is greater, it is substituted for the initial-time-delay gap.

Two values are given for t_I, one at a seat just to one side of the centerline of the main floor, about halfway between the most protruding balcony front (if there is one) and the stage, and the second at a seat in the balcony about halfway between the front of the balcony and the last row of seats in the balcony. Hence $t_I = 45$; 22 msec means the initial-time-delay gap for the mid-main-floor seat is 45 msec, and for the mid-balcony seat is 22 msec. When there is no balcony, only one value for t_I is given.

In using drawings to determine the time delays of the reflections, we measure first the length of the path that the direct sound travels. As an example, let us consider the drawing for Symphony Hall in Boston, Figure A3.1. The direct sound D travels a distance of 65 ft. between the violinist and the

listener in the center of the main floor. Next we measure the length of the paths that the first, second, third, fourth, and so forth, reflections travel to this position. All reflecting surfaces are considered, including walls, ceiling, balcony faces, and the rear of the stage. Assume that R_1, R_2, R_3, and R_4 measure 82, 87, 91, and 108 ft, respectively. The differences between these distances and the distances that the direct sound travels yield four differences: $D_1 = 17$; $D_2 = 22$; $D_3 = 26$; and $D_4 = 43$ ft.

To convert these numbers into time delays, we must divide by the speed of sound. Hence, the delay in arrival of the first reflection after the arrival of the direct sound is 17 ft divided by 1130 ft/sec or 0.015 sec. This number multiplied by 1000 gives us the time delay, t, in thousandths of a second, i.e., 15 msec. Therefore, the values of t_1, t_2, t_3, and t_4 corresponding to D_1, D_2, D_3, and D_4 above are, respectively, 15, 19, 23, and 38 msec. These results are then plotted to form a reflection pattern shown in Figure A3.2.

All reflections whose intensities are within 10 db of the intensity of the direct sound, that is to say, at least half as loud as the direct sound, are included as part of the reflection pattern. In a hall like Symphony Hall, reflections from balcony faces are included in making up a reflection pattern because, owing to scattering, they arrive at

573

the ears of listeners on the main floor at levels within 10 db of the level of the direct sound.

An alternate way of measuring the reflection pattern of Figure A3.2 would be to construct a model of the auditorium in which the audience is simulated by sound-absorbing material and to measure the direct sound and the reflections at the desired locations using an ultrasonic source of sound and a tiny microphone. In order for this kind of test to be more meaningful than drawings alone, the model of the hall must be very accurate and the audience simulation must be excellent. Crude models are no better than drawings and may even be inferior. The number of man-hours required to make an accurate model is generally so excessive that this procedure cannot be used in the preliminary stages of design of a hall. Obviously, in the later stages, the usefulness of a model would be limited to determining minor factors in design. Note that the orchestra must also be simulated.

The third method of measuring the reflection pattern of Figure A3.2 is to perform the tests in the completed hall, with *orchestra and audience*, using an explosive type of sound (small pistol or electronic simulation of one) or a pulse wave. This test comes too late to affect the design, of course, but it may be useful as a check on the original design.

CONVERSION FACTORS

To Convert	Into	Multiply by	Conversely Multiply by
inches (in.)	centimeters (cm)	2.54	0.394
	feet (ft)	0.0833	12
	meters (m)	0.0254	39.4
square inches (in.^{2})	square centimeters (cm^2)	6.45	0.155
	square feet (ft^2)	$6.94 \text{ times } 10^{-3}$	144
	square meters (m^2)	$6.45 \text{ times } 10^{-4}$	1550
cubic inches (in.^{3})	cubic centimeters (cm^3)	16.39	$6.10 \text{ times } 10^{-2}$
	cubic feet (ft^3)	$5.787 \text{ times } 10^{-4}$	1728
	cubic meters (m^3)	$1.639 \text{ times } 10^{-5}$	$6.10 \text{ times } 10^{4}$
feet (ft)	centimeters (cm)	30.5	$3.28 \text{ times } 10^{-2}$
	meters (m)	0.305	3.28
square feet (ft^2)	square centimeters (cm^2)	929	$1.076 \text{ times } 10^{-3}$
	square meters (m^2)	0.0929	10.76
cubic feet (ft^3)	cubic centimeters (cm^3)	$2.83 \text{ times } 10^{4}$	$3.53 \text{ times } 10^{-5}$
	cubic meters (m^3)	0.0283	35.3
pounds (lb)	grams (gm)	454	$2.205 \text{ times } 10^{-3}$
	ounces (oz)	16	0.0625
	kilograms (kg)	0.454	2.205
yards (yd)	inches (in.)	36	0.0278
	centimeters (cm)	91.4	0.01094
	meters (m)	0.914	1.094
pounds per square foot (lb/ft^2)	grams per square centimeter (gm/cm^2)	0.488	2.048
	kilograms per square meter (kg/m^2)	4.88	0.2048
pounds per cubic foot (lb/ft^3)	grams per cubic centimeter (gm/cm^3)	0.016	62.4
	kilograms per cubic meter (kg/m^3)	16.0	$6.24 \text{ times } 10^{-2}$

Note: $10^{-2} = 0.01$ $10^{2} = 100$
$10^{-3} = 0.001$ $10^{3} = 1000$
$10^{-4} = 0.0001$ $10^{4} = 10,000$
$10^{-5} = 0.00001$

Name Index

Gendt, A. L. van, 369
George, G., 219
Gesellschaft der Musikfreunde, 193, 197
Ghiringhelli, A., 359, 363
Gibson, A., 76, 300, 306, 321, 338, 427
Gigli, B., 359
Gilford, C. L. S., 294, 296, 301, 302, 306, 314, 328, 333, 345
Giulini, C. M., 359
Goldberg, A., 76
Goldovsky, B., 34
Gropius, P., 277
Grossman, M., 350
Gumppenberg, F., 283
Gutbrod, R., 290
Gye, F., 335

Haas, H., 421, 422
Hallé Orchestra, 341, 344
Hannikainen, T., 76, 225, 229, 426
Hansen, H., 228
Hansen, T. R. von, 197
Harrington, H., 132, 133
Harris, A., 335
Harris, C. M., 457, 543, 545, 549
Harrison, J., 76
Harrison, S., and Sons, 302
Harrison, W. K., 507, 512
Harrison and Abramovitz, 152, 164, 491, 507, 512, 525
Harshaw, M., 536
Harvard University, 2, 55, 56, 542, 554
Helm, E., 187, 190
Helsinki City Symphony Orchestra, 229
Heyworth, P., 77, 312, 331, 338
Hoffman, I., 76, 215, 218
Holzmeister, C., 192
Hopper, C. R., 324
Horta, Baron Victor, 208
Howes, F., 77, 306, 312, 322, 328, 335, 433
Howitt, L. C., 345
Hughes, S., 508
Hume, P., 76

Ingemansson, S. N. P., 569
Inness-Brown, H. A., 254
International Pan-American Congress, 387, 389
Israeli Philharmonic Orchestra, 347, 353, 356
Iturbi, J., 356
Izenour, G. C., 503

Janlet, P., 208
Jellinek, G. A., 213
Johnson, F. R., 76, 145, 220, 525
Johnson, H. E., 98
Jordan, V. L., 197, 224, 228, 333, 422, 544, 562, 565, 566, 568, 569
Judd, G. C., Jr., 513, 514

Juilliard School of Music, 408, 532
Julian, A. M., 241

Kaelber, G. E., 174
Karajan, H. von, 5, 74, 76, 93, 168, 196, 218, 240, 249, 285, 329, 330, 359, 375, 427, 480, 508
Karmi, D., 358
Keibs, L., 46
Keidel, L., 290
Keilberth, J., 248
Kelly, R., and Associates, 526
Kessler, J. A., 99, 568
Kidd, F. J., 103
Kidd, W. A., 103
Klein, R., 187
Kleinhans Music Hall Management, Inc., 103
Klepper, D. L., 145, 351, 352, 525
Knudsen, V. O., 455, 542, 543, 545, 549
Kolodin, I., 4, 76, 150, 156, 168, 181, 184, 248, 508
Kostelanetz, A., 532
Koussevitsky, S., 55, 56, 353
Kraglund, J., 219
Krawitz, H. E., 164
Krehbiel, H. E., 542
Krips, H., 291
Kuhl, W., 46, 57, 58, 277, 283, 543, 563, 566, 568, 569
Kuttruff, H., 271, 541, 553, 563, 566

Lacovich, P., 233
Lang, P. H., 57, 76
Lansburgh, G. A., 175, 179
Lauritzen, V., 224
Le Brun, N. E. H. C., 170
Lee, E. J., 115
Lehtinen, N., 236
Leinsdorf, E., 52, 74, 76, 403, 426, 443, 532
Leitner, F., 287
Liepmann, K., 108
London Philharmonic Orchestra, 322
London Symphony Orchestra, 356
Luce, C. B., 251
Luukkonen, R. V., 236

McClure, J., 532, 534
McDonald, G., 309, 314
McKay, R. L., 525
McKim, C. F., 96
McKim, Mead and White, 98, 174
McLean, E., 77, 141, 168, 219
McMullen, R., 241
McNair, W. A., 434

Marchal, A., 108
Markevich, I., 76, 371, 427
Marsh, R. C., 76, 114, 121, 126, 331
Martin, J. L., 333
Mason, C., 77, 312, 322, 331, 344

Mason, H. T., 170
Massachusetts Institute of Technology, 108, 562
Mathew, R., 333
Mattoni, A. von, 203
Meano, V., 185
Meredith, J. N., 296
Metropolitan Opera Association, 89, 111, 114, 135, 159, 164, 171, 403
Meyer, E., 267, 271, 277, 283, 333, 422, 541, 543, 544, 553, 563, 565, 566, 568
Miller, L. N., 525
Mingotti, A., 77, 190, 287
Mitropoulos, D., 76, 249, 356, 375, 428, 508
Mocken, F., 255
Monteux, P., 76, 83, 141, 168, 426, 427, 428, 480
Moseley, C., 532
Mueller, H., 283, 287, 290, 563, 568
Muncey, R. W., 421
Munch, C., 74, 76, 83, 108, 109, 139, 285, 347, 356, 427, 428
Münchinger, K., 379

Netherlands Kamerorkest, 350
Newman, R. B., 145
New York Philharmonic Society and Orchestra, 389, 408, 496, 511, 513, 514, 515, 517, 527, 535, 536
Nickson, A. F. B., 421
Nordell, R., 394
Northwood, T. D., 213, 541, 562, 565
Nüll, E. van der, 203

Oenslager, D., 526
Oistrakh, D., 229
Orcutt, W. D., 541
Ormandy, E., 1, 74, 76, 83, 144, 168, 225, 285, 371, 426, 427, 528, 480
Ormestad, H. J., 127, 562, 565
Ozawa, S., 511, 532

Paolini, E., 567
Paray, P., 132, 350
Parkin, P. H., 296, 301, 302, 307, 312, 314, 328, 333, 345, 541, 543, 563, 564, 566, 567, 568, 569
Patti, A., 317, 359
Peress, M., 532, 534
Perry, T. D., Jr., 98, 109, 141, 145
Philadelphia Orchestra Association, 55, 56, 165, 168, 513
Piermarini, G., 359, 363
Pinkham, D., 31, 33, 531
Piston, W., 33
Platner, W., 145
Podd, S. C., 103
Potwin, C. C., 568
Purkis, H. J., 328, 333, 541, 543

Subject Index

Seating (*cont.*)
capacity of 54 halls, 556–561
density, 485–487
dimensions, 398, 399
in Philharmonic Hall, 516
near stage, 468, 469
sound absorption, 458, 541, 547
spacing in 54 halls, 556–561
Secular music, 45, 46
Sender Freies (*see* Berlin)
Severance Hall (*see* Cleveland)
Shapes of halls, 10, 411, 490–493
Shell, orchestra, 501–503
Shrine Auditorium, Los Angeles, 484
Sight lines and acoustics, 468
Size, and acoustics, 9, 411, 482–489
Sound, absorption coefficients, 541, 547
decay, 16
diffusion, 23
direct, 22, 35
how created, 13
outdoors, 17
reverberant, 22, 35
speed of, 13
systems, 519
Southern Methodist University, McFarlin Auditorium, Dallas, 484
Speed of music, 38–40
Speed of sound, 13
Staatsoper (*see* Hamburg and Vienna)
Staatstheater, Grosses Haus, Kassel, 483
Stadt-Casino (*see* Basel)
Städtische Bühnen, Grosses Haus, Frankfurt, 483
Städtische Bühnen Nürnberg-Fürth, Opernhaus, Nuremburg, 483
Städtische Bühnen, Opernhaus, Dortmund, 483
Städtische Oper, Berlin, 483
Stadttheater, Duisburg, 483
Stadttheater, Gelsenkirchen, 483, 507
Stages, areas of, 498, 524
dimensions of, 496–506
heights in 47 halls, 556–559
in newer halls, 497
in older halls, 496, 497
in Philharmonic Hall, 517, 518, 533–538
mechanically operated, 492, 493
with ceilings, high, 496, 497
low, 497
with stagehouses, 501–506
without stagehouses, 496
Stockholm, Konserthus, 397, 483
Street noise, 518, 519, 521
Stuttgart, Liederhalle, 285–290, 442, 483, 487, 496, 497, 516, 558, 563, 566

Stuttgart (*cont.*)
Württembergisches Staatstheater, 483
Subjective judgments, 404–408, 475, 479, 532, 533
Subway noise, 518, 519, 521
Symphony Hall (*see* Boston)
Synthetic audience, 528, 529

Tanglewood Music Shed (*see* Lenox)
Teatro alla Scala (*see* Milan)
Teatro Carlo Felice, Genoa, 483
Teatro Colón (*see* Buenos Aires)
Teatro dell'Opera, Rome, 483
Teatro Massimo Bellini, Catania, 483
Teatro Massimo, Palermo, 483
Tel Aviv, F. R. Mann Auditorium, 77, 99, 347, 350, 353–358, 394, 434, 461, 463, 484, 487, 541, 558, 563, 566
Terminology, 571–574
Texture, acoustical, attribute of, 69, 413, 448–450
defined, 23, 24, 69
requirements, 448–450, 493
typical, 449
Théatre National de l'Opéra (*see* Paris, Opéra)
Thomaskirche, Leipzig, 31, 46
Timbre, affected by acoustics, 42
defined, 16, 41, 42
Tivoli Koncertsal (*see* Copenhagen)
Tonal distortion, attribute of, 70, 413, 457–459
Tonal quality, attribute of, 70, 413, 457–459
Tone color, affected by acoustics, 42
defined, 42
Tonhallesaal (*see* Zurich)
Toronto, O'Keefe Auditorium, 484
Treble, loudness of, 23
Tuning of halls, 511, 526–540
Turku, Konserttisali, 233–236, 483, 558, 562, 565, 568
Twentieth Century music, defined, 49, 50
electronic, 50, 51
halls for, 50, 51
reverberation times for, 472

Uniformity of sound in hall, attribute of, 70, 413, 460–462
in boxes, 466, 467
near stage, 468, 469
rating, 469
sight lines, 468
under balcony overhangs, 462–466
variations in intimacy, 468
Units of loudness, 17
Uses for halls, 399, 400
Usher Hall (*see* Edinburgh)

Validation of rating system, 471–480
Vancouver, Queen Elizabeth Theatre, 77, 215–220, 484, 487, 556, 560, 562, 565
Variable acoustics, 492, 493, 522, 523
Venice, La Fenice, 51, 335
St. Mark's Basilica, 32, 44
Ventilation grilles, absorption of sound by, 437
noise of, 495, 518
Ventilation systems, noise of, 495, 518, 522
Vertical definition, 37
Vibration isolation, 521
Vibration, normal mode of, 14, 21
Vienna, Musikvereinssaal, 11, 41, 49, 93, 96, 193–197, 199, 205, 276, 287, 300, 301, 303, 307, 351, 357, 365, 368, 393, 427, 428, 433, 434, 436, 439, 445, 483, 487, 496, 513, 514, 515, 516, 556, 562, 565, 568
Redoutensaal, 47
Staatsoper, 41, 51, 159, 162, 165, 175, 181, 199–203, 237, 240, 249, 338, 398, 420, 439, 483, 487, 505, 506, 508, 509, 560, 564, 567
Violin and acoustics, 53
Vocabulary, musical-acoustic, 61–71
Volume (*see* Cubic volume)

War Memorial Opera House (*see* San Francisco)
Warmth, affected by wood, 8, 434–438, 494
attribute of, 65, 413, 433–436
defined, 65, 435
related to materials, 434, 436–438, 494
related to reverberation times, 434–436, 515, 516
Washington, D.C., Constitution Hall, 484
Westminster Abbey, London, 33
Whispering gallery, 6
Wood, effect on bass, 8, 434–438, 494
effect on warmth, 8, 434–438, 494
sound absorption by, 437, 541, 547
thin, 8, 436–438, 494
Wuppertaler Bühnen, Opernhaus, Wuppertal, 483
Württembergisches Staatstheater, Grosses Haus, Stuttgart, 483

Years 54 halls dedicated, 556–561

Zurich, Grosser Tonhallesaal, 383–386, 395, 434, 445, 483, 487, 496, 558, 563, 566
Kleiner Tonhallesaal, 386